UNIVERSITY OF STRATHCLYDE

Dust explosion

prevention and protection

Dust explosion

prevention and protection

The information in this book is given in good faith and belief in its accuracy, but does not imply the acceptance of any legal liability or responsibility whatsoever, by the Institution, or by the authors, for the consequences of its use or misuse in any particular circumstances. This disclaimer shall have effect only to the extent permitted by any applicable law.

Published by
Institution of Chemical Engineers (IChemE),
Davis Building,
165-189 Railway Terrace,
Rugby, Warwickshire CV21 3HQ, UK
IChemE is a registered Charity

© 2002 John Barton

ISBN 0 85295 410 7

Typeset by Techset Composition Limited, Salisbury, UK
Printed by Bell & Bain Limited, Glasgow, UK

Preface

This IChemE guide, *Dust explosion prevention and protection*, was originally published in three parts. *Part 1 — Venting* by Dr C. Schofield was published in 1985. A substantially revised and updated *2nd edition of Part 1* by Dr G.A. Lunn was published in 1992. *Part 2 — Ignition Prevention, Containment, Inerting Suppression and Isolation* by C. Schofield and J.A. Abbott was published in 1988. *Part 3 — Venting of Weak Explosions and the Effect of Vent Ducts* by G.A. Lunn was published in 1988. These three parts formed the first authoritative and comprehensive guidance for dust explosion prevention and protection published in the UK in a form accessible to engineers, scientists, safety specialists and managers.

Since the three parts of the guide were published much research has been done and information published, particularly in relation to containment and venting of dust explosions. It was felt that the new information required incorporation in a single volume edition of the guide. This new edition of the guide stands on its own as a complete document. The reader will not need to refer to the original parts of the guide.

This guide is a compilation of current best practice for measures either to prevent dust explosions occurring (by control of ignition sources or inerting), or, if they do occur, to protect the plant and personnel from their destructive effects (by applying the techniques of explosion containment, explosion suppression, or explosion venting, either singly or in combination; and by suitable siting of plant). Worked examples are included where appropriate.

The guide assumes on the part of the reader some basic knowledge of dust explosions and their potential. It should be noted that this guide does not cover hybrid mixtures unless otherwise stated and it does not cover dusts that exhibit the properties of explosives (i.e., can give rise to detonation). Special consideration is necessary for hybrid mixtures and specialized safety precautions are required for the processing and handling of explosive dusts. They are not dealt with here. If you are unsure where to start, the Institution of Chemical

Engineers is able to advise on consultancies and laboratories that can offer assistance.

The recommendations presented in this guide will provide a basis for good practice for explosion prevention and protection of plant and processes where dust explosions could occur. The guide aims to help those responsible for the design, supply and operation of plant to comply with the provisions of Health and Safety legislation. It must be recognized, however, that on occasions strict adherence to these recommendations would be inappropriate and further advice may have to be sought. In addition it would be expected that further research and other developments will lead to improved methods and it is not the intention that this guide should inhibit such developments.

Note: throughout the book 'bar' means 'bar g'.

Acknowledgements

Much of the new information in this guide resulted from various dust explosion projects, funded jointly by Government Departments, HSE and individual companies under the auspices of the British Materials Handling Board. Permission to use this information is gratefully acknowledged.

The editor wishes to thank all the members of the IChemE Advisory Panel for their invaluable help and guidance. Particular thanks are due, for their substantial contributions to the writing of certain chapters, to Peter Moore (chapter 6), Geoff Lunn (chapters 5 and 7–11), and Steven Manchester (chapter 12); also to David Pritchard of the Health and Safety Laboratory (chapters 2 and 3).

Thanks are also due to Ken Marshall (Fike) and Paul Cooke (Stuvex) who kindly agreed to make available their experience as users or manufacturers by reading and commenting on all or part of the draft.

Membership of the Advisory Panel

N. Gibson	Burgoyne Consultants Limited
N. Hubbard	DCE Donaldson Limited
G. Lunn	Health and Safety Laboratory
S. Manchester	FRS, Building Research Establishment Limited
P. Moore	Kidde International
A. Tyldesley	Health and Safety Executive

Contents

Background to dust explosions

1

1.1 Introduction

The danger of a dust explosion is difficult to avoid in processes where combustible powders are handled. Many fine materials — for example, coal, wood, flour, starch, sugar, rubber, plastics, some metals, pharmaceuticals, etc. — can explode once they are dispersed in air as a cloud with a suitable concentration and when an effective ignition source is present. Statistics on the frequency and occurrence of fire and explosion incidents reveal the wide range of ignition sources, materials and industries that can be involved[1,2]. Case histories of incidents can be interesting and informative, but it is not the remit of this guide to dwell on them. However, some illustrative examples of more recent incidents are given in Appendix 1.

Dust cloud explosions confined in vessels or other process equipment cause a rapid increase in pressure. If the dust-handling plant cannot contain such pressures then measures have to be taken either to prevent the explosion or to protect the plant against the destructive effects. There is a statutory requirement to take appropriate precautions. These requirements are embodied in legislation as outlined in Appendix 2.

A dust explosion can take place if a number of conditions are satisfied simultaneously:

- The dust must be explosible.
- The dust must have a particle size distribution that will allow the propagation of flame.
- The atmosphere into which the dust is dispersed as a cloud or suspension must contain sufficient oxidant to support combustion.
- The dust cloud must have a concentration within the explosion range.
- The dust cloud must be in contact with an ignition source of sufficient energy to cause an ignition.

The hazard from an explosion depends on several factors concerning both the dust and the environment in which it is dispersed:

- The dust itself. Dusts vary in their explosibility and the consequent explosion violence generated. The explosion violence may be measured in standard tests (see Chapter 2), by two parameters, which define the maximum explosion pressure that can be generated, and maximum rate of explosion pressure rise (explosion speed) that is related to the K_{St} value. It is important to know the speed of an explosion (K_{St} value) in order to design appropriate protective measures, but it must be recognized that a relatively slow event (low K_{St} value) can still cause enormous damage, if high pressures develop. Coal dust, for example, exhibits relatively low explosibility and explosion violence (low K_{St} value); it is less explosible than aspirin and much less explosible than fine aluminium powder. But coal dust explosions can have devastating effects, as witnessed by coalmine disasters over the years. Also, for comparison, gas explosions can be characterized by a similarly defined parameter (K_g value). The value for methane is low, only 55 bar m s^{-1}, but the ability of natural gas explosions to destroy buildings and process plant is widely understood.
- The composition of the dust. Some dusts — coal is a prime example — are not homogeneous and can have very different compositions and thus explosion properties, depending on the source. Coal dust generally is more highly explosible and exhibits higher explosion violence the greater its volatile content. Some anthracite is non-explosible because the volatile content is low. Other examples include the variation of fat content in milk and the presence of de-dusting agents.
- The particle size and particle size distribution. Finer particles have a greater surface area and are thus more likely to be explosible. When the dust is made up of a series of particle sizes ranging from fine to coarse, the fines play the most prominent part in an ignition and in the propagation of an explosion.
- The concentration of dispersed dust. When this concentration is below the lower explosion limit (LEL), typically 10–100 gm^{-3}, an explosion cannot be propagated. The explosion violence of the cloud increases as the dust concentration increases until an optimum concentration is reached giving the highest explosion violence; this concentration is usually well in excess of the amount of dust theoretically required to react with the available oxygen. At still higher concentrations the explosion violence either decreases or stays roughly constant. The upper explosion limit (UEL) — the dust concentration above which an explosion cannot be propagated — is not as clearly

defined as the lower limit. At high concentrations of coal dust, for example, the flame travels rapidly through a reactive volatiles/air mixture as soon as this mixture is produced and leaves the partly devolatilized particles in its wake[3]. Only at very high dust concentrations is the inerting effect of these particles sufficient to quench the flame.

- Moisture content. The explosion violence falls as the moisture content of a dust increases. Eventually the dust is no longer explosible.
- Ambient temperature and pressure. Although at a given dust concentration an increase in the ambient temperature results in a decrease in the maximum explosion pressure in an enclosed explosion, it has very little effect on the rate of pressure rise. If the ambient pressure increases, both the maximum pressure and the rate of pressure rise increase.
- Turbulence of the dust cloud. Dust clouds are usually turbulent to some degree because there must be some air movement if the dust is to remain dispersed. At low levels of turbulence the explosion violence of a dust cloud may be relatively mild, but at high states of turbulence, when the flame front is broken up and its effective area much increased, the explosion will propagate much more rapidly and the explosion violence will reach high values.
- The presence of flammable gas. The explosion violence of a dispersed dust cloud increases markedly if admixed with even a low concentration of flammable gas to give a so called 'hybrid mixture'.
- The scale of the vessel. The violence of a dust explosion — as indicated by the rate of pressure rise – depends on the size of the vessel. Pressure rise is slower the larger the vessel, although the potential for destruction will be greater because of the increased scale of the explosion. One of the simplest scaling laws is the cubic law, which relates the rate of pressure rise in an explosion to the cube root of the vessel volume.

1.2 Approach to handling dust explosion hazards

A practical approach to handling dust explosion hazards and risks can be found in the Essential Health and Safety Requirements described in Annex II of the EC ATEX Directive[4].

The approach, summarized below, is one of integrated explosion safety, involving **prevention** methods aimed at ensuring that conditions under which an explosion becomes possible do not occur, and **protection** methods aimed at minimizing the effects of explosions it is assumed will occur:

(1) **Prevent**, if possible, the formation of explosive atmospheres. For example:
  - Replace flammable materials with non-flammable ones. For example, the addition of inert diluent dust (generally of limited application; applied in coal mines).
  - Select less dusty alternatives for materials and minimize attrition.
  - Minimize handling of dusty materials and design handling systems to minimize dust generation and the size of dust clouds.
  - Avoid the accumulation of dust (which can be disturbed to form a dust cloud) by the detailed design of equipment, buildings and working practices.
  - Avoid explosible dust concentrations — for example, by using a wet process[5,6,7].
  - Carry out the process under an inert atmosphere, a technique known as inerting.
(2) **Prevent** the ignition of explosive atmospheres:
  - Anticipate possible ignition sources and eliminate them, as far as reasonably practicable. For example, by appropriate equipment design, earthing, maintenance and working practices.
(3) **Protect** against the worst effects of an explosion should it occur, by halting it immediately and/or limiting the range of explosion flames and explosion pressures to a sufficient level of safety, with:
  - Containment — the vessel or plant is built to be strong enough to withstand the pressure of a confined explosion. Plant can be designed to be either explosion pressure resistant or explosion pressure shock resistant.
  - Isolation — explosions must be isolated from other parts of dust-handling plant to limit destructive effects. Rotary valves, fast acting valves, extinguishing barriers and explosion diverters are methods for doing this.
  - Suppression — inject suppressant material into an explosion as soon after ignition as possible to keep explosion pressures low.
  - Venting — weak panels in the walls of a plant open early in the development of the explosion. The main force of the explosion is dissipated in the open air.
  - Suitable siting of plant.

The correct application of prevention and protection techniques relies on a thorough knowledge of the plant, the dust and the dust-handling process.

There is no 'best' technique when it comes to taking precautions against dust explosions. Each piece of plant or process step must be assessed separately and appropriate precautions taken with due consideration of the possible explosion effect on other items of plant or parts of the process. Careful thought and attention must be given to the approach. For example, it is not sufficient merely to install a protection technique such as venting without first having done all that is practicable to prevent an explosion.

1.3 Selection of a basis for safety

The selection of appropriate prevention and protection techniques, and a record of the reasoning behind their application, defines the basis of safety of dust handling plant, i.e. an explanation of why the plant is safe in terms of the specific precautions taken. A rationale for arriving at a basis of safety for a plant handling flammable dusts is outlined in Logic diagram 1 at the end of this chapter.

The first step in defining a basis for safety is to conduct a screening procedure that will identify dusts with explosive properties. An explosive material rapidly decomposes with the evolution of large amounts of energy and large volumes of gas, generally resulting in a detonation. Decomposition often involves the oxygen contained in the molecule, and the presence of air is not necessary. The specialized safety precautions required for the processing and handling of explosive dusts are not covered in this guide. The screening procedure is described in the IChemE guide *Prevention of Fires and Explosions in Dryers*[8]. Briefly, three factors must be considered:

The chemical composition of the material — the influence of groups in the molecule can modify the behaviour markedly.

The oxygen balance of organic molecules — the availability of oxygen often indicates the explosive potential of the material and the oxygen balance enables the availability of oxygen to be compared with known explosives. In the calculation of the oxygen balance only carbon, hydrogen and oxygen are taken to be involved:

$$C_xH_yO_z + (x + y/4 - z/2)O_2 \rightarrow xCO_2 + y/2\,H_2O \qquad (1.1)$$

And the oxygen balance is:

$$-16(2x + y/2 - z) \times 100/\text{Molecular weight} \qquad (1.2)$$

The reactions of the material in standard flammability tests — material must be submitted for testing for explosive properties if the material structure suggests it may be explosive and if the oxygen balance is more positive than -200.

If the screening procedure indicates that the dust possesses explosive properties, then separate specialist advice should be sought, and the guidance that follows in subsequent chapters of this guide is not applicable.

If the screening procedure establishes that the dust under investigation does not possess explosive properties, then further testing can proceed to determine the explosibility characteristics of the powder, for example, can the dust give rise to a deflagration. The tests are described in Chapter 2, together with a logic diagram to guide the user through the testing regime. A conclusion is reached as to whether an explosion hazard exists or not based on the results of the explosibility tests. The tests take into consideration process conditions such as temperature, dust concentration, state of the dust and whether flammable vapours are present. If it is determined that a hazard exists, explosion prevention and protection techniques need to be applied. These techniques are described in subsequent chapters. For explosion prevention, see Chapters 3 (control of ignition) and 4 (inerting). Explosion protection is covered in Chapters 5 (explosion containment), 6 (explosion suppression), and 7 to 13 (venting). Chapters 2, 3, 4, 5, 6 and 7 contain logic diagrams to aid the selection of appropriate prevention and protection techniques.

References in Chapter 1

1. Abbott, J.A., *BMHB Survey of Dust Fires and Explosions in the UK 1979–84*, ISBN 0 85624 455 4 (British Materials Handling Board, UK).
2. Porter, B., 1989, Industrial incidents, Paper presented at *Dust Explosions: Assessment, Prevention and Protection, 24 November 1989, London* (IBC Technical Services Ltd).
3. Hertzberg, M. and Cashdollar, K.L., 1987, Introduction to dust explosions, in Cashdollar, K.L. and Hertzberg, M. (Eds), *Industrial Dust Explosions, ASTM Special Technical Publication 958* (American Society of Testing and Materials).
4. Council Directive of 23 March 1994 (ATEX-100A-Directive) on Equipment and protective systems intended for use in potentially explosive atmospheres (94/9/EC), European Communities Council, *Official Journal of the European Communities*, 19 April 1994, 37 (L100).
5. The Magnesium (Grinding of Castings and Other Articles) Special Regulations 1946 (S.R. & O. 1946 No. 2107, as amended by S.I. 1992 No. 1811 and S.I. 1992 No. 2966) (HMSO, UK).
6. NFPA, 1993, *Standard for the Processing and Finishing of Aluminum* (NFPA 65) (National Fire Protection Association, Quincy, USA).
7. NFPA, 1987, *Standard for the Production, Processing, Handling, and Storage of Zirconium* (NFPA 482) (National Fire Protection Association, Quincy, USA).
8. Abbott, J.A., 1990, *Prevention of Fires and Explosions in Dryers*, ISBN 0 85295 257 0 (Institution of Chemical Engineers, Rugby, UK).

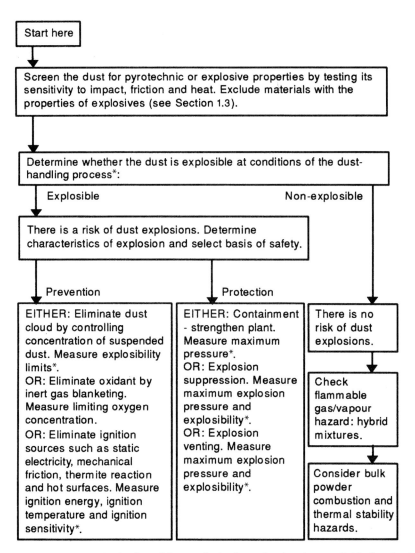

Logic Diagram 1 Evaluation of dust explosion hazard and options available for a basis of safety.

* The testing regime and the appropriate tests for determining or measuring the various parameters or properties referred to are discussed in Chapter 2.

Determination of dust ignitability, flammability and explosibility characteristics

2

The standard tests for assessing the fire and explosion characteristics of a dust and quantifying the explosibility are described in this chapter (some examples are given in Table 2.1). These characteristics are listed in Table 2.2 alongside the precautionary methods to which they apply. A comprehensive tabulation of test results for a wide range and a large number of dusts is given in a BIA publication[1].

2.1 Explosibility classification

The first stage in the design of explosion prevention and protection systems is to obtain a qualitative assessment of the ability of a dust to participate in an explosion by carrying out explosibility tests. In the UK these are used to divide dusts into two groups:

Group A — dusts able to ignite and propagate a flame;
Group B — dusts that do not propagate a flame.

As in all explosion testing, the sample selected for testing must be representative of the material in the plant at risk. Best practice is to ensure that the sample is as dry as the driest material in the plant and that the size distribution of the test dust is similar to the finest size fractions that are likely to occur in any part of the process.

Also it is important that the classification pertains to the conditions, for example, the temperature, under which the dust will be handled. It is not sensible to conduct an explosibility assessment at room temperature when the process temperature is to be substantially higher. Some dusts, classified as Group B at room temperature, can ignite at higher temperatures. A series of tests has been devised allowing explosibility classification under increasingly severe conditions.

The sequence to be followed for performing these tests is given in Logic diagram 2 at the end of this chapter. Explanatory notes are given with the diagram; the bracketed numbers in the notes relate to those on the logic diagram. The most commonly used explosibility tests are described in Appendix 3.

Table 2.1 Explosibility parameters for a number of dusts*

Type of dust	Min cloud ignition energy mJ	Cloud ignition temp. $^{\circ}$C	Layer ignition temp. $^{\circ}$C	Max. explosion pressure bar a	K_{St}** bar ms^{-1}	Minimum explosible conc. g m^{-3}	Limiting O_2 conc. volume %
Anthraquinone	3	550	Sublimes	9.1	298	30	–
Pea flour	40	560	260	–	–	–	15
Lignite	30	390	180	11.0	151	60	12
Aluminium	15	550	740	13.0	750	60	5
Coal	60	610	170	9.8	114	15	14
Cellulose	80	480	270	11.0	125	30	9
Cornflour	40	380	330	10.3	125	60	9
Wood	40	470	260	10.2	142	60	10
Wheat flour	50	380	360	9.8	70	125	11
Charcoal	20	530	180	10.0	10	60	–
Cotton linter	1920	560	350	8.2	24	100	–
Skimmed milk	50	490	200	9.8	125	60	–
Sugar	30	370	400	9.5	138	60	–
Sulphur	5	280	113	6.8	151	30	–
Magnesium	80	450	240	18.5	508	30	–
Zinc	9600	690	540	7.8	93	250	–
Paraform-aldehyde	–	460	>480	10.9	178	60	6

*Examples of recorded values. For illustrative purposes only: not to be used in the calculations for explosion precaution methods.
**1 m^3 vessel

Table 2.2 Common methods used in controlling dust explosions

Precautionary measure	Comments	Parameter
PREVENTION		
Replacement of combustible materials (addition of diluent dust to reduce dust explosibility).	Non-flammable diluent well mixed with dust, acts as heat sink reducing explosibility of dust. Limited application because of contamination.	Flammability. Heat of combustion. Explosibility.
Concentration limitation (exclusion of explosive dust cloud).	Material can be rendered less dusty and handling system designed to minimize dust, or changed to a wet process.	Lower explosion limit.
Inerting (exclusion of oxygen using N_2, CO_2 or other suitable gas).	Reduces oxygen content below minimum necessary to support combustion (typically <5–15%). Requires monitoring of oxygen content. Usually requires closed system to conserve inert gas.	Limiting oxygen concentration.
Avoidance of ignition sources.	All practical measures must be taken to exclude ignition sources. Sources are often unknown, so it is difficult to guarantee exclusion and other precautions are usually taken.	Layer ignition temperature. Cloud ignition temperature. Decomposition temperature. Spontaneous ignition temperature. Minimum ignition energy. Electrostatic behaviour.
PROTECTION		
Explosion-resistant construction (containment).	Sufficiently strong construction of vessel and associated pipe work, to withstand the maximum explosion pressure.	Maximum explosion pressure.
Isolation.	Ensure explosions cannot propagate between items of plant, using rotary valves, fast-acting cut-off valves, extinguishing barriers and so on.	Maximum rate of pressure rise and maximum explosion pressure. Flame speed.

(continued)

Table 2.2 (*continued*)

Precautionary measure	Comments	Parameter
Explosion pressure relief (venting).	Vents provided in walls of vessel to allow escape of dust and combustion products to limit pressure rise to an acceptable level. Widely used.	Maximum rate of pressure rise and maximum explosion pressure.
Explosion suppression.	Start of explosion detected by instruments triggering release of fire suppressants. Useful where venting is unacceptable or impracticable, for example, when the dust is toxic.	Maximum rate of pressure rise and maximum explosion pressure. Cloud ignition temperature.
Detection of smouldering particles (wood flour industry, metal working).	Detection of smouldering particles in pneumatic transport or dust extraction lines by infrared sensors and quenching by a triggered water spray to reduce the probability of ignition.	

2.1.1 Standard explosibility tests

The standard explosibility test currently accepted by the UK Health and Safety Executive, for the initial classification of dusts as Group A or Group B, is the vertical tube test (see Appendix 3). If flame propagation is observed in this test, the dust is designated Group A. If flame propagation is not observed, the test is repeated under a range of conditions, for example, the sample is dried and sieved and the amount of dust used and the method of dispersing it are varied to ensure that a Group B classification is based on exhaustive testing.

It should be borne in mind that the classification by the vertical tube test is only valid in air at ambient conditions of temperature and pressure. In dust-handling processes where high temperatures exist (for example drying), Group B classification may not be valid. It is possible for a dust classified in Group B at room temperature to have a dust cloud minimum ignition temperature. Therefore, it is general practice for further testing to be done if a Group B dust is to be used at a temperature above 110°C. Group A dusts need no further testing.

2.1.2 Tests at elevated temperatures

The Godbert-Greenwald furnace apparatus (see Appendix 3) is most commonly used to assess explosibility of a Group B dust at elevated tempera-tures. If flame propagation occurs during a sequence of tests, the dust is re-classified to Group A. If no flame is observed the dust remains in Group B.

This result can be accepted as the final assessment, but further testing can be done if process conditions are known to be less severe than those in the test. The test can be performed at the known process temperature and with a localized ignition source inside the furnace tube. If flame propagation is observed the dust is classified as Group A.

Dusts that remain in Group B may require further testing for explosibility to take into account, for example, more energetic ignition sources, or higher pressures, or other process conditions.

2.1.3 Further explosibility tests

Further explosibility testing most commonly is done in either the 20 litre sphere with a central 2 kJ ignition source, or a 1 m^3 vessel with a central 10 kJ ignition source (see Appendix 3). Explosibility is judged on the basis of pressure rise. If a pressure rise of less than 0.5 bar is recorded for all dust concentrations across a potential explosible range, the dust is considered to be non-explosible, and remains in Group B. Otherwise the dust is allocated to Group A.

2.2 Explosibility characteristics

The tests for explosibility described in Section 2.1 give only a qualitative assessment of the risk. A quantitative assessment requires further testing to measure explosion characteristics that are important to the design of explosion protection methods such as venting, suppression, and containment.

These explosion characteristics are:

- The maximum explosion pressure, P_{max}. This is the highest explosion pressure developed by an enclosed dust explosion. It is measured in a standard test at the optimum dust concentration.
- The maximum rate of pressure rise, $(dP/dt)_{max}$. This is the highest rate of pressure rise generated by an enclosed dust explosion. It is measured in a standard test at the optimum dust concentration.

The procedures for measuring these characteristics are given in an ISO standard available as BS 6713 (1986)[2]. The standard test vessel for these determinations is the $1\,m^3$ vessel, but the standard also allows the use of alternative vessels provided it can be shown that they give comparable results. The criteria for demonstrating conformity are given in the standard. Descriptions of the $1\,m^3$ apparatus and the alternative 20 litre sphere apparatus, are given in Appendix 3. CEN Technical Committee 305 is refining the ISO procedure. They will recommend use of the $1\,m^3$ apparatus as the standard apparatus, but will also allow the use of alternatives such as the 20 litre sphere if conformity can be demonstrated, and new European Standards for the determination of P_{max} and $(dP/dt)_{max}$ will be issued.

The peak value of the maximum rate of pressure rise $(dP/dt)_{max}$, is used to calculate a dust specific explosibility characteristic called the K_{St} value. The K_{St} value is given by:

$$K_{St} = (dP/dt)_{max} V^{1/3} \tag{2.1}$$

where $(dP/dt)_{max}$ is the peak maximum rate of pressure rise $(bar\,s^{-1})$ and V is the total volume of the vessel (m^3). The units of K_{St} are $bar\,m\,s^{-1}$. The K_{St}

Table 2.3 Definition of dust explosion classes ($1\,m^3$ apparatus, $10\,kJ$ ignition source)

Dust explosion class	K_{St} $(bar\,m\,s^{-1})$	Characteristics
St 0	0	Non-explosible
St 1	$0 < K_{St} \leqslant 200$	Weak to moderately explosible
St 2	$200 < K_{St} \leqslant 300$	Strongly explosible
St 3	$300 < K_{St} \leqslant 800$	Very strongly explosible

value is derived only from measurements in either the $1\,m^3$ vessel or the 20 litre sphere.

The K_{St} value can be used to classify dusts into one of several groups. Table 2.3 shows the classification that is generally adopted.

Comparisons of results from the $1\,m^3$ vessel and the 20 litre spherical tester generally show[3] that:

- The values for the maximum explosion pressure, P_{max}, measured in the 20 litre sphere are slightly lower than those measured in the $1\,m^3$ apparatus;
- The K_{St} values are equal up to about $600\,bar\,m\,s^{-1}$.

Equation (2.1) is known as the 'cubic law' or 'cube root law'. K_{St} is considered to be a constant for any dust, independent of vessel size, and Equation (2.1) acts as a simple scaling law. However, there are limitations to the conditions under which this scaling law is strictly applicable. In practical terms this means that if any other apparatus is used to measure the K_{St} value, it must be calibrated against the $1\,m^3$ or 20 litre standard test vessels.

Any deviation from the established procedure requires an alteration in the ignition delay, t_d, until concurrence with measurements in the $1\,m^3$ vessel is obtained.

2.3 Other explosibility and ignitability characteristics

2.3.1 Explosion limits

Explosion limits describe the concentration range of dust/air mixtures in which explosions are possible. Usually, only the lower explosion limit (LEL) is determined. These measurements are important if the avoidance of an explosible dust cloud forms part of the basis for safety.

For the determination of the lower explosion limit both the $1\,m^3$ apparatus and the 20 litre sphere apparatus are commonly used. CEN Technical Committee 305 is currently preparing a standard for the test procedure. Essentially the concentration of an explosible dust is systematically reduced in a series of tests until the dust suspension can no longer be ignited. The highest dust concentration at which the dust/air mixture can no longer be ignited in the tests is specified as the LEL.

2.3.2 Minimum ignition energy

The minimum ignition energy (MIE) of a dust air mixture is defined as the lowest value of electrical energy stored in a capacitor that just ignites the most ignitable dust/air mixture following the discharge of the energy across a spark gap. This measurement is important when considering the elimination of ignition sources as part of the basis of safety.

A single MIE value for a substance cannot be defined with universal agreement because the value depends on the physical and chemical properties of the dust as well as the test apparatus used (for example, the electrical circuit used to generate the spark). CEN Technical Committee 305 is preparing a standard for the determination of MIEs. In the meantime methods can be found in BS 5958 (1991)[4] and IEC 61241-2-3 (1994)[5]. A commercially available apparatus, the Mike 3 apparatus, is in common use[6].

The MIE is usually quoted as a pair of values. The lower value specifies the energy at which ignition no longer took place. The higher value specifies the energy at which the most ignitable dust/air mixture could just be ignited. In view of the dependency of the MIE on the apparatus used, the method used should be stated when values are quoted.

2.3.3 Minimum ignition temperature of a dust cloud

The minimum ignition temperature (MIT) of a dust cloud describes the ignition behaviour of a dust/air mixture at a hot surface. The MIT is specified as the lowest temperature at which the most ignitable dust/air mixture could just be ignited. A test method is given in IEC 61241-2-1 (1994)[7]. Measurement of the MIT is not only important when considering the elimination of ignition sources, but is also required for the specification of electrical equipment, and is a design parameter for explosion suppression.

The MIT is usually determined using either the Godbert-Greenwald furnace (as in IEC 61241-2-1 (1994))[7] or the BAM furnace (for a description of these two furnaces see Appendix 3). Lower values of MIT are usually determined in the BAM furnace, because, due to the nature of the apparatus, delayed ignition of the gases produced from the dust that settles on the bottom of the furnace makes a contribution.

2.3.4 Limiting oxygen concentration

The limiting oxygen concentration (LOC) is defined as the highest oxygen concentration in a dust/air/inert gas mixture at which an explosion just fails to take place. Typical values when nitrogen is the inert gas range from 5–15%. The LOC depends on both the dust and the inert gas used. Measurement of the LOC is important if inerting forms part of the basis for safety.

Determinations of the LOC are usually carried out in the 1 m^3 vessel or the 20 litre sphere. A standard test procedure based upon the use of these test vessels is currently in preparation by CEN Technical Committee 305.

2.4 Dust layer flammability characteristics

A layer of a combustible dust can ignite and burn. If this happens it presents a considerable fire hazard whether the fire starts inside process plant, a storage container or in some deposit on the floor of a building.

Also it presents a potential ignition source for a dust cloud. It is important to be aware of the flammability characteristics of layers of the dust being processed. The following tests commonly are used for this purpose.

It is not the remit of this guide to cover fire hazards in any depth. A short discussion on dust fires is given in Appendix 4.

2.4.1 Flammability

The flammability of a dust deposit or layer specifies the ease with which the dust can be ignited by one or more ignition sources. If the dust deposit can be ignited in the test the dust is considered to be flammable.

The test consists of placing a triangular shaped dust deposit with base dimensions of 2 cm wide by 4 cm long on a ceramic plate and trying to ignite it with different ignition sources — for example, a gas flame, cigarette, match, etc. Further details on the procedure are given in an ISSA (1997)[8] publication. Details of the ignition source must be given.

2.4.2 Burning behaviour

If a dust deposit is flammable, the burning behaviour is used to describe the nature of the fire in the deposit.

The UN rules[9] for the transportation of dangerous goods describe a burning rate test that is commonly used. A mould is used to make a train of dust 200 mm

Table 2.4 Burning behaviour of dust layers

Type of reaction	Class
No burning, no ignition	1
Brief burning, rapid extinction	2
Localized combustion or smouldering (no or only very minor propagation)	3
Spread of a smouldering fire or slow, flameless decomposition	4
Spread of an open fire (burning with flame development)	5
Very rapid burn through with flame development or rapid, flameless decomposition	6

long and one end is ignited with a small flame or hot wire. The speed of spread of burning through the train is measured, as is the ability of the burn to pass through a section of wetted dust. The test can be performed either at room temperature or at an elevated temperature (usually 100°C). Burning rates are often greatly increased if the dust is ignited at an elevated temperature. A class number according to the definitions given in Table 2.4 then rates the burning behaviour of the dust sample.

The higher the combustion class, the more effective an ignition source the burning deposit is.

2.4.3 Minimum ignition temperature of a dust layer

The minimum ignition temperature (MIT) of a dust layer is the lowest temperature at which a dust layer on a hot surface ignites. For a dust layer of thickness 5 mm, the MIT is often referred to as the smoulder temperature, or sometimes the glow temperature. The measurement is important to assess the need for limiting the temperatures obtained in dust handling plant. Layer ignition temperatures are almost always lower than cloud ignition temperatures.

Procedures for determining the layer MIT are given in the ISSA (1997)[8] publication and in IEC 61241-2-1 (1994)[7]. There are slight differences between the procedures, but both methods use an electrically heated circular plate (200 mm diameter) upon which a dust layer 100 mm in diameter and 5 mm thick is placed. The plate is maintained at a constant temperature for a specified period and the condition of the dust sample noted. The layer MIT is the temperature at which ignition just takes place. This temperature cannot be divorced from an induction time, defined as the time between initial heating and the onset of glowing.

Caution must be exercised in using this layer MIT as a universal value for assessing the ignition risk where there is an accumulation of a dust. The geometry of the accumulation as well as the state of the accumulation can have a marked influence on the ignition temperature. A thin layer of a dust is likely to have a higher ignition temperature than a bulk deposit of the same dust, due to the difference in heat loss. The ignition temperature will also be different if air flows over the dust layer or through the dust (for example, in a fluidized bed dryer). Material held in bulk storage for long periods can also undergo spontaneous ignition as a result of slow exothermic reactions with oxygen or biological reactions. Test methods for determining the ignition temperature more appropriate to these different situations can be found in the ISSA (1997)[8] publication and the IChemE (1990) dryers guide[10].

2.5 Where to go for tests

The following laboratories in the UK are able to carry out the above tests and/or provide advice on testing, on a commercial basis:

FRS, Building Research
Establishment Ltd.
Garston
Watford
WD2 7JR

Burgoyne Consultants Ltd.
Burgoyne House
Chantry Drive
Ilkley
West Yorkshire
LS29 9HU

Chilworth Technology Limited
Chilworth Research Centre
Beta House
Southampton
SO16 7NS

Hazard Evaluation Laboratory
50 Moxon Street
Barnet
Herts
EN5 5TS

Health and Safety Laboratory
Harpur Hill
Buxton
Derbyshire
SK17 9JN

Syngenta Technology
Process Hazards Section
South Bank
Huddersfield Manufacturing Centre
PO Box A38
Huddersfield
HD2 1FF

References in Chapter 2

1. BIA Report 13/97, *Combustion and explosion characteristics of dusts*, Hauptverband der gewerblichen Berufsgenossenschaften, Sankt Augustin, Germany, ISBN 3-88383-469-6.

2. BS 6713 (1986). British Standard 6713: Part 1: 1986. *Method for the determination of explosion indices of combustible dusts in air,* British Standards Institution. [Note this is identical to EN26184-1: 1991 and ISO 6184/1: 1985].

3. Bartknecht, W. (1989), *Dust explosions: Course, prevention, protection*. Springer-Verlag, ISBN 0 387 50100 2.

4. BS 5958 (1991), British Standard 5958: 1991, *Code of practice for the control of undesirable static electricity,* Part 1: General considerations, Part 2: Recommendations for particular industrial situations, British Standards Institution.

5. IEC 61241-2-3 (1994), *Electrical apparatus for use in the presence of combustible dust*, Part 2: Test methods, Section 3: Methods for determining the minimum ignition energy of dust/air mixtures.

6. MIKE 3.2 Minimum Ignition Apparatus, February 1994, Adolf Kuhner AG, Dinkelbergstr. 1, CH-4127, Birsfelden, Switzerland.

7. IEC 61241-2-1 (1994), *Electrical apparatus for use in the presence of combustible dust*, Part 2: Test methods, Section 1: Methods for determining the minimum ignition temperatures of dusts.

8. International Safety Security Association (1997), *Determination of the combustion and explosion characteristics of dusts*, ISSA Prevention Series No. 2018 (E), Mannheim, ISBN 92-843-1092; ISSN 1015-8022.

9. Recommendations on the Transport of Dangerous Goods — Model Regulations (11th revised edition) United Nations NY 1999, ISBN 92-1-139067-2.

10. Abbott, J.A., 1990, *Prevention of Fires and Explosions in Dryers*, ISBN 0 85295 2570 (Institution of Chemical Engineers, Rugby, UK).

11. Hertzberg, M. and Cashdollar, K.L., 1987, Introduction to dust explosions, in Cashdollar, K.L. and Hertzberg, M. (Eds) *Industrial Dust Explosions, ASTM Special Technical Publication 958* (American Society of Testing and Materials).

12. Banhegyi, M. and Egyedi, J., 1983, Method for determining the explosive limits of a mixture of coal dust, methane and inert matter, Paper presented at the *20th International Conference of Safety in Mines Research Institutes, Sheffield*, UK, 3–7 October.

13. Feng, K.K., 1983, Hazardous characteristics of Canadian coal dusts, Paper presented at the *20th International Conference on Safety in Mines Research Institute, Sheffield*, UK, 3–7 October.

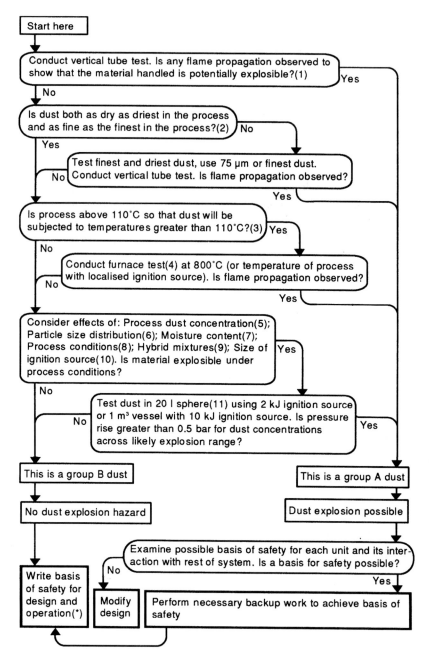

Logic Diagram 2 Testing and design (the numbers in brackets relate to those in the notes on the following pages).

      * It is strongly recommended that the basis of safety for the design should be formally recorded.

(1) Explosibility testing

Satisfactory designs for controlling dust explosion hazards must always be based on the results of tests performed on the materials involved in the process concerned. If material is unavailable for testing, it must be considered explosible and sensitive to ignition unless there is contrary evidence.

Dusts are considered to be Group A if they ignite and propagate flame in the vertical test apparatus. If there is no flame propagation, the dust is considered to be Group B.

(2) Retest/sieving and drying

Tests are often made on samples as received. If the sample does not ignite it should be re-tested under conditions of dryness and fineness appropriate to the process. Materials classified as Group B at ambient temperature may be explosible when process temperatures are higher than ambient, or larger ignition sources are potentially present.

(3) Retest at process temperature

A process temperature of $110°C$ is usually considered to be the temperature above which further testing of the likelihood of explosibility is considered necessary. Such a test is desirable in order to assess explosibility and sensitivity to ignition sources in heated environments.

(4) Test at elevated temperature

Although there is no nationally accepted test, the effect of elevated temperature is usually measured in the Godbert-Greenwald furnace set at $800°C$. This is a rigorous test for explosibility on account of the high temperature and large ignition source. If flame propagation is observed, the dust is re-classified as Group A. This result can be accepted as the final assessment but, because of the test's severity, further testing may be necessary to take into account less severe process conditions. This can be done by performing the furnace test at the known temperature of the process and with a localized ignition source inside the furnace tube. If flame propagation is observed the dust is classified as Group A.

Dusts which remain classified as Group B may require further testing in the 20 litre or $1\,m^3$ test vessels.

(5) Effect of process dust concentration on explosibility classification

When the concentration of dispersed dust is below a certain value, an explosion cannot be propagated. This concentration is the lower explosion limit (LEL), typically $10–100\,g\,m^{-3}$ (Note: compare this with the occupational hygiene limit that is measured in $mg\,m^{-3}$). The explosion violence of the cloud increases as the dust concentration increases until an optimum concentration is reached giving the highest explosion violence; this concentration is usually well in excess of the amount of dust theoretically required to react with the available oxygen.

At higher concentrations still the explosion violence either decreases or stays roughly constant. The upper explosion limit (UEL) is the dust concentration above which an explosion cannot be propagated. It is not as clearly defined as the lower limit. At high concentrations of coal dust, for example, the flame travels rapidly through a reactive volatiles/air mixture as soon as this mixture is produced and leaves the partly devolatilized particles in its wake[11]. Only at very high dust concentrations is the inerting effect of these particles sufficient to quench the flame.

Exclusion of an explosible dust cloud is one prevention method, but in practice it is difficult to prevent the formation of a hazardous dust cloud, although choice of plant can do much to minimize the problem. If the dust concentration normally exceeds the upper explosion limit there will be times (starting up, shutting down or in the event of a breakdown) when the concentration will be in the explosion range. It is difficult to maintain the necessary high dust concentration, except possibly in dense phase pneumatic transfer operations. Safety can be achieved by operating at concentrations below the LEL, for instance, in certain extraction ducts of powder/air conveying systems where only a small concentration of explosible dust is present.

Nevertheless, it is difficult to guarantee that the dust concentration will always remain below the lower explosion limit. Dust particles readily settle out as layers that can then be dispersed easily by flow disturbances, producing a cloud with a concentration that will more than likely exceed the lower explosion limit. Secondary explosions are a case in point: an explosion of a relatively small dust cloud can produce sufficient air movement to disperse dust which then fuels the flame and leads to extensive explosions, causing much damage.

Dust dispersion in dust-handling plant is not homogeneous. Dividing the known amount of dust by the known volume is unlikely to give a true value of the dust concentration at any point in the vessel. Operating at a mean concentration below the LEL can be useful, but this can only assist other precautionary methods.

An increase in temperature decreases the LEL, the effect increasing with higher concentrations of the room temperature LEL.

(6) Effect of particle size/distribution on explosibility and sensitivity to ignition

Finer particles have a proportionally greater surface area and are therefore more explosible. When the dust is made up of a series of particle sizes ranging from fine to coarse, the fines play the most prominent part in an ignition and in the propagation of an explosion; the effect of the coarse particles on the explosion violence is not significant unless the fraction of coarse particles is high.

Fine particles are more readily dispersible and stay in suspension longer but can agglomerate in some circumstances, depending on the dust and the forces attempting to disperse it. Careful consideration sometimes has to be given to the effective particle size in an explosion. Particles greater than about 500 µm in diameter are unlikely to cause dust explosions, although the possibility of coarser materials producing fine dust by attrition during handling must be anticipated.

For material that can form dust clouds, a Group B classification can only be given after testing a sieved sample. If the material contains both fine and coarse particles, then explosibility tests should be done on a sample that has a particle size less than 75 µm or the finest dust likely to be present in practice. An explosion can be propagated by fine material even when it constitutes only a small percentage of the total material in the cloud.

Particle size does not have a marked effect on the LEL. There are no means of precisely predicting the effect of particle size and/or distribution on explosibility and work in this area would be both long-term and expensive to provide a general solution. Acceptance as a basis for safety would also require plant control to maintain the specified distribution. In processes where the particle size distribution can be closely defined, explosibility testing to determine the sensitivity under process conditions can be carried out on representative samples having the size distribution existing in the process.

(7) Effect of moisture content on explosibility

Explosion violence falls as the moisture content of a dust increases. Eventually the dust is no longer explosible.

Guidelines for the effect of moisture content are as follows:

- 0–5% little effect;
- 5–25% decrease in sensitivity;
- >25% the dust is unlikely to be held in suspension and even if it is there will be a further decrease in sensitivity.

To avoid the sample being classified unrealistically, it is important that tests are not carried out on over-dried materials, that is, on samples containing less than the minimum moisture content found under normal process conditions.

In processes where the minimum moisture content can be closely defined, explosibility testing to determine the sensitivity under process conditions should be carried out using a sample containing the minimum moisture content found in the process.

(8) Effect of process conditions on explosibility

Process conditions that can affect the situation are pressure, temperature and inventory. Consideration should be given to the explosibility of a cloud and the violence of an explosion. Although at a given dust concentration an increase in the ambient temperature results in a decrease in the maximum explosion pressure in an enclosed explosion, it has very little effect on the rate of pressure rise. If the ambient pressure increases, both the maximum pressure and the rate of pressure rise increase.

(8.1) Pressure

Up to the pressures normally used, namely 2–3 bar, there is no significant effect on explosibility classification.

(8.2) Temperature

It is generally considered that a dust classified as Group B at ambient temperatures will remain non-explosible unless the temperature is greater than 110°C.

(8.3) Dust inventory

The dust inventory has no effect on explosibility of a dust cloud for a given concentration, but can have a marked effect on the self-heating of bulk material.

(9) Effect of hybrid mixtures (more than one phase) on explosibility

The presence of flammable gas or vapour as an admixture of low concentration can increase the explosion violence of a dispersed dust cloud markedly. These are so called 'hybrid mixtures'.

A mixture containing a flammable gas or vapour and an explosible dust may be more explosible than the explosibility characteristics of the individual components might suggest. If both the gas and dust in such a mixture are present in concentrations less than their individual LELs, the mixture may still be explosive. At present, no method exists for predicting limits for such mixtures from theoretical considerations but some experimental data has been published[12,13]. Such mixtures, if necessary, need to be tested using standard methods.

The admixture of a small quantity of flammable gas to a dust cloud can reduce the lower explosion limit; reduce markedly the minimum ignition energy; decrease the dust concentration at which the highest values of explosibility occur; and, increase markedly the rate of pressure rise in an enclosed explosion of carbonaceous dusts with weak values of explosibility.

(10) Size of potential ignition sources

The localized ignition source used in the vertical tube test may not adequately simulate the potential ignition sources in the real process. The larger the ignition source the greater the probability of a dust being classified explosible.

(11) Further testing in 20 litre or 1 m³ vessels

Further testing can be done using either a 20 litre test vessel using an ignition source of energy 0.5 kJ to 2.0 kJ or a 1 m^3 vessel with a 10 kJ ignition source. If a pressure rise of less than 0.5 bar is recorded for all dust concentrations across the likely explosion range, the dust is considered to be non-explosible.

Control of ignition 3

3.1 Introduction

Dust explosions cannot occur unless an effective ignition source of sufficient energy to initiate flame propagation is present. Avoidance or elimination of potential sources of ignition therefore is a crucial step in preventing dust explosions. A careful analysis of all aspects of plant design, plant operation and product reactivity is required if all potential ignition sources are to be identified and the hazard they represent reduced or eliminated.

The considerations necessary before exclusion of ignition sources can be accepted as a basis of safety are summarized in Logic diagram 3 (at the end of this chapter). However, the total elimination of all ignition sources is difficult to guarantee. The exclusion of all obvious ignition sources is normally the first step in safety rather than a basis for safety. A risk-based approach is a more realistic alternative (see Section 3.3).

3.2 Ignition sources

Ignition sources responsible for the majority of explosions are:

1. flames;
2. hot surfaces;
3. burning material;
4. spontaneous heating;
5. welding or cutting operations;
6. friction generated heating or sparks;
7. electric sparks;
8. electrostatic discharge sparks.

How they arise and the measures that can be taken to reduce the risk of their occurrence are discussed below.

3.2.1 Flames

Almost any flame is capable of igniting an explosible dust. Common sources of flames present in industrial plant are described below.

Direct-fired space and process heating

Direct-fired heating should be avoided wherever possible. Indirect heating of buildings by hot water or low-pressure steam is preferred. Special care should be taken to ensure that standby or temporary heating does not introduce additional ignition sources.

Where direct heating is used to provide hot air for the process, for example in drying, a separate combustion chamber should be provided to keep flames well away from the explosible dust. Direct heating should never be used where a flammable vapour may arise. Hot particles from the heater can be a source of ignition. To avoid this danger the following precautions are recommended[1]:

1. Draw combustion air and dilution air from a reasonably dust-free zone and filter it. Filters should be inspected regularly and cleaned in a safe place.
2. Clean burners regularly and operate them at the correct air-fuel ratio. Erratic burning and flame blow-off should be investigated and remedied immediately. In most applications the correct air-fuel ratio is that which gives complete combustion, although in some applications excess air is used to prevent the generation of noxious fumes.
3. Powder must not enter the combustion chamber. This should be borne in mind when considering recirculation of air from the dryer.
4. Precautions should be taken to prevent large particles entering the dryer. A 3 mm mesh is recommended if large particles can otherwise enter the dryer with the hot gases.

Detailed advice on the use of gas or oil burners is available in Codes of Practice[2,3]. While shut down the plant should be isolated from the burners to prevent leakage of gas into the plant and at start-up combustion products should not be fed to the process until the flame is established[1]. Consideration should be given to the effects of an emergency burner shutdown on the safe operation of process plant. In most circumstances safe shutdown will involve shutting off the material feed to the plant. The design and operation of boilers or furnaces for burning pulverized coal, wood dust or similar fuels is a specialized topic not covered in this book, although dust explosion precautions will inevitably be needed[4].

Dislodged layers of smouldering dust

Layers of smouldering dust can become dislodged and burn with flame. The formation of smouldering dust as a result of contact with hot surfaces or from spontaneous combustion is discussed separately.

Cigarettes and other smoking materials

Smoking should be prohibited in areas where there is a dust explosion hazard. It may be necessary to set up 'no smoking' areas, on entry to which all smoking materials must be given up. Where contract workers and staff unfamiliar with the plant are involved, additional supervision may be necessary.

Internal combustion engines

Internal combustion engines can cause ignitions by ingestion of an explosible dust cloud, resulting in explosions within the exhaust, or inlet manifolds which then propagate to the external atmosphere, or via ignition of dust layers that accumulate on the hot surfaces of the engine. Normally internal combustion engines should not be used in the presence of any explosible powder. However, it is possible to flameproof internal combustion compression ignition engines (diesel engines) so they can be operated in locations where an explosible dust cloud may arise for short periods. There is a European standard[5] that specifies the requirements.

Welding and cutting flames

Welding and cutting produce localized heating of plant and sparks which are known to have caused dust explosions. Similar hazards arise from operations such as soldering, burning and the use of power tools. Work carried on outside equipment can easily heat up any dust left inside the equipment. Any flammable material left in the vicinity of welding operations (for example, wooden structures, tarpaulins) can be ignited by welding sparks and remain smouldering for several hours.

Welding and cutting and other repair work involving the application of heat are subject to statutory requirements. Work should only be permitted after the plant has been shut down, emptied and cleared of dust or the dust has been rendered non-explosible. The surrounding area should also be cleared of dust. The introduction of a 'permit to work' system, where permits are issued daily or sometimes hourly is useful, particularly where outside contractors are involved. Particular care should be taken where the work is undertaken in a confined space. For example, it may be necessary to ventilate the space both to keep the atmosphere fresh and to remove any leaking gas. On no account should the atmosphere be oxygenated. Protective systems and services should be isolated before entry is made. Further advice on entry into confined spaces can be found in an HSC Approved Code of Practice[6].

Any flammable materials in the vicinity of welding and cutting activities should be cleared away or at least protected by non-flammable sheeting. Wooden structures and floors can be similarly covered or at least wetted before repairs commence. Flammable materials in adjacent rooms should also be removed if there is any possibility of sparks passing through cracks or openings. Suitable fire-fighting equipment should be to hand and the maintenance team competent in its operation.

Equipment should not be left unattended. Particular care should be taken to ensure that electrical equipment is adequately earthed.

Accidental fires elsewhere in the factory

The presence of fires started accidentally, elsewhere in a factory, is a serious ignition risk. Precautions to prevent the spread of fire are described below. In the case of a fire, great care must be taken when attempting to extinguish it. An explosible dust cloud should be prevented from contacting the fire. In the case of burning settled dust the attempt to put out the fire should not stir the dust into suspension. Although small confined volumes of dust may be allowed to burn themselves out under continuous surveillance, the usual approach is to extinguish the fire. Selection of the most suitable extinguishing agent will usually depend on factors such as the composition of the dust, its situation, and the presence of other hazardous material and equipment nearby.

3.2.2 Hot surfaces

Hot surface ignition is related to surface temperature and geometry, contact time, airflow, contamination and the chemistry and history of the material on it. Preventing the build-up of dust layers on hot surfaces, by good housekeeping, can significantly reduce the risk of ignition from this source.

In the standard test for determining the minimum ignition temperature of a dust layer, the layer is 5 mm thick (see Chapter 2, Section 2.4.3). However, layer thickness can strongly influence the layer ignition temperature or glow temperature. Thicker layers require lower layer ignition temperatures. A general rule of thumb is that the decrease is approximately $5°C\,mm^{-1}$ of layer thickness.

If the air above the layer is at a temperature higher than normal room temperature, layer ignition temperature will fall. A typical decrease is 40°C–60°C at an air temperature of 100°C. It is preferable to check this by measurement, especially for dryers, where hot air flows are passed over layers by design or pass over layers deposited on internal surfaces in normal running.

It is important that ignition temperatures are measured under conditions that reflect as closely as possible those in the intended application by using tests[1] developed to simulate conditions in various types of dryers and obtain measurements of the temperature at which exothermic reaction begins.

The aerated powder test simulates conditions in dryers where a hot air stream passes through material. The powder is held in an 80 mm long, 50 mm diameter glass cylinder closed at each end by sintered glass. The cylinder is placed in a fan-assisted oven and air is passed downwards through the powder at the same temperature as the surroundings. A screening test may be performed, but a more thorough study is made with isothermal tests at different temperatures and for periods exceeding the drying time. The number of isothermal tests will depend on the precision required in the result.

Impurities, slight changes in composition and autocatalytic reactions can have a marked effect on the temperature at which exothermic activity begins. Performing the test with a temperature cycle akin to that likely to occur in the dryer is a useful addition to the isothermal tests. In order to minimise the hazard, a material temperature 30–50°C below the measured temperature is generally recommended, but this safety factor should not be the only basis for safety.

A layer test for dryers where hot air passes over deposits or layers uses a layer 75 mm by 40 mm and 15 mm deep. A screening test can be used, but isothermal tests, each lasting perhaps for several hours, are the tests mainly used to obtain ignition temperatures. If the layer depth properly simulates the dryer conditions, the temperature at which an exotherm can progress to red heat can be used as a basis for safe procedures rather than the somewhat lower temperature at which exothermic activity begins. An adequate safety margin is usually 20°C.

A bulk powder test uses the same apparatus as the aerated powder test but the hot air flows around the sample and not through it. Screening tests, isothermal tests, low heat loss tests and simulation of process cycles can be performed. If the operating temperature is 50°C less than the measured exotherm onset temperature from the screening tests, dangerous decomposition is unlikely to occur up to at least 1 tonne capacity. However, if this temperature difference is less than 50°C, or the operating cycle is longer than the test duration, or the measured temperature is less than 200°C, isothermal tests should be performed. These should be done at 50°C above the process temperature and with a longer duration than the operational time. A low heat loss test using a Dewar flask should follow. The build-up of bulk powder at the base of dryers should be prevented, possibly by use of a level detector.

The temperature measured in tests that assess the capability of bulk powders to undergo thermal decomposition governs the maximum safe discharge temperature from dryers. Bulking can occur in cyclones, filters and packages. If these tests reveal that time, bulk or rate of heat loss are important factors, tests with simulated process conditions should be carried out.

Temperatures higher than normal in the dryer cycle should be minimized, for example, at start-up or shutdown. Disturbance of a smouldering dust layer can cause inflammation and so create an ignition source for a dust cloud. Contamination of the layers with oil or other substances can lead to a marked reduction in the ignition temperature.

The minimum ignition temperature (MIT) of a dust cloud gives a measurement of the surface temperature at which a dust cloud can be ignited (see Chapter 2, Section 2.3.3). Ignition must be anticipated if surface temperatures higher than the MIT are known to be present. Usually a safety factor of $50°C$ is adequate. In areas outside the plant liable to contamination with combustible dusts, surface temperatures must not exceed $75°C$ below the measured ignition temperature of a 5 mm thick layer, and should not exceed $\frac{2}{3}$ of the ignition temperature of a dust suspension.

3.2.3 Spontaneous heating

The source of heating for ignition of a dust does not necessarily have to be a flame or hot surface. Layers of dust accumulating in and around process plant and material held in bulk storage can undergo spontaneous heating if left undisturbed for a period of time. The heating may occur as a result of slow exothermic reactions of the material with oxygen or biological reactions. Ignition can then occur if the temperature of the material is raised to a level at which the heat liberated by the exothermic reaction is sufficient to exceed heat losses, leading to a runaway increase in temperature. Spontaneous heating is not necessarily rapid and usually there is considerable delay before ignition occurs.

The minimum temperature for self-ignition will depend mainly on the overall dimensions of the mass of material and the time of exposure to the heat. The onset temperature for self-heating varies greatly with the size of the sample tested. For example, the UN test for the transport of dangerous substances[7] uses a 10 cm cube (1 litre) sample. An onset temperature of $140°C$ at this scale is assumed to be equivalent to an onset temperature of $40°C$ with a cargo stored in a 3 m cube (27 m^3). However, a reliable assessment of the ignition risk can be made from the results of small-scale laboratory tests by applying thermal ignition theory[8]. Other variables, such as the rate of airflow across or through the material, the local oxygen concentration and whether the material is disturbed, have some effect on the minimum ignition temperature.

For the minimum ignition temperature test to give an accurate indication of the risk of spontaneous heating it is, therefore, important it is carried out on a sample representative of the material in the process and it simulates the conditions that exist in the plant. The tests described in Section 3.2.2, on hot surfaces, can be used to simulate the various process conditions that may arise.

One of the main ways of preventing spontaneous heating is to ensure that material does not remain undisturbed in storage for long periods of time. Bins and hoppers for storing materials liable to spontaneous heating may be either mass-flow or core-flow. Mass-flow bins in which all of the material in the bin moves during discharge do not need complete emptying if the material has only a short hold-up time. In core-flow bins not all of the material moves during discharge and so it is necessary to empty them completely on a regular basis.

Many materials heat up spontaneously from atmospheric ambient temperatures, particularly when stored in bulk. These include coal, sawdust, reactive metals, and dusts impregnated with vegetable oils. Special care should be taken when storing such materials. Highly reactive materials should not be allowed to form dust layers around a plant and it is often recommended that they are stored in airtight containers. Reactive metals may cease to be reactive after initial oxidation of the surface. Allowing the oxidation to proceed under controlled conditions is one way of inerting the material prior to storage.

Attention should be given to changing weather conditions affecting the temperature of stored material. It may, for instance, be desirable to deflect the sun's rays from storage hoppers.

Spontaneous heating can be restricted to some extent by storing the material in several small stores rather than one large one. Periodic recirculation of the stored material in hoppers or reblending of materials in stockpiles can achieve cooling of large stores. The addition of water to cool material should be used with caution since it may increase heat generation or cause hazardous side reactions (for example, water on pulverised coal can produce hydrogen and carbon monoxide which then may explode). Spontaneous heating often produces carbon monoxide. Thus monitoring for carbon monoxide emissions from the material is one way of detecting the onset of heating.

Deep-seated fires within a large silo, for example, a pulverized coal silo, can be very difficult to extinguish. Discharging the product creates the risk that the fire could flare up or a dust explosion could occur as smouldering material meets a supply of fresh air. Sometimes the only safe way of dealing with the problem is to displace the air above the powder level in the silo with an inert gas. It is then necessary to wait days or even weeks for the fire to extinguish when it runs out of oxygen, and for the powder to cool so it will not flare up when discharged.

3.2.4 Thermite ignition

Many Group A dusts can be ignited by thermite reaction. The normal requirements for a thermite ignition by impact are for a light alloy containing, for example, aluminium or titanium to be used; for rust to be present; and, for an impact to occur. All three requirements must coincide for ignition to occur, consequently, one or more must be excluded.

3.2.5 Friction (impact and rubbing) and mechanical sparks

These ignition sources have been implicated in 25% of dust explosions. Tramp metal, hot bearings, moving vanes and belts are the most common sources of ignition. There has been a limited amount of work carried out on the ignition of dust clouds by these sources and no recognized methods for characterizing dust clouds with respect to their sensitivity to the different forms of ignition sources produced by friction and impact are known.

There are several different ways in which the dust cloud can be ignited by mechanical ignition sources. In flammable gas situations, potential ignition mechanisms are the heated contact area produced by rubbing or impact, and any hot particles of the contacting materials that are projected into the gas/air mixture. The heated contact area and the hot particles from the contact materials can also ignite dust clouds, but the presence of powder in the contact region can also result in an ignition, particularly in rubbing friction situations. For this latter situation, the frictional heating does not have to produce the temperature levels required to ignite the dust cloud, but only the lower temperature levels required to initiate exothermic decomposition of the powder. Burning powder produced by the progression of the reaction to red heat can present an additional hazard.

A number of studies are now in hand to develop methods for determining the conditions, in terms of the minimum energy and/or minimum velocity between contact surfaces, required for frictional ignition of dust clouds. CEN (Technical Committee 305) is developing European Standards for mechanical equipment, safe for use in powder handling areas.

In the majority of powder handling plants, the consequences of a frictional ignition will be a fire or a dust explosion. Certain chemicals (for example, azides, nitro-compounds, perchlorates, nitrates, and so on) can react violently in bulk when exposed to energy sources. Such materials should not be processed in mechanical equipment where they would be subjected to friction. At present no test method is available to characterize powders in terms of their reaction in bulk to localized heat sources produced by friction.

3.2.6 Electricity

Electric power either from mains or batteries can produce sparks with sufficient energy to ignite dusts. As a general precaution, the installation of electrical equipment should be avoided where an explosible dust is likely to occur. If installation in such areas cannot be avoided, electrical equipment should be totally enclosed and dust-tight. Flame-proof or intrinsically safe equipment designed for gases should not be assumed to be suitable for dusts. Requirements for the use of electrical equipment in dusty areas are available[9,10].

3.2.7 Electrostatic discharges

In any powder handling operation electrostatic charge can build up on bulk powder, powder suspension, process equipment and fittings, personnel and objects nearby. Electrification can be expected whenever a powder comes into contact with a dissimilar surface, in mixing, grinding, sieving, pouring, micronising and pneumatic transfer. The presence of the charged powder may then result in a charge being transferred to objects in contact with it or induced on nearby objects. Rapid discharge of the accumulated charge in the form of a spark may provide a source of sufficient energy to ignite an explosible dust cloud. There are various types of discharge associated with the handling and processing of powders[11].

Over a period of time the charge will gradually leak away to earth by conduction resulting in a decrease in or relaxation of the charge. The time taken for relaxation depends on the overall resistivity of the leakage path to earth. The major electrostatic hazards are associated with:

1. Isolated conductors, such as non-earthed metal containers (Figure 3.1), insulated pipes and ducts (Figure 3.2), small metal plant components, and dipsticks and metal probes. If isolated conductors come into contact with a powder stream they may collect charge until they release this charge as a distinct spark when an earthed metal object is brought near.
2. High resistivity non-conducting construction materials, particularly those of high dielectric strength. If these are found in thin layers in close contact with a metal object they may store high charges on the surface, until released in a form known as a propagating brush discharge.
3. Containers, silos, FIBCs, drums, etc. made from non-conducting plastic materials may sometimes cause an increased risk.
4. Powders with high volume electrical resistivities ($>10^{10}$ ohm.m), which store any charge they collect for an extended period.

The electrostatic hazard associated with a particular powder material may be assessed by means of measurements[12] of the minimum ignition energy (MIE)

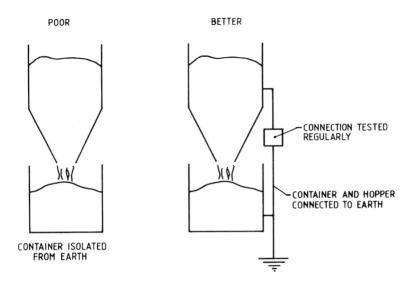

POOR

BETTER

CONNECTION TESTED
REGULARLY

CONTAINER AND HOPPER
CONNECTED TO EARTH

CONTAINER ISOLATED
FROM EARTH

Figure 3.1 Hazard associated with non-earthed metal container

and volume resistivity of the dust. Test results are strongly influenced by the method of measurement, and care must be used when interpreting data drawn from different sources.

Table 3.1 gives general guidance on precautions to take for low and medium resistivity powders with volume resistivities less than about 10^{12} ohm.m. Increased precautions are necessary for high resistivity powders with volume resistivities greater than 10^{12} ohm.m. Advice on precautions against the risk of

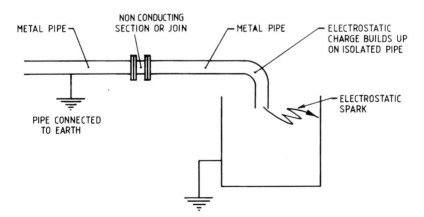

NON CONDUCTING
SECTION OR JOIN

METAL PIPE

METAL PIPE

ELECTROSTATIC
CHARGE BUILDS UP
ON ISOLATED PIPE

ELECTROSTATIC
SPARK

PIPE CONNECTED
TO EARTH

Figure 3.2 Hazard associated with isolated pipes

35

Table 3.1 General guidance on electrostatic precautions for powder suspensions in air in metal plant

Minimum ignition energy (BS 5958)	Precautions
500 mJ	Low sensitivity to ignition. Earth plant when ignition energy is at or below this level.
50 mJ	Earth personnel when ignition energy is at or below this level.
25 mJ	The majority of ignition incidents occur when ignition energy is below this level.
10 mJ	High sensitivity to ignition. Particular attention should be paid to the use of high resistivity non-conductors when ignition energy is at or below this level.
1 mJ	Extremely sensitive to ignition. The presence of an explosible dust cloud should be avoided wherever possible. Handling operations should be such that they minimize the possibility of suspending the powder in air. All possible steps should be taken to encourage the dissipation of charge and to discourage charge generation.

The above applies only to metal plants. Where plastic plants or components are in use, other considerations are necessary. See References 12 and 13.

ignition by static discharge in a range of common industrial operations is given in standards[12] and in European Guidelines[13]. Consultation of these references is recommended before deciding safety measures.

Earthing of plant[12,13] is the primary safety measure against electrostatic discharge but additional precautions will sometimes be needed. Earthing metallic parts in contact with moving dust will almost always be appropriate. It is important that the integrity of the bond to earth is maintained. A monitoring system should be established. All earthing devices should be inspected visually on a regular basis. In addition, measurements of earthing resistance should be made before the plant is brought into use after a scheduled maintenance shutdown, and after any other modification or maintenance. A log of measured resistance should also be kept in order to bring to light any changes.

It is important to bear in mind that the MIE of a dust cloud and thus its sensitivity to ignition by electrostatic discharge can be significantly altered by changes in process conditions. Particle size has a marked effect on the MIE (decreasing with decreasing particle size). There is no means of precisely predicting the effect of particle size and/or distribution, so determinations need to be carried out on representative samples having the size distribution existing in the process. Basing the safety case on a given particle size always being present would also require plant control to maintain the specified distribution.

The drier the samples the lower the MIE. To avoid the sample being classified as unrealistically sensitive, it is important that tests are not carried out on overdried materials, that is, on samples containing less than the minimum moisture content found under normal process conditions. In processes where the minimum moisture content can be closely defined, testing to determine the ignition sensitivity under process conditions should be carried out using a sample containing the minimum moisture content found in the process. There is no available method for predicting the effect of moisture content on ignition sensitivity.

The sensitivity to ignition of an explosible dust can be markedly affected by relatively small increases in temperature. The MIE value can decrease by a factor of 10 for a temperature change from 20–100°C[14,15].

The admixture of a small quantity of flammable gas or vapour to a dust cloud can reduce markedly the MIE. In general, flammable gases have very much lower minimum ignition energies than dusts and are of the order of 0.1–1.0 millijoules. For a mixture of a flammable gas and an explosible dust the MIE may be lower than the characteristics of the individual components might suggest. Ignition is, therefore, much more likely to occur when a dust cloud exists in the presence of a flammable gas.

3.3 Assessment of ignition hazards and risks

The total elimination of all potential sources of ignition is difficult to guarantee and could be very expensive. The possibility of self-heating of any material involved in the process must also be excluded. An alternative and more flexible approach is a risk based one. This would involve assessing the risk from each potential ignition source and then implementing prevention measures to make that risk as low as reasonably practicable (the ALARP principle). It may be that the risk of ignition cannot be reduced to acceptable levels, in which case explosion protection measures, such as explosion relief, would be required to reduce the consequences of an ignition. There should not be total reliance on protective measures alone as the basis of safety. Important ignition sources that should be excluded as far as possible no matter what other precautions are taken include hot surfaces, electrical and mechanically generated sparks, static electricity, flames and spontaneous ignition of dust deposits.

3.3.1 Risk assessment

A risk assessment would include the following elements:

1. Identification of all potential ignition sources.
2. Determining whether an explosive atmosphere is likely to occur and the amount of material involved.
3. Determining the likelihood of the ignition sources igniting the explosive atmosphere.
4. Determining the possible effects of an ignition and the resulting explosion.
5. Evaluating the risk.
6. Consideration of measures for minimizing the risks.

Further guidance on undertaking a risk assessment can be found in BS EN 1127-1[16]. When ATEX 137[17] comes into force in 2003 it will make documenting the elements of this risk assessment a specific legal requirement.

3.3.2 Zoning

The risk of an ignition and the measures required to reduce the risk will depend on the likelihood of an explosible dust cloud being present. For practical purposes it is convenient to use a zone classification based on the frequency and duration of occurrence of an explosible atmosphere[16].

Zoning of dust handling plant has not been widely carried out in the past, but it will become a requirement once the ATEX 137 user Directive[17] is in force after June 2003. The prime purpose of the zoning exercise is to identify areas where installed equipment needs to be of an explosion protected design, and this now covers mechanical as well as electrical equipment. It is also useful as a basis for deciding where special controls are needed during maintenance activities that create a risk of fire or explosion. The risk of an ignition and the measures required to reduce the risk will depend on the likelihood of an explosible dust cloud being present. The standard[16] and Directive[17] recognize three zones for dusts, which mirror those that have been in common use where flammable gases and vapours are present. Dust layers may form over an extended period of time from small releases that never reach a concentration within the explosion range. The zoning of such places remains a matter of debate, as ignition sources are much more likely to cause a fire than an explosion, and in a strict sense zoning concerns only the probability that an explosive atmosphere may form. In practise, it is usually sensible to select equipment to prevent fires and explosions, and the selection criteria are essentially the same. The definitions of the zones are given in BS EN 1127-1[16], and will

also appear in the regulations implementing the ATEX 137 user Directive[17].
They are as follows:

Zone 20
A place in which an explosive atmosphere in the form of a cloud of explosible dust in air is present continuously, for long periods or frequently.

Zone 21
A place in which an explosive atmosphere in the form of a cloud of explosible dust in air is likely to occur in normal operation occasionally.

Zone 22
A place in which an explosive atmosphere in the form of a cloud of explosible dust in air is not likely to occur in normal operation, but, if it does occur, will persist for a short period only.

They are accompanied by the statement that: Layers, deposits and heaps of explosive dust shall be considered as sources which can form an explosive atmosphere. For a particular plant and dust, there may be no way of forming a cloud from a dust layer if the dust is comparatively dense, low air speeds are always expected, the dust is hygroscopic or has a strong tendency to agglomerate or for other reasons. A local assessment of these factors is needed.

The results of a zoning study are usually documented in the form of drawings, using different symbols for the different zones (recommended symbols are given in the standard [16]).

Zone 20 is most likely to be assigned to areas inside containers, pipes and vessels. Within zone 20, many places may sometimes be completely submerged in dust. Inside a storage hopper or silo conditions will vary from no explosive atmosphere, above the powder level, soon after filling ceases, to submerged in powder, perhaps some metres deep. Although flow patterns of dust during filling of silos and operation of cyclones and similar equipment may be measured, these should not in general be used to define some internal parts of individual vessels as zone 20 while others are zone 21. Many conditions may lead to abnormal flow patterns and alter the extent of dust clouds above the lower explosion concentration.

Dust clouds within the explosion range are dense, and no one can see through them more than a metre or so. Accordingly, the extent of zone 21 during powder filling and emptying can to some extent be assessed visually. No one can work effectively in zone 21 except briefly, and proper design of extraction ventilation at predictable points of release will in nearly all cases eliminate zone 21 in the general open parts of buildings. Wind speeds out of doors are such that any zone 21 is unlikely to exist or will have minimal extent. Zone 21 may apply to the inside of process plant that is filled infrequently enough not to justify designation as zone 20.

A location is most likely to be assessed zone 22 as a result of the possibility of dust clouds forming where the dust containment system can spill substantial amounts of dust.

Examples are:

1. holding bins that can be overfilled and spill product;
2. unenclosed filters and bags below such filters, which can tear or come loose[18];
3. large bags which could tear or release product from a bottom opening while being moved;
4. flexible connections between items of plant;
5. explosion vent panels which could fail for reasons other than an explosion;
6. pneumatic conveying systems that could overpressurize weak systems leading to failure of a coupling joint or vessel.

Correct design of such systems should prevent this.

Well fitting doors with a self-closing device will normally be adequate to prevent the spread of significant quantities of dust from one room to another. If there are other openings in the building wall, however, dust can easily spread through and form deposits in rooms remote from the source of release.

The inside of ductwork for local extraction ventilation systems should normally run with dust loading below the lower explosion limit. However, if abnormal conditions could allow the dust concentration to exceed the lower explosion limit, the inside may need to be zoned as 21 or 22.

Zone 22 may well extend above any foreseeable source of release if the finest dust is fine enough to be carried on thermal currents up to high levels within a building. An explosion in a process vessel may well produce a shock wave sufficient to disturb dust layers in an adjacent room. If housekeeping standards are good, this adjacent area may not need to be assigned as zone 22.

Newly installed plant may well be dust tight and rooms containing this plant may then not be considered as zone 22. However, over time leaks in plants often develop, and dust layers then form. Similarly, poor operation, e.g., leaving inspection hatches open, may lead to dust escapes where none were expected by the plant designers. Area classification needs to consider these possibilities.

Once the zones are established, equipment can be selected, and one of the most important criteria is the maximum surface temperature. EN 1127-1[16] specifies safety margins between the maximum surface temperature of equipment, and the cloud or layer ignition temperature of the dust. Layer ignition temperatures are usually lower than cloud ignition temperatures, and layer temperatures normally are the controlling factor for equipment selection.

Often a fire in a dust layer precedes a dust explosion. Clearly, in selecting equipment to avoid explosions, the risk of igniting a dust layer or deposit should be considered. Some dusts however can char or degrade but do not produce smouldering or flaming combustion in the form of a layer, even though they may explode as a cloud. This may have a bearing on equipment selection. It may also be necessary to consider the possibility that a dust layer on equipment acts as insulation, causing the equipment to overheat, and develop a fault.

Further advice on zoning is contained in prEN 50281 Part 3. (This was distributed for final voting with a closing date of June 2001. It received a positive vote.)

3.4 Examples of ignition prevention measures

No code of practice exists to cover all situations and careful consideration of ignition sources and their relative hazard is required for each and every plant handling explosible dusts. Ignition hazards should be assessed separately for each plant and appropriate precautions taken. Precautions against ignition are not usually sufficient on their own and explosion protection measures (for example, explosion containment — Chapter 5, explosion suppression — Chapter 6, or explosion venting — Chapter 7), will usually be necessary to protect people and equipment in the event that ignition prevention measures fail. Some precautions against the possibility of ignition, specific to some particular types of equipment are given below. This section should not be read in isolation. In addition to the particular precautions listed for the various types of equipment, as a general point it should be noted that any electrical equipment should conform to a recognized standard for dust equipment — for example BS EN 50281-1-1/2[9,10].

3.4.1 Size reduction processes

1. Remove ferrous metal from the feed with magnets.
2. Remove tramp non-ferrous metal and stones from the feed with a pneumatic separator.
3. Ensure separators are regularly maintained and emptied.
4. Control feed input rate.
5. Install overload monitor on drive motor.
6. Maintain and lubricate bearings regularly.
7. Check and maintain the alignment of mechanical components and tolerances regularly.
8. Periodically check for excessive heating of mechanical components.
9. Regularly maintain drive chains and lubrication. Maintain correct tension.
10. Ensure that the correct number of V-belt drives is fitted and that they are maintained at the correct tension. V-belt drives should be fire-resistant and, for dusts with low minimum ignition energies, be anti-static.
11. Open mesh metal machinery-guards should be fitted to prevent dust accumulation and aid ventilation.
12. All components should be checked for earth connection, including frames and guards. Earth resistance should be less than 10 ohms. Lubricant-isolated components may, under certain circumstances, be permitted resistances to earth up to 10^6 ohms. Special earthing connections may be necessary and will require regular inspection (BS 5958)[12].
13. Feedstock should not be kept within the size reduction enclosure.

3.4.2 Pneumatic conveying lines

1. All components should be regularly checked for earth connection, which should have a resistance less than 10 ohms.
2. Where flexible connections are required, flexible metal parts are preferred.
3. Pipework either side of sight-glasses and flange connections should be connected to earth with resistance less than 10 ohms.
4. Conveying air should be drawn from a clean, ignition free source.
5. Blower, fan, pump, or compressor motors should be fitted with an overload trip.
6. Air pressure relief and non-return valves may also be fitted.
7. Feed to the system should be controlled at the optimum rate.
8. Detectors to sense hot material and/or sparks which initiate shutdown if hot material or sparks are detected in the feed may be installed at the feed point.
9. At start-up, the air supply should first be established and then powder fed in at its optimum rate as quickly as possible.

10. At shutdown the powder supply should be stopped quickly and the air continued at the optimum rate until all powder has been removed.
11. Pneumatic conveying lines should not contain any dead areas where dust can accumulate.
12. Non-conducting plastic conveying lines should be used with care. Anti-static plastics should be used if the material is sensitive to ignition by static electricity[13].

3.4.3 Screw conveyors
1. Top and bottom covers should be securely attached and should not be readily removable. Maintenance procedures should state clearly that covers must be replaced before the plant is started.
2. Drive motors should incorporate an overload cut out.
3. All components should be connected to earth with an earthing resistance less than 10 ohms. Earthing resistance should be checked regularly.
4. Maintain and lubricate bearings regularly. Check that bearings do not overheat.
5. Maintain correct tension on drive chains and ensure regular lubrication.
6. Maintain the correct tension on V-belt drives where fitted. V-belts should be fire resistant and anti-static, if the material is sensitive to ignition by static electricity.
7. Open-mesh metal machinery-guards should be fitted.

3.4.4 Drag link or en masse conveyors
Similar precautions to screw conveyors. The volume of the return leg should be as small as possible.

3.4.5 Belt conveyors
1. Not recommended for explosible dusts, except where totally enclosed by a suitably protected enclosure.
2. Similar precautions to screw conveyors should be taken.
3. Belting should be made of antistatic material if the material is sensitive to ignition by static electricity (see BS 5958)[12].
4. Bearings should be external to the dust carrying components and should give, if possible, an alarm if overheating occurs.
5. A harmonized European standard for belt conveyors is in preparation, as EN 620. An example of an assessment of the ignition risks from belt conveyors is given in EN 13463-1[19].

3.4.6 Bucket elevators

1. Dust-tight casings should be fitted and should not be readily removable. Maintenance procedures should make clear the importance of replacing casings.
2. Belt alignment sensors should be provided particularly where metal buckets are used.
3. All buckets should be securely fixed. Damaged or missing buckets should be replaced by buckets of the correct size. Oversize buckets increase the risk of impact with the casing.
4. Belt speed meters should be incorporated to detect belt slip. Belt slip detection should result in shutdown.
5. Anti-runback devices should be installed.
6. Bearings should be inspected regularly and lubricated. Bearing temperature sensors may be desirable.
7. The drive should be external to the casing.
8. Antistatic belting should be used if the material is sensitive to ignition by static electricity (see BS 5958)[12].
9. The feed rate should be controlled within the design limits, and overloading should not be permitted.
10. An overload trip should be installed on the drive.
11. Bucket elevators should be installed if possible outside of buildings.
12. A harmonised European standard is in preparation for continuous bulk handling equipment, including bucket elevators, as EN 618.

3.4.7 Dryers

1. Ignition prevention precautions for dryers are described in an IChemE guide[1].
2. The temperature of flammable materials should be kept a safe margin below the relevant ignition temperatures. Recommended safety margins are given for individual dryer types in the IChemE guide[1]. During start-up and shutdown the heat input should be regulated to prevent the exhaust air temperature exceeding a predetermined value.
3. Layers of dust should not be allowed to accumulate inside vessels and regular inspection and cleaning is necessary. Ledges, corners and crevices where dust can accumulate should be eliminated. Any smouldering deposits should be extinguished, for example by using a gentle water spray, before removing them.
4. Dust spills and any dust accumulations outside the dryer should be removed. Oil leaks should be remedied immediately.

5. Direct heating systems should not be used if the dryer contains flammable vapour.
6. A separate combustion chamber should be provided to keep flames away from flammable dust.
7. Combustion and dilution air should be clean.
8. Operate burners according to relevant codes of practice[2,3].
9. Hot gases should pass through a mesh not exceeding 3 mm before entering the dryer. The mesh should be cleaned regularly.
10. Equipment should be earthed.
11. Low conductivity materials of construction and other non-conducting items should be avoided for static-sensitive dusts.

3.4.8 Storage bins

1. All metal storage bins are preferred if the dust is sensitive to ignition by static electricity. The resistance to earth should be less than 10 ohms and should be checked regularly. Special precautions may be necessary for plastic containers for high resistivity powders. BS 5958[12] gives details.
2. Electrical wiring should not be strapped to the outside of bins.
3. Metal items, such as chain measures or metal tapes, should not be lowered into the bin. Level indicators of approved dust tight design should be used. They must be adequately earthed and electricity supply cables should not run inside the bin.
4. Material feed to the bin should be shut off if it contains excessively hot material. Infrared sensors may be used to detect hot material.
5. Cutting and welding operations on the bin should only be carried out after removal of all flammable materials and in accordance with a safe system of work.
6. Provision should be made for safe and isolated discharge of bins used to store materials liable to spontaneous heating .
7. Carbon monoxide monitors may be used to detect spontaneous combustion.

3.4.9 Dust filters

1. Ideally, fans should be located on the clean side of the collector. If this is not practical, the fan could present an ignition risk, which needs to be considered.
2. All-metal collecting bins are preferred. The resistance to earth should be less than 10 ohms and should be checked regularly. Special precautions may be necessary for high resistivity powders. BS 5958[12] gives details.
3. Precautions should be taken to prevent overfilling of the collecting bin.

4. Level indicators of approved dust-tight design must be adequately earthed. Electricity supply cables should not run inside the collecting bin. Electrical wiring should not be strapped to the outside of the collecting bin.

5. Filter bags made from epitropic fibres, which conduct electricity, can be used to prevent the build up of static electricity on the bags, but steps must be taken to ensure that the bags are earthed. The use of filter bags incorporating metal wires in the weave requires some caution, because if the connection between a metal wire and earth is broken, for example through wear, the isolated wire will create an electrostatic hazard.

6. Material feed to the filter should be shut off if it contains excessively hot material. Infrared sensors may be used to detect hot material. Provision should be made for safe and isolated discharge of filters collecting materials liable to spontaneous heating.

7. Cutting and welding operations on the collecting bin should only be carried out after removal of all flammable materials and in accordance with a safe system of work.

References in Chapter 3

1. Abbott, J.A., 1990, *Prevention of Fires and Explosions in Dryers*, ISBN 0 85295 2570 (Institute of Chemical Engineers, Rugby, UK).

2. BS 799 (1991), British Standard 799: Part 4:1991, *Oil burning equipment. Specification for atomising burners (other than monobloc type) together with associated equipment for single and multi burner installations*. British Standards Institution.

3. BS EN 676 1997: *Automatic forced draught burners for gaseous fuels.*

4. NFPA 8503: *Standard for Pulverised Fuel Systems, 1997.*

5. CEN Standard EN 1834-3, *Reciprocating internal combustion engines — Safety requirements for design and construction of engines for use in potentially explosive atmospheres — Part 3: Group II engines for use in flammable dust atmospheres*. CEN.

6. Health and Safety Commission, 1997, *Safe work in confined spaces. Confined spaces regulations 1997. Approved code of practice, regulations and guidance* (HSE Books, UK).

7. Recommendations on the Transport of Dangerous Goods, *Model Regulations (11th revised edition)* United Nations NY 1999, ISBN 92-1-139067-2.

8. Bowes, P.C., 1984, *Self-Heating: Evaluating and controlling the hazards* (Building Research Establishment, HMSO).

9. BS EN 50281-1-1 (1999), *Electrical apparatus for use in the presence of combustible dust, construction and testing*, British Standards Institution.

10. BS EN 50281-1-2 (1999), *Electrical apparatus for use in the presence of combustible dust, selection, installation and maintenance*, British Standards Institution.

11. Glor, M., 1985, *Hazards due to electrostatic charging of particles*, Journal of Electrostatics, 16: 175191.

12. BS 5958 (1991), British Standard 5958:1991, *Code of practice for the control of undesirable static electricty*, Part 1: General Considerations, Part 2: Recommendations for particular industrial situations, British Standards Institution.

13. CENELEC Technical Report RO44-001 1999, *Safety of Machinery — Guidance and recommendations for the avoidance of hazards due to static electricity.*

14. Bartkenecht, W. (1989), *Dust explosions: Course, prevention, protection.* Springer-Verlag, ISBN 0 387 50100 2.

15. Glarner, T., *Temperatureinfluss auf das explosions — und Zund — verhalten brennbarer Staube*, Diss. ETH Zurich Nr. 7350.

16. BS EN 1127 (1998), European Standard EN 1127-1: 1997, Explosive atmospheres — Explosion prevention and protection Part 1 — Basic concepts and methodology, British Standards Institution.

17. Directive 1999/92/EC on minimum requirements for improving the safety and health protection of workers potentially at risk from explosive atmospheres (15th individual directive within the meaning of Article 16(1) of directive 89/391/EEC).

18. HSE Contract Research Report 176/1988, *Dust explosions from unenclosed sock filters.*

19. BS EN 13463 (2002), Non-electrical equipment for use in potentially explosive atmospheres Part 1 — Basic method and requirements.

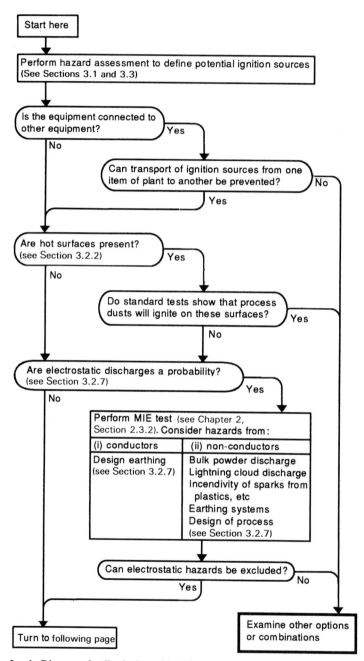

Logic Diagram 3a Exclusion of ignition sources.

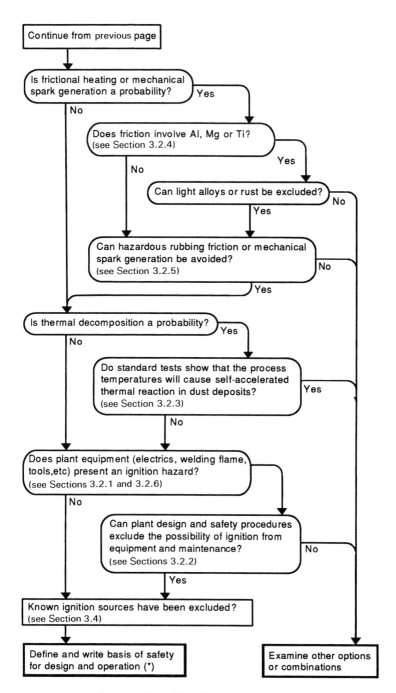

Logic Diagram 3b Exclusion of ignition sources.

　　　　　　　　　* It is strongly recommended that the basis of safety for the design
　　　　　　　　　should be formally recorded.

49

Inerting

4

4.1 Outline of principles

Inerting involves the addition of inert substances to either the dust or the atmosphere to prevent the formation of explosible dust clouds. Inerting can be an effective method of explosion prevention.

4.1.1 Diluent dust addition

Explosible dusts are made non-explosible by diluting them with an inert dust such as calcium sulphate, limestone, sodium bicarbonate, common salt, various silicates or stone dust. Such materials may act as a heat sink or otherwise interfere with flame propagation. In most cases at least 60% diluent dust is required and it is necessary for the diluent dust to be intimately mixed with the explosible dust. The quantity of diluent dust required can be determined by means of the explosibility tests described in Chapter 2. Except in coalmines, where it is extensively applied, diluent dust inerting is rarely used because of the large quantities needed and the consequent contamination issue involved. It is not discussed further herein.

4.1.2 Use of inert gas

This involves the partial or complete substitution, by an inert gas, of the air (or any other reactive atmosphere) with which the dust is mixed. Dust explosions can be eliminated if oxygen is excluded completely, or is reduced to a concentration (the limiting oxygen concentration (LOC)) below which flame propagation in the dust cloud, and consequently an explosion, cannot occur.

Inerting, using an inert gas, is applicable to enclosed plant. Plant that is substantially open to the atmosphere cannot be inerted effectively because significant fluctuations in oxygen concentration are likely. Furthermore the loss of inert gas would be uneconomic and may lead to a build-up of inert gas in places accessible to people, with the risk of their asphyxiation. HSE guidance[1] gives advice on entry into confined spaces where inert gas may be present.

Typical equipment in which explosions are prevented by inerting includes:

- Processing equipment: enclosed reactors, mixers, pulverizers, mills, dryers, ovens, filters, screens, cyclones, dust collectors;
- Storage equipment: hoppers and silos;
- Conveyors and elevators: pneumatic conveyors, screw conveyors, en masse conveyors, bucket elevators.

Inerting is of particular use for very strongly explosible dusts ($K_{St} > 600$ $bar\,m\,s^{-1}$). It is also used where flammable solvent vapours are present. Inerting is often used for grinding and drying operations that would otherwise be subject to frequent explosions.

A major consideration when designing inerting systems is the need for continuous monitoring of oxygen. Estimates of leakage rates from plant items and of the efficiency of gas mixing in plant are necessary. It is recommended that the advice of a specialist supplier of such systems be sought.

4.1.3 Inerting gases

Typical inert gases used include nitrogen, carbon dioxide, argon, helium, flue gases and steam. The choice of inert gas depends on a number of factors including:

- cost;
- availability;
- reliability of supply;
- likelihood of contamination of the dust by inert gas constituents, including moisture;
- volume effectiveness in reducing explosibility.

Table 4.1 shows the relative merits of some commonly used inert gases.

Greatest consideration should be given to ensuring that the supply of inert gas is reliable and that adequate back-up facilities are available in the event of failure.

4.2 Inerting as a basis of safety

The considerations necessary before inerting can be accepted as a basis of safety are shown in Logic diagram 4 at the end of this chapter. Explanatory notes are given with the diagram; the bracketed numbers in the notes relate to those on the logic diagram.

Table 4.1 Relative merits of inert gases

Gas	Advantages	Disadvantages
Carbon dioxide	Readily available in compressed form, from proprietary inert gas generators, and in some cases as a waste gas from on-site processes.	Some metal dusts react violently with carbon dioxide (for example, aluminium).
	Effective – higher oxygen levels (per cent by volume) are permissible compared with nitrogen.	Flow of carbon dioxide can generate considerable electrostatic charge.
	Moderate cost.	
Nitrogen	Readily available in compressed or cryogenic form, and in some cases as a waste gas from on-site processes.	Less effective in volume/volume terms than carbon dioxide.
	Moderate cost.	Some metal dusts react with nitrogen (for example, magnesium) at high temperature.
Flue gases	Often readily available as a waste gas from on-site processes or from inert gas generators.	Requires additional equipment to cool the gas, remove contaminants, monitor or remove flammable vapours and remove incandescent material.
	Often available at low cost.	May react with dusts.
		Storage of flue gas may not be practical, so that adequate quantities may not always be available, for example, during a furnace shutdown.
Argon or helium	Unlikely to contaminate products or react with them.	Expensive.
Steam	May be generated by the process	May not be available during start-up and shut-down.
		Incompatible with many products.
		Will condense if temperature falls leading to loss of inert atmosphere.

Measurement of the LOC (see Chapter 2, Section 2.3.4) is the important parameter for the application of inerting.

4.3 LOC for preventing explosion

The concentration of inert gas required to prevent explosion is determined by testing and measurement of the LOC (see Chapter 2, Section 2.3.4). The LOC for preventing explosion for many dusts is in the range 8–15% with carbon dioxide and 6–13% with nitrogen. Generally, a greater volume concentration of nitrogen is required than carbon dioxide. Although rules of thumb relating the LOC in atmospheres inerted, respectively, with carbon dioxide and nitrogen exist, for design purposes it is best practice for the LOC to be determined by testing (see Chapter 2, Section 2.3.4).

Where flammable solvent vapours are also likely to arise in practical applications, steps should be taken to create a test atmosphere corresponding to that likely to arise in practice. Similarly, when the dust/air mixture is likely to be present in the plant at temperatures above atmospheric, the test should be modified to simulate actual plant conditions. It should be noted that smouldering fires in deposits of dust might continue to burn in atmospheres with oxygen concentrations less than the LOC for preventing the explosion of a dust cloud.

In practical applications it is usual to employ a safety margin in the application of the test results to the design of the plant. The safety margin depends on the size of the plant, the explosibility of the dust and the level of monitoring and accuracy of oxygen monitors. It is unlikely to be less than 2% (for example, if the LOC were determined as 10% in the test, the concentration in the plant would not exceed 8%). Greater margins are necessary if large plant volumes are involved, extended hot surfaces are present, or St3 dusts are concerned.

In situations where dangerous oxidation can occur at low oxygen concentrations, it is safest to replace all or nearly all the air in the plant by inert gas. Leaving a trace of oxygen will prevent the subsequent spontaneous ignition of pyrophoric materials, for example metal powders, when they are removed from the process. The trace of oxygen reacts with the metal to form a protective oxide coating on the surface.

4.3.1 Use of steam for inerting

Some types of dryer use the steam generated by evaporation from a wet feed to maintain inert conditions within the plant. This can be effective while the process is operating under steady conditions, but the inert atmosphere needs also to be maintained during start up and shut down. This may be achieved by supplying steam or another inert gas into the system whenever the system is not 'self inerting'. Continuous monitoring of the oxygen concentration within the plant will be needed, and the sensors used must be suitable for operating over a range of temperatures, be unaffected by steam, and be designed to prevent condensation blocking access of the atmosphere to the sensor head.

LOC is normally measured at room temperature, but such values are inapplicable to steam inerted systems operating at temperatures over 100°C.

In such cases, the LOC needs to be measured under conditions that are representative of normal processing temperatures.

The LOC required to prevent the explosion risk may not prevent the onset of smouldering ignition if, for instance, a hot product is held for an extended period within a dryer. This risk from smouldering material carried forward into later parts of the process needs to be assessed for individual plants.

4.4 Supply, distribution and monitoring of inert gas

The aim of the inert gas distribution system is to ensure that the oxygen concentration is maintained at a safe level throughout the plant. The inert gas is usually introduced at several points on the plant, usually where pressure in the plant is low and hence the leakage of air into the plant is most likely. Special care should be taken to avoid the development of air pockets within the plant that are not in the main stream of flow. The NFPA 89 standard[2] gives guidance on the supply, distribution and monitoring of inert gas. Impurities such as rust, moisture, harmful gases and so on should be removed from the inert gas by means of suitable traps and filters before introduction to the plant.

Non-return check valves should be provided at each connection between the inert gas application point and the distribution system to prevent contamination of the distribution system through a drop in inert gas pressure or excessive pressure in the vessel. This precaution is particularly necessary where inert gas is introduced at several points around the plant.

Excessive flow of inert gas in one part of the distribution system is prevented by suitable valves and pressure monitoring devices, in order that a high demand in one part of the distribution system does not substantially reduce supply pressures elsewhere.

Inert gas leaving the plant is usually cleaned by means of gas cleaning equipment such as cyclones and fabric filters. Special care should be taken to ensure that the gas is vented to a safe place where build-up of inert gas in places accessible to people cannot occur. Where the inert gas is recycled, special care is needed to remove fine fractions of dust that would otherwise accumulate within the system.

Simple systems provide inert gas at a constant rate sufficient to match peak demand. The flow rate of inert gas is continuously monitored and controlled. An example of a constant rate supply system is shown in Figure 4.1. Such systems have the advantage that they need relatively little maintenance. The main disadvantage is that excessive inert gas is used and where solvent vapours or very dusty materials are present there is a possible substantial loss of product.

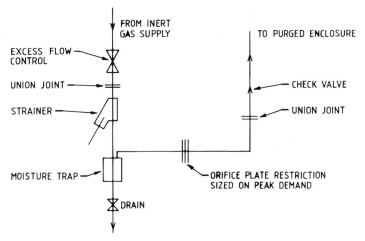

Figure 4.1 Constant rate supply of inert gas

More commonly, variable rate systems are used in which there is an attempt to match fluctuations in demand. An example of a variable rate supply system is shown in Figure 4.2. The control system responds to, for example, decreases in pressure in the protected vessel, or to the start-up of a feeder discharging material from the vessel, by increasing the flow rate of inert gas.

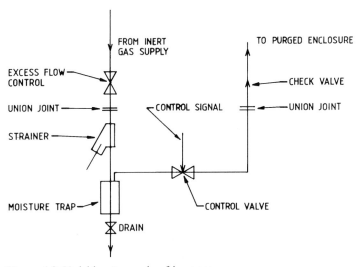

Figure 4.2 Variable rate supply of inert gas

For both constant rate and variable rate systems, the main control variable is the oxygen concentration. The oxygen level is monitored continuously and automatically at points throughout the plant and the flow rates of inert gas are increased whenever the oxygen concentration increases. In the event that a failure in the monitoring equipment or an unacceptable increase in oxygen concentration occurs, the control system is designed to shut down the plant in a safe manner. Blockage in the sampling line to the monitor should raise an alarm. In cases where flammable vapours may be present, the concentration of vapours should also be monitored to ensure that it does not exceed the design concentration.

4.5 Peak demands for inert gas

The distribution system is designed to cope with the peak demand for inert gas. The peak demand is controlled by such factors as:

- bulk material flow-rates;
- maximum withdrawal rate through vents, etc;
- recycle rate;
- leaks;
- temperature changes.

Whenever bulk powder is fed to a processing plant, air is carried with the powder in the voids between the powder particles. The oxygen content of the air thus fed to the plant affects the oxygen concentration in the plant. When bulk powder is discharged from closed plant, the volume of powder discharged needs to be replaced with inert gas. If it is not replaced, leakage of air into the plant may occur as a result of the reduced gas pressure.

Cooling of gas or vapours in a container as a result of internal or external temperature changes can lead to the pressure in the container falling. Enough inert gas should be supplied to the container to prevent pressure falling significantly.

In estimating inert gas requirements, careful consideration should be given to material and gas flow patterns. For example, the consequences of material tending to core flow or rathole in a silo should be investigated to make sure that the rathole does not cause oxygen to enter the protected plant. Similarly, if all the inert gas were fed to the top of the hopper there would be a tendency for the gas to bypass the hopper and go straight out through the dust filter. Care should be taken to ensure that the inert gas flows through the whole system and does not bypass any sections of it.

56

4.6 Examples

4.6.1 Grinding installation

Figure 4.3 shows a simple grinding installation protected by inert gas. Material is conveyed intermittently to the feed hopper by means of a screw conveyor. A screw feeder controls the rate of discharge of the material from the feed hopper

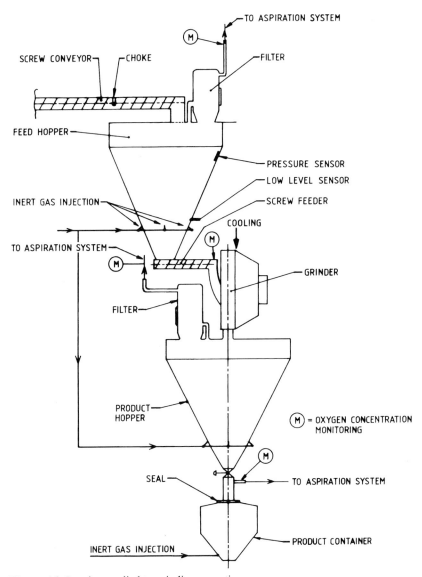

Figure 4.3 Inerting applied to grinding operations

into the grinder so that the grinder is continuously fed with material at a constant rate. The ground material is then collected in a product hopper from where it is loaded into product containers.

The plant has an inert gas system installed, designed to maintain the concentration of oxygen in the grinder, product hopper, and product container below the LOC. Inert gas is introduced into the feed hopper, product hopper, and product container. The oxygen concentration is monitored continuously in the grinder-input chute, in the air outlets of the product and feed hopper filters and in the container-loading spout. Any increase in oxygen concentration at these four monitoring points during operation results in automatic shutdown. The oxygen concentration is also monitored during initial purging. The plant is only started-up when the oxygen concentration throughout is below the limit. The screw feeder is disabled if the level of material in the feed hopper drops below a low-level sensor.

Material that is conveyed into the feed hopper entrains with it a substantial quantity of air in the voids between particles. The air is most effectively removed by feeding the inert gas to the bottom of the feed hopper so that the inert gas flows upwards through the material in the hopper.

4.6.2 Spray drying installation

Figure 4.4 shows the application of inerting to a spray drying installation. Recycled gas passes through a natural gas fired air heater. The combustion products are mixed with the recycled gas. The hot gas stream is then used to dry the droplets of slurry sprayed into the spray dryer. Exhaust air, together with some fines are fed to a cyclone where the fines are removed. The coarser product is conveyed pneumatically using recycled gas as the carrying medium to a second cyclone, where the product is collected.

At start-up, no slurry is fed to the dryer until the concentration of oxygen in the recycled gas falls below the LOC. The drying system is thus 'self inerted' by the combustion products[3].

The oxygen concentration is monitored in the gas stream as it leaves the air heater and in the air streams as they leave the two cyclones. Any increase in oxygen concentration above the limit results in plant shutdown. The gas stream leaving the air heater is also monitored to detect the presence of unburned gas.

Some materials are liable to spontaneous exothermic decomposition. The cyclones therefore are vented to prevent pressure increasing to an unacceptable level. The spray dryer and cyclones are also protected by an automatic water deluge system that operates whenever spontaneous decomposition is detected.

58

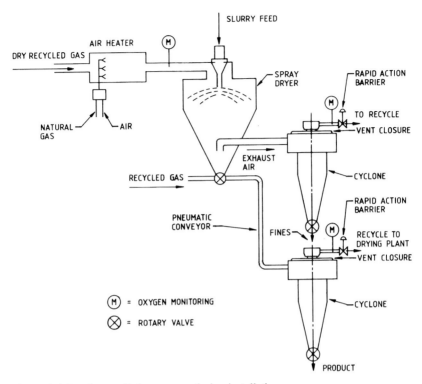

Figure 4.4 Inerting applied to a spray drying installation

4.6.3 Application of steam inerting in a sewage sludge drying plant

Sewage sludge drying plants have become the preferred route for treating material that can no longer be dumped at sea. A range of diverse designs is in use, or proposed. A cloud of the dry powder is capable of exploding, so appropriate precautions are required. During continuous operation, the atmosphere in the dryer chamber can be kept inert because the steam driven off displaces most of the air. It is necessary, however, to ensure that an inert atmosphere can be maintained during start-up and shutdown phases of operation. Other parts of the plant may not be inerted by the steam driven off by the drying plant, in which case the techniques of venting, suppression or containment will need to be considered.

Precautions against smouldering ignition will also be needed (see Appendix 4). Sewage sludge is capable of reacting with air, and spontaneously self-heating. Furthermore, if dry material picks up moisture from the atmosphere, adventitious microbial contamination may cause self-heating from room temperature.

Steam inerting of the dryer chamber is therefore but one technique in a selection of techniques needed for the protection of sewage sludge drying plants.

4.7 Inerting/venting and inerting/suppression combinations

In some instances it is not economic to reduce the oxygen concentration to below that required for flame propagation. By reducing the oxygen concentration somewhat by means of inert gas the rate of pressure rise in an explosion can be reduced. The presence of the inert gas enables the vent size, or the amount of suppressant, necessary to protect a vessel in the event of an explosion, to be reduced. Tests to determine the rate of pressure rise in the presence of a reduced oxygen concentration can be carried out in the 20 litre sphere (see Appendix 3).

4.8 Worked example of the calculation method for inerting

Three explosible materials are being mixed in a vessel. Vessel volume $= 5\,m^3$, Vessel design pressure $= 2.0\,bar$, Vessel yield pressure $= 5.0\,bar$.

Materials	Bulk Density $(kg\,m^{-3})$	Feed Rate $(kg\,hr^{-1})$	LOC % V/V
A	400	600	10.1
B	500	500	15.9
C	625	450	5.0

(Assume that 50% by volume of the dust feed is air.)

1. Calculate the number of purges to achieve the required nitrogen concentration in the mixer (3 bar nitrogen is available) assuming a mixing efficiency of 0.5.

The worst case LOC value is for powder C (LOC 5.0%); hence the target value is $5.0 - 2.0 = 3.0\%$. Note that, as the materials are fed into the mixer individually, there will be periods of high local concentrations of each powder.

The vessel design pressure of 2.0 bar, not the available nitrogen supply pressure, governs the upper purge pressure.

$$C_n = C_1(P_1/P_2)^n \quad \text{or} \quad n = \frac{\log_e(C_n/C_1)}{\log_e(P_1/P_2)} \times \frac{1}{K}$$

where $C_n = O_2$ concentration after n purges
$\quad C_1 =$ initial O_2 concentration (% v/v)
$\quad P_1 =$ lower purge pressure (abs)
$\quad P_2 =$ upper purge pressure (abs)
$\quad n =$ number of purge cycles
$\quad K =$ mixing efficiency

$$n = \frac{\log_e(3.0/21.0) \times 1}{\log_e(1.0/3.0) \times 0.5}$$

Answer: n $= 3.5 \therefore$ 4 purge cycles are needed.

2. Calculate the required nitrogen flow rate to maintain an oxygen concentration of 3% by volume during feed of powder B.

Assuming that the mixer is already below this value following the initial purging sequence and 50% of the flow rate by volume is air:

Feed rate Powder B $= 500$ kg hr^{-1}
Bulk density $= 500$ kg m^{-3}
Volumetric 'solids' rate $= 1.0$ m^3 hr^{-1}
Air ingress rate $= 0.5$ m^3 hr^{-1}
O_2 ingress rate $= 0.21 \times 0.5 = 0.105$ m^3 hr^{-1}
N_2 ingress rate $= 0.79 \times 0.5 = 0.395$ m^3 hr^{-1}.

If the oxygen ingress rate of 0.105 m^3 hr^{-1} represents a 3.0% oxygen concentration, then the total flow is given by:

$$\frac{0.105 \times 100}{3.0} = 3.5 \text{ m}^3 \text{ hr}^{-1},$$

the total nitrogen flow is given by:

$$3.5 - 0.105 = 3.395 \text{ m}^3 \text{ hr}^{-1}.$$

therefore, the required additional nitrogen flow is given by:

$$3.395 - 0.395$$

Answer: 3.0 m^3 hr^{-1}.

3. Assuming the nitrogen supply fails, how long does it take for explosible concentrations to form during feed of powder A?

Build up of oxygen (using modified NFPA89[2] Appendix D, Equation 8)

$$\log_e(1 - ((C_f - C_1)Q/100G) = -KN$$

and

$$time = \frac{vessel\ volume}{air\ ingress\ rate} \times N$$

where C_f = final O_2 concentration (%)
$\quad C_1$ = initial O_2 concentration (%)
$\quad G = O_2$ ingress rate ($m^3\,hr^{-1}$) [0.21 × airflow]
$\quad Q$ = air ingress rate ($m^3\,hr^{-1}$)
$\quad N$ = No. of air changes
$\quad K$ = Mixing efficiency

Assuming $K = 1.0$,

the worst case LOC = 5.0% v/v

therefore $C_f = 5.0\%$

the target LOC = 5.0 − 2.0 = 3.0% v/v

therefore $C_1 = 3.0\%$

The volumetric 'solids' ingress rate = 600/400 = 1.5 $m^3\,hr^{-1}$, and assuming 50% by volume is air, the air ingress rate = 0.75 $m^3\,hr^{-1}$

therefore $Q = 0.75$

Oxygen ingress rate = 0.75 × 0.21 = 0.1575 $m^3\,hr^{-1}$

therefore $G = 0.1575$

$$thus\ \log_e\left(1 - \frac{(5.0 - 3) \times (0.75)}{(100 \times 0.1575)}\right) = -1.0 \times N$$

therefore $N = 0.10$

$$The\ time\ to\ reach\ LOC = \frac{5 \times 0.1}{0.75}$$
Answer: 0.67 hr

Intuitively, it might be thought that assuming poor mixing would err on the side of safety, but in fact that is not so. For example, if $K = 0.2$ (i.e., poor mixing is assumed), then:

Time to reach LOC $= 5 \times 0.5/0.75$
Answer: 3.33 hrs

References in Chapter 4

1. Health and Safety Commission, 1997, *Safe Work in Confined Spaces*. Confined Spaces Regulations 1997, Approved Code of Practice, Regulations and Guidance (HSE Books, UK).
2. National Fire Protection Association, 1978, *Standard on Explosion Prevention Systems*, NFPA 89-1978 (NFPA, Quincy, Massachusetts, USA).
3. Masters, K., 1991, *Spray Drying Handbook*, 5th edition, ISBN 0-582-06266-7, pp 43–53 (Longman Scientific & Technical).
4. Bartknecht, W., 1989, *Dust Explosions: Course, Prevention, Protection*, ISBN 0-387-50100-2 (Springer-Verlag).

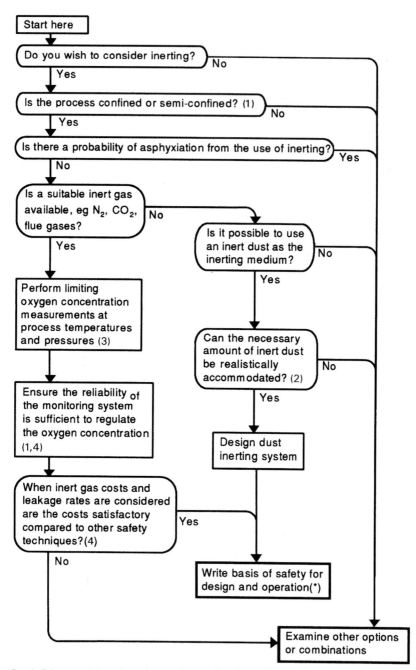

Logic Diagram 4 Inerting (the numbers in brackets relate to those in the notes on the
following pages).

*It is strongly recommended that the basis of safety for the design
should be formally recorded.

(1) Limiting the oxygen concentration

Limiting the oxygen concentration by feeding in inert gases is a highly effective method of preventing dust explosions if circumstances favour its application. Inerting is only suitable when the system is either closed or well confined. It can be expensive both on initial outlay for equipment and monitoring devices and on running costs, depending on the leakage rate from the plant. Reliable monitoring of the oxygen concentration at various points in the plant is crucial, with reliable alarm and shutdown procedures.

(2) Design dust inerting system

Generally, 70–80% inert dust is required for dust inerting to be effective.

(3) Design gas inerting system

The limiting oxygen concentration (LOC) for a given explosible dust/air system varies with the particular inert gas used. The process temperature can also affect the LOC.

Reactions can occur between dusts and otherwise inert gases, e.g. metal dusts and carbon dioxide. Such a possibility must be investigated and another inerting agent substituted.

The safety margin in practical applications depends on the efficiency of the oxygen monitoring system, the explosibility of the dust and size of plant. Typical values range from 1–4% below the limiting oxygen concentration, the lower values used only when monitoring is multi-point, and highly accurate, with dusts of low explosibility. If the dust is an St 3 dust, or there are likely to be extensive hot surfaces, the safety margin will be at the higher end of the range.

(4) Is inerting feasible?

If inerting is to be considered as a basis for safety it must be considered in relation to cost and operability. Factors to assess are:

1. inert gas costs;
2. typical inert gas leakage rates;
3. risks of asphyxiation;
4. monitoring system reliability and compatibility.

Explosion containment

5

5.1 Introduction

Explosion containment is a protection measure that involves the use of either explosion-pressure-resistant or explosion-pressure-shock-resistant equipment designed to withstand, without rupture, the maximum explosion pressure likely to be encountered. Explosion containment is used, in particular, when a hazard assessment indicates that an emission of process material or combustion products could present an unacceptable risk. It may be a valid option for explosion protection even when emissions are not hazardous. For instance, containment is frequently used to protect plant operating at sub-atmospheric pressure (for example, vacuum dryers). It is often a suitable option for mills and other plant of small volume that can be built to be strong enough to withstand the maximum explosion pressure, P_{max}, generated by a dust explosion, without excessive cost. Increasingly, containment is being used on larger items of plant.

Practical application of containment depends on knowledge of P_{max}. In single vessels maximum pressures can be in the range 7–10 times the operating pressure. P_{max} can be measured in standard tests (see Chapter 2 Section 2.2) and the vessel is then designed to withstand P_{max} without rupture. P_{max} is insensitive to vessel size and can be measured in the standard small-scale tests to estimate directly the maximum explosion pressure that a single vessel must withstand. Although it is not difficult to estimate or measure directly the maximum explosion pressure in a closed single vessel, with more complex configurations problems arise. Pressure-piling effects associated with multi-volumes or long ducts can lead to pressures in excess of that expected from an explosion starting from ambient pressure.

Pressure piling occurs when an unburned explosible dust cloud is compressed in one part of a plant by an oncoming explosion in another. When this pre-compressed dust cloud is ignited the explosion begins at above ambient pressure and the resulting maximum pressure is correspondingly higher. The classic case is transmission of an explosion from a large vessel into a much smaller one.

If dust-handling plant does consist of several connected items of equipment, consideration must be given to strengthening the plant to cope with pressure-piling effects, increasing the level of explosion protection, and isolating the various units to prevent transmission of flame or other ignition sources. Isolation measures are described in Chapter 14.

5.2 Explosion containment as a basis of safety

The considerations necessary before explosion containment can be accepted as a basis of safety are shown in Logic diagram 5 at the end of this chapter. Explanatory notes are given with the diagram. The bracketed numbers in the notes relate to those on the logic diagram.

5.3 Explosion containment in linked vessels

Dust handling plant almost invariably consists of vessels connected by dust carrying pipelines. If isolation techniques are not applied, an explosion in one vessel can propagate through the pipeline into another. The explosion in a linked system can be significantly more violent than an explosion in a single vessel because of the combination of increased turbulence, pressure-piling effects and a large flame-jet ignition source. When the linked vessels are contained, very high explosion pressures can result, the level depending on such factors as the relative sizes of the vessels, and the relative sizes of the vessels in relation to the diameter of the linking pipeline. Guidance on estimating the maximum explosion pressures in some linked vessel systems has been published[1].

5.4 Guidance on explosion containment in linked vessels

5.4.1 General

The guidance is based on a simple mathematical model of pressure-piling behaviour, and the results of an experimental programme[2]. Figure 5.1 compares calculations from the model analysis and pressure measurements from the series of experimental trials.

The analysis produces the Calculated Maximum Possible Explosion Pressure in the linked vessel system, and the experimental results are presented in terms of the maximum explosion pressure measured in the system. The volume

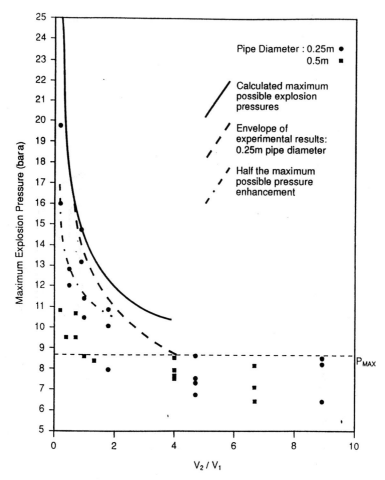

Figure 5.1 Maximum explosion pressures, calculated and experimental

ratio V_2/V_1 is calculated by taking V_2 as the volume of Vessel 2 and V_1 as the volume of Vessel 1 plus the volume of the interconnecting pipe. Vessel 1 is where the primary ignition takes place. It is clear from the pressure measurements that the maximum explosion pressure falls when the diameter of the interconnecting pipe increases. This is because back venting of the secondary explosion is more effective when the pipe diameter is greater.

The guidance gives estimations of the explosion pressures that linked, contained vessels should be designed to withstand. The highest pressures are 'worst-case' estimations; the analysis assumes slow transmission of the explosion. In practice, these conditions are not met because the speed of actual explosions is higher than assumed, and because of the back-venting effect. The back-venting effect is, however, taken into account in the guidance on the basis of the measured pressures. The K_{St} value is not a factor in this guidance.

A summary of the guidance for practical application is given in the notes and worked examples below.

5.4.2 Notes for guidance

1. It is rarely possible to predict with certainty in which vessel the primary ignition will occur in a system of linked vessels. The maximum pressures obtainable depend on the volume ratio of the vessels and will become very high when this ratio is less than 0.25. That is, ignition occurs in the larger vessel.

2. Volume ratios are always taken to be less than 1 in the advice which follows. That is, V_1 is larger than V_2 and it is assumed that primary ignition occurs in the larger of the two vessels. The volume of the pipework should be calculated and this guidance is not applicable if the pipe volume is large relative to the vessels. The pipe volume should be added to the larger vessel when calculating the ratio V_2/V_1.

3. P_{max} (bar a) is the maximum explosion pressure for a given dust as measured in the standard 20 litre sphere. The pressure compression factor (CF), derived from the model analysis, is estimated from the graph in Figure 5.2, but should not be used if P_{max} exceeds 10 bar a.

4. The flow chart in Figure 5.3 describes the relevant considerations. Depending on the system, the design pressure may be:

    P_{max},
    $P_{max} \times CF$
    $P_{max} \times (CF + 1)/2.$

5. P_{max} is expressed as bar a. If P_{max} is not known, and is not thought to exceed 10 bar a, set P_{max} to 10 bar a.

6. This guidance does not apply if the pipe is long enough to allow the flame front to accelerate significantly. Protection of pipelines is discussed in Chapter 14.

7. The larger vessel should not exceed 20 m^3 in volume.

5.4.3 Worked examples

The following worked examples demonstrate the application:

(a) Dust with parameters $K_{st} = 250$ bar m s^{-1}, $P_{max} = 8.5$ bar a
    Vessels of volumes 1.5 and 4.5 m^3
    Pipeline: diameter 0.3 m, length 5 m, so volume $= 0.35$ m^3

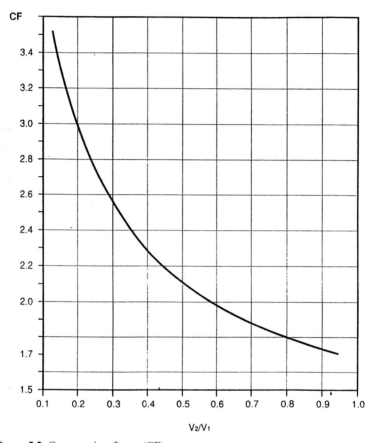

Figure 5.2 Compression factor (CF)

$$\frac{V_2}{V_1} = \frac{1.5\text{m}^3}{(4.5 + 0.35)\text{m}^3}$$

Vessel ratio = 0.31
Figure 5.2 gives CF = 2.52
Theoretical maximum pressure = 8.5 × 2.52 = 21.4
Design systems to withstand 21.4 bar a

(b) Same dust
Vessels of 8 and 10 m³
Pipe diameter 0.55 m, length 8 m, and volume 1.9 m³
Vessel ratio = 0.67
Figure 5.2 gives CF = 1.9
Theoretical maximum pressure = 8.5 × 1.9 = 16.2
Design pressure = (1.9 + 1) × 8.5/2 = 12.3 bar a

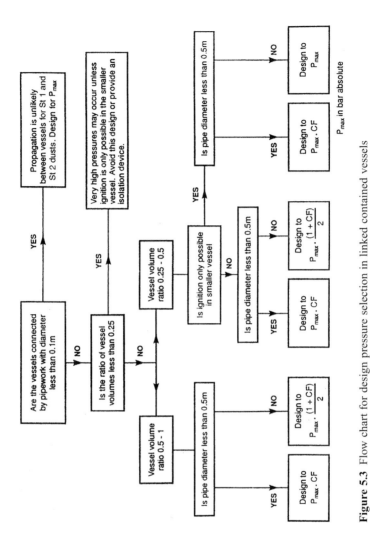

Figure 5.3 Flow chart for design pressure selection in linked contained vessels

References in Chapter 5

1. Holbrow, P., Lunn, G.A. and Tyldesley, A., 1999, Dust explosion protection in linked vessels: containment and venting, *J Loss Prev Process Industries*, 12: 227.

2. Lunn, G.A., Holbrow, P., Andrews, S. and Gummer, J., 1996, Dust explosions in totally enclosed interconnected vessel systems, *J Loss Prev Process Industries*, 9: 45.

3. Bartnecht, W., 1981, *Explosions: Course, prevention, protection*, ISBN 0 387 10216 9 (Springer Verlag).

4. IChemE, 2000, *Process vessels subject to explosion risk: design guidelines for the pressure rating of weak vessels subject to explosion risk*, Pilkington, S. (Ed.), ISBN 0 85295 428 X.

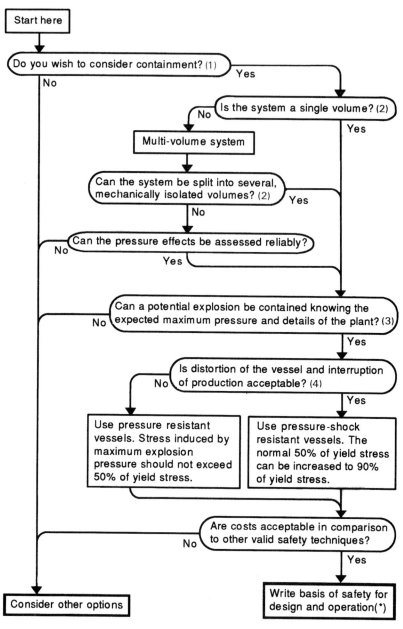

Logic Diagram 5 Explosion containment (the numbers in brackets relate to those in the notes on the following pages).

* It is strongly recommended that this basis of safety for the design should be formally recorded.

(1) Explosion containment – guidelines for assessment

Measurement of the maximum explosion pressure (P_{max}) in a totally confined vessel is the relevant parameter for explosion protection by containment. The standard tests for measurement of P_{max} are discussed in Chapter 2, Section 2.2.

Containment is of possible use for toxic materials where hazard quantification indicates that an emission could present an unacceptable risk. Containment may still be a valid option even if emission of material does not present an unacceptable risk. Containment is often a suitable option for plant operating at sub-atmospheric pressures, and for mills which can be built strong enough to withstand maximum explosion pressures. Due consideration must be given to preventing flame propagation into adjacent equipment and to the workspace via open air inlets.

(2) Configuration of plant

If the system consists of several connected items of plant, consideration must be given to isolating the various units to prevent transmission of flame or other ignition sources. Possible isolation devices often used are:

- rotary valves;
- inter-linked slide valve combinations;
- suitably designed screw feeders with no free volume and where compaction of powder impedes pressure transmission.

Before any of these are used, their ability to withstand the pressure and to prevent transmission of flame, burning particles or blast pressure must be checked. Guidance on the estimation of maximum explosion pressures in linked contained vessels is given in Section 5.3.

(3) Containment – assessment of pressure effects

In single vessels, the maximum pressures produced from dust explosions are in the range 7–10 times the operating pressure, depending on the process conditions. With multi-volumes or long ducts, pressure-piling effects can occur leading to pressure ratios in excess of 10. Guidance on the estimations of maximum explosion pressures in linked contained vessels is given in Section 5.4.

(4) Distortion of the vessel

In some processes it may not be necessary to prevent vessel deformation during an explosion. In some applications the vessel is designed to withstand the maximum explosion pressure, P_{max} without rupture. P_{max}, measured in the standard tests, can be used, because of its insensitivity to vessel size, to estimate directly the maximum explosion pressure in the vessel.

Explosion-pressure-resistant vessels are designed to contain an explosion without rupture or deformation. The stress induced by the maximum explosion pressure should therefore not exceed 50% of the yield stress of the weakest part of the vessel or any attachment. It is recommended that yield stress = 1.5 design stress[3].

Explosion-pressure-shock resistant vessels are designed to withstand maximum explosion pressure but are liable to permanent deformation. Stresses induced by the maximum explosion pressure should not exceed 90% of the yield stress of the weakest part of the vessel or any attachment. It is recommended that yield stress equal design stress[3]. However, there is still a substantial safety margin up to the ultimate tensile strength.

In some small enclosures, the maximum explosion pressure is reduced below that measured in standard tests because of the large internal areas provided by components; mills are an example. In others, the process entry and exit ports may provide a satisfactory amount of venting, although due consideration must be paid to preventing the propagation of an explosion into other items of plant and other parts of the process. With full information as to how the maximum explosion pressure is limited by internal components and by the enclosure's inherent venting it may be that small vessels especially can be designed so that no extra strengthening is required. A convincing case would need to be made, and the justification for this option would need to be well documented.

When a vessel is not designed to pressure vessel codes, the difficulty of estimating its strength should not be underestimated. It is the strength of the weakest link that must be known, be it, e.g., a bolted joint, a riveted joint, or a door fastener etc., and this determines the explosion pressure that the vessel can withstand.

Quantifying the strength of weak plant, especially when it is old and has been in service for some time is not easy. IChemE guidance on the estimation of the strength of weak components of plant is available[4].

Explosion suppression

6.1 Introduction

Following ignition an explosion typically takes some 30–100 ms to build up before destructive pressures arise in an enclosure. Explosion suppression requires that the incipient explosion is detected very soon after ignition, and that sufficient suppressant is discharged into the growing fireball in the enclosure at a fast enough rate to extinguish all flame before a destructive overpressure develops (see Figure 6.1).

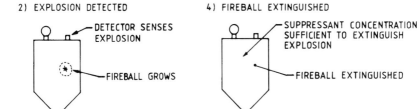

Figure 6.1 Principles of suppression

Explosion suppression is often used where it is not possible to protect by containment or explosion relief venting, and in particular where the pressure and flame of the explosion cannot be vented to a safe location. Explosion suppression is particularly important in cases where loss of process containment could cause the emission of toxic dusts or other substances harmful to people or the surroundings.

Sometimes suppression is used in combination with venting to protect a container. The main uses of venting/suppression combinations are where it is not possible to provide sufficient vent area for venting alone to protect the container or where it is necessary to minimize the size of the fireball emitted from the vent. By dispersing suppressant in the container shortly after ignition the rate of pressure rise can be reduced, thereby allowing smaller vent sizes to be used. The size of the fireball can be considerably reduced by means of suppressant injected into the flame-front in the vicinity of the vent. Specialist knowledge is required to design such vent/suppression protection measures.

Practically it is viable to suppress explosions in vessels with volumes as small as $0.25\,m^3$ [1], and in volumes up to $1000\,m^3$ [2,3]. Volumes that are larger than $1000\,m^3$ can also be protected by explosion suppression provided that it is admissible to locate suppressors within the volume boundaries.

In practice most applications of explosion suppression are to provide protection against St 1 and St 2 dusts. Protection is viable against some St 3 dusts, although the resultant suppressed explosion pressures are higher[4].

For an explosion in a closed vessel without suppression, the pressure rises in a manner illustrated in Figure 6.2 (curve A). Typically the explosion pressure may rise to a maximum of 10 bar, which is higher than much plant can withstand (e.g., many silos can withstand a pressure of only 0.4 bar). If such an explosion is detected and sufficient suppressant is dispersed within the vessel before destructive explosion pressures have been attained, the maximum pressure excursion will be limited as illustrated (curve B). This lower pressure is the reduced explosion pressure, P_{red}.

For a given explosion hazard in a vessel P_{red} is dependent on:

- The type and setting of the explosion detector(s) and thus the threshold level of detection (pressure or radiation) at which the explosion is recognized.
- The suppression efficiency of the suppressant.
- The number of suppressors fitted and thus the resultant suppressant concentration.
- The discharge rate of suppressant from the explosion suppressor(s).
- The temporal and spatial dispersion of the suppressant from the explosion suppressor(s).

- The geometric deployment of the explosion suppressor(s) in the volume to be protected.

An explosion suppression system comprises explosion detectors, explosion suppressors, and a central control unit (see Figure 6.3).

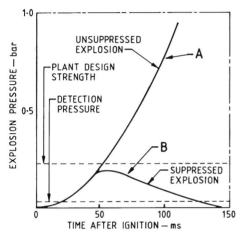

Figure 6.2 Typical pressure time history of suppressed dust explosion

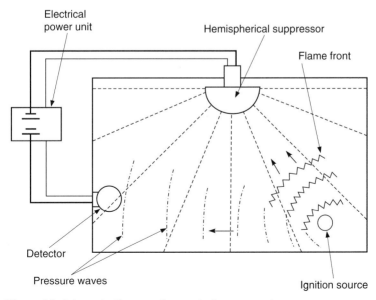

Figure 6.3 Schematic diagram of an explosion suppression system

77

6.2 Suppression as a basis of safety

The considerations necessary before explosion suppression can be accepted as a basis of safety are shown in Logic diagram 6 at the end of this chapter. Explanatory notes are given with the diagram; the bracketed figures relate to those on the logic diagram.

The K_{st} value, the maximum explosion pressure (P_{max}) and the minimum ignition temperature (MIT) of a dust cloud are the relevant parameters to be measured (see Chapter 2) for the design and efficacy of explosion suppression systems.

The following sections in this chapter describe the principal components used. Design, installation and maintenance of suppression systems should normally be left to one of the small number of specialist companies in the field.

6.3 Methods of detection of an incipient explosion

The pressure created at an early stage of an explosion within an enclosure expands from the flamefront at the speed of sound. A low-inertia pressure detection device located at the vessel boundary is well suited to detect reliably the onset of an explosion within milliseconds. Pressure detectors are designed to alarm when a pre-set threshold pressure or a pre-set rate of pressure rise is exceeded in the vessel. The set detection point(s) must be above the process induced pressure fluctuations and be independent of process temperature. The detectors are often programmable so that a detection algorithm can be set up specific to their location and application in the process.

Figure 6.4 shows a membrane pressure threshold detector and Figure 6.5 shows a rate of rise dynamic pressure detector. The sensing membrane is a large diameter pressure sensitive diaphragm, used because it will neither become occluded by product nor be affected by build up of product on the diaphragm surface. To reduce the incidence of nuisance alarms triggered by shock, some suppliers deploy two detectors, mutually perpendicular, configured in AND logic at each detection station. Other suppliers incorporate two or more sensing diaphragms within each detector device.

More recently, multi-parameter explosion detectors of the type shown in Figure 6.6 have come to market. These include pressure and infrared (IR) sensors that can be configured and pre-programmed to an appropriate algorithm for the specific explosion detection application.

It is essential that explosion detectors are tolerant to the impact of temperature excursions, vibration and shock, and further that they are resistant

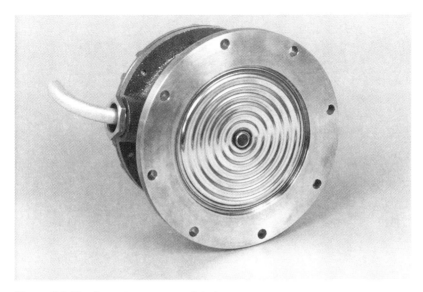

Figure 6.4 Membrane type pressure detector

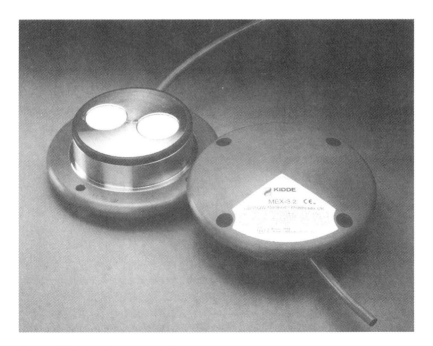

Figure 6.5 Dynamic pressure detector

79

Figure 6.6 Multi parameter sensor (2 × dynamic + I × IR flame)

to corrosion and moisture ingress. They should also be resistant to abrasion and attrition by the process conditions and provide a hermetic seal between the plant process and the environment. For use in hazardous areas the appropriate ATEX-100A Directive classification for protective systems is a prerequisite (see also Appendix 2). ATEX demands that there is no possibility of a breach of integrity between the explosible (process) side of the detector membrane and the normally non-explosible (air) side of the detector membrane.

6.4 Control systems

The active explosion suppression hardware — the explosion detectors and explosion suppressors, plus any explosion isolation hardware such as high speed gate valves are all connected to a central control and indicating system. Field connection between these components may be radial, or in a loop configuration. The control system of an explosion suppression system serves four key purposes:

- It ensures the availability of the system, and, through interlocks, prevents plant operation unless the explosion suppression system is fully functional.
- It activates ALARM closure actions that may be an integral part of the efficacy of the system design, such as blower shut off and isolation valve closure.
- It enunciates system status, thus providing information on an ALARM status or a TROUBLE status condition.
- It facilitates power back-up — such that in any power outage the process is fully protected through the plant shutdown process.

It is often the case that an explosion suppression system will be designed into logical zones. An explosion incident in any one location actuates only the explosion suppressor(s) necessary to suppress the explosion at that location. ALARM shutdown actions specific to that location (zone) are also initiated. For such multi-zone configurations (see Figure 6.7), the control system design allows for individual zones to be isolated for maintenance and service as necessary.

The control system automatically shuts down the plant in a safe manner in the event of a critical system fault. It provides, as a minimum, full field wiring continuity, ground fault monitoring, and field device fault monitoring. Through appropriate interlocks, the control system prevents the plant restarting without the fault being corrected.

For some applications, the control system will include detection algorithms in AND or OR logic to determine action.

The control system will facilitate standby power — either from battery or from an independent resilient USP. Failure of the standby power will initiate a TROUBLE alarm and start the controlled process shutdown system.

Electronic control systems are usually installed in a safe dust-free environment — usually the process control room, or mounted in an appropriate enclosure. For application in classified hazardous areas, control systems are installed in an appropriately certified enclosure.

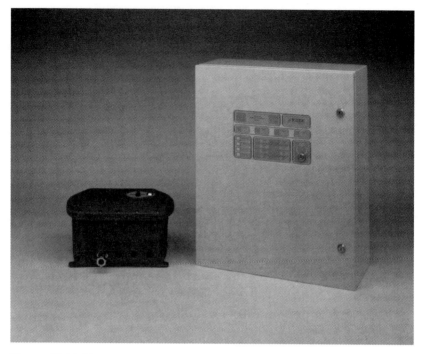

Figure 6.7 Multi-zone control panel with a field connection node (one node per zone uses fibre optic connections between nodes to eliminate electromagnetic interference)

6.5 Methods of injecting suppressant

The hardware used to store the suppressant comes in various forms depending on the manufacturer.

Hemispherical suppressors, as illustrated in Figure 6.8 are operated by a chemical detonator. The firing of the detonator causes 'petalling' of the specially weakened dome allowing the discharge of the suppressant. The initial velocity of the suppressant (usually water) is about $200\,\text{ms}^{-1}$ and the suppressor is typically completely discharged in 10–30 ms. Hemispherical suppressors contain relatively small quantities of suppressant, typically up to 5 litres, and are used for liquid suppressants only. They are fixed on the inside of the plant and because of their limited discharge distance (<2.5 m) are mainly used to protect small volumes and ducting. They are not suited to high temperature process operation ($>60°\text{C}$).

Figure 6.8 Hemispherical suppressors

High rate discharge (HRD) suppressors, similar to those shown in Figure 6.9, are the most frequently used explosion suppressor type. The HRD suppressor comprises a canister containing a charge of suppressant (liquid, vaporising liquid or dry powder) pressurised with nitrogen to a high pressure, usually in the range 20–120 bar. The HRD suppressor has a large diameter valve closure designed to open in a few milliseconds to provide an unimpeded discharge path for the suppressant to be expelled from the canister through a discharge nozzle into the plant component. The valve opening time and the mass discharge rate of suppressant from the HRD suppressor is critical to the effectiveness of the suppression system. The suppressant mass discharge rate dm/dt increases proportionally with the discharge outlet area, A, and the root of the stored pressure, P_{N_2}:

$$\frac{dm}{dt} \propto A.\sqrt{P_{N_2}} \tag{6.1}$$

Thus increasing the diameter (area) of the HRD suppressor has a greater influence than increasing the stored pressure.

Proprietary HRD suppressors (see Figures 6.10 (a)–(d)) are available with sizes ranging from 3 litres to 60 litres, and outlet diameters ranging from 20 mm

Figure 6.9 High rate discharge bottle with elbow and telescopic nozzle

to 130 mm. A large HRD suppressor may contain 40 kg of suppressant. Valve activation may be by an explosive device (detonator or cartridge), a non-explosive pyrotechnic actuator or piston actuator, or an electromechanical device such as a solenoid or motor. Some HRD suppressors incorporate a 90° elbow — these provide a faster discharge when the suppressor is to be mounted on a vertical surface of the plant component. Other HRD suppressors use two smaller outlets as an alternative to a single larger outlet to attain a sufficient suppressant mass discharge rate.

HRD suppressors are installed on the outside of the protected vessel. Suppressant travels through a short outlet spur, possibly via a bend, to the inside of the vessel, where it is discharged into the vessel through a 'pepperpot' nozzle. The suppressor is sometimes sealed from the plant by means of blow off cups, rupture foils or glass discs which are broken when the suppressor is activated: the nozzle then expands telescopically into the vessel. This prevents ingress of process material into the HRD suppressor fittings and provides a smooth (aerodynamic) surface that does not impede process flow. Nozzle design is dependent on suppressant type — superheated water arguably needs

Figure 6.10a Example of an HRD suppressor with dual outlet (2×35 mm with flexible connectors, $P_{N_2} = 60$ bar)
Reproduced courtesy of DEGRA

Figure 6.10b Example of an HRD suppressor with integral $90°$ bend (outlet diameter 100 mm, $P_{N_2} = 62$ bar)
Reproduced courtesy of FIKE

Figure 6.10c Example of an HRD suppressor that uses an electromechanical valve (outlet diameter 80 mm, $P_{N_2} = 60$ bar)
Reproduced courtesy of INCOM

Figure 6.10d Pyrotechnic gas generating HRD suppressor
Reproduced courtesy of Stuvex

only a simple nozzle, whereas deployment of some dry chemicals can be very dependent on the nozzle geometry.

The performance requirements of a HRD suppressor are:

1. High suppressant mass discharge rate.
2. High suppressant discharge velocity to give effective throw.
3. Good angular dispersion of suppressant.

The mass discharge rate and discharge velocity depend to a great extent on the diameter of the suppressor outlet and on the propelling agent pressure. They also depend on the restrictions to flow such as bends between the outlet and the nozzle. The angular dispersion of the suppressant depends on the suppressant velocity and on the detailed design of the nozzle. Typically a HRD suppressor discharges its entire contents in about 100 milliseconds, with the suppressant first entering the plant within 10 milliseconds of explosion detection. They are capable of throwing the suppressant charge distances of 6–8 m. Individual manufacturers of suppressors have a proprietary knowledge of their own products' performance under different conditions of operation and are usually able to tailor the performance to meet specific application requirements.

A variant on the HRD-suppressor replaces the stored pressure charge with a pyrotechnic gas-generating cartridge. Thus a controlled burn of pyrotechnic materials generates the expelling gas. These hot gases drive the suppressant charge through a controlled discharge port. Deployment of suppressant from this type of HRD-suppressor is initially slower, but the sustained generation of propelling agent gases retains the bulk dispersion of the suppressant charge at a high velocity throughout the discharge. The suppressor performance is very dependent on the gas generation characteristics of the pyrotechnic device, and, in the case of dry powder suppressants, the fluidity of the powder as it is expelled from the discharge port. (Note: pyrotechnic devices are 'lifed' items and must be replaced at set intervals to ensure system reliability.)

6.6 Suppressant materials

An explosion is a freely propagating combustion wave in a combustible fuel-air mixture. The propagation mechanism may be physically or chemically controlled. Heat transfer between dust particles is usually considered to control the propagation rate of dust explosions. Hence, in order to suppress most dust explosions it is essential to quench the combustion wave. Discharging a spray of liquid or powder suppressant into a growing fireball results in a number of complex effects, which include:

- Quenching — Heat abstraction from the combustion zone by energy transfer.
- Free radical scavenging — Active species in the suppressant compete with chain propagating reactions in the combustion wave.
- Wetting — Unburned dust particles are rendered non-explosible by absorption of liquid suppressant.
- Inerting — Concentration of suppressant in suspension in the unburned explosible mixture renders the mixture non-explosible.

For dust explosions quenching is usually the most important mechanism. Explosion propagation is dependent on a heat transfer mechanism between the suspended dust particles, whilst the combustion of each particle is controlled by combustion chemistry. The energy transfer between the suppressant and the combustion zone is limited by residence time of the suppressant droplets or particles in the combustion zone, by the droplet or particle size distribution, and by the concentration of suppressant in the combustion zone. The heat capacity of the suppressant material, including any latent heat contributions, and its thermal conductivity and radiation properties all influence suppression efficiency.

Other mechanisms are affected by other properties. For example, the effectiveness of the free radical scavenging mechanism depends on the extent to which free radicals take part in the explosion reactions. In many gas explosions, the chemistry of combustion dominates the rate of flame propagation, and in this case a chemical inhibition effect of an explosion suppressant is more important to the suppressant effectiveness. It is for this reason that water, which acts only as a quenching agent, is much less effective against a gas explosion than a dust explosion of the same explosion intensity.

6.6.1 Common suppressants

Dry powders

Dry chemical suppressants are usually variants of the proprietary dry chemical fire extinguishants that have been conditioned to have a low median particle size and a high degree of fluidity. Powders used include the alkali metal bicarbonates, ammonium phosphates and substituted ureas. Where the explosion hazard involves pharmaceutical or food materials, food grade compatible suppressants must be selected. Dry powder suppressants are usually pressurised to quite high pressure (60 bar to 120 bar). This is necessary because the interstitial stored energy between powder particles fluidizes the agent at discharge — thus overcoming any compaction or settling that may have occurred in the HRD suppressor container. Dry powder suppressants settle out relatively quickly after they have been discharged. Plant shutdown is essential to protect against purging of the suppressant and thus any risk of re-ignition in the plant component after the initial activation.

Fluorinated hydrocarbons

Vaporizing liquid fluorocarbons have similar extinguishing properties to the Halon[a] extinguishants[5,6]. The most widely used are FE36[b] and FM200[c]. Fluorocarbons injected late into the hot combustion products of an explosion rather than the flame front may decompose resulting in an increased pressure in the vessel. In such an event the explosion is not suppressed.

Water

For many dust explosions water has been shown to be a satisfactory suppressant[7]. Water based suppressors mounted outside the plant are subject to freezing. Certain suppliers offer salt-based antifreeze to provide a measure of protection. Superheated water has the advantage that a proportion of the suppressant flash vaporizes to steam during the suppressant discharge, thus adding an inerting effect to the suppression effect.

6.6.2 Performance

The performance of any suppressant material is dependent on a large number of factors. For example, different types of ammonium phosphate extinguishant may have markedly different performance[8] because of their different physical characteristics of particle size, specific surface, bulk density etc. For this reason substantial effort has gone into developing standard tests for explosion suppressant delivery systems. ISO 6814[9] recommends that a given system be

---

[a] Prior to 1995 halogenated hydrocarbons (Halons) were widely used as an explosion suppressant. These chlorinated and brominated alkanes are ozone depleting substances, and are now not admissible under the terms of the Montreal Protocol ["Montreal Protocol on Substances that Deplete the Ozone Layer", Final Act, United Nations Environmental Program, September 1987 (HMSO, CM977)].

[b] FE36 is a fluorinated streaming-agent $-CF_3CH_2CF_3-$ with a boiling point of $-1.5\,^{\circ}C$ manufactured by DuPont who own the trade mark.

[c] FM200 is a fluorinated vaporizing agent $-CF_3CHFCF_3-$ with a boiling point of $4\,^{\circ}C$ manufactured by Great Lakes Chemical Corp., who own the trade mark.

tested in a suitably large vessel for explosions of defined severity (i.e., K_{St} value), using a range of detection pressures.

For a given suppression system the tests result in limiting values for explosion severity, K_{St}, and an explosion detection threshold beyond which it will not be possible to suppress the explosion satisfactorily. A new European Standard is being drafted currently by CEN TC 305[10] that builds on the principles established in ISO 6814 and derives more detailed criteria for the validation of the efficacy of the technology chosen for an explosion suppression system.

In general it has been found that specific vaporizing liquids, dry powders and water are all capable of extinguishing St 1 explosions. In general fluorocarbons are not suitable for the more intense explosions.

It has been shown recently that the more intense St 3 dust and hybrid explosions can be protected by explosion suppression[4]. A measure of protection can also be provided against some metal-dust explosion hazards[11].

These are all special cases, and no general guidance is available. Suppliers of explosion suppression hardware will be able to advise on the suitability and limitations of their hardware for such extreme explosion challenges.

Table 6.1 summarizes the relative advantages of common suppressants.

Table 6.1 Relative merits of common suppressants

Consideration	Powder	Fluorocarbons	Water (pure)
Toxicity	No	Slight	No
Contamination	Yes	Negligible	Wets Product
Decomposition	Slight	Yes	No
Explosion Dust Classes	St 1, St 2 and some St 3	Some St 1 only	St 1 and St 2

6.7 Design procedures

6.7.1 Background

Design procedures are required to determine the number and type of suppressors and the threshold level for the explosion detector that will initiate suppression sufficiently early and prevent the pressure in a vessel exceeding its strength. Designs are based on interpretation of experimental data derived from suppressed explosions in test vessels and on experience. Test explosions are carried out in a chosen test volume for a particular type of explosion suppression system, and the resulting suppressed explosion pressure measured.

To assess the efficacy of explosion suppression ISO6814 sets out the criterion that system performance needs to be quantified against three independent parameters:

Explosion intensity — achieved by systematic tests against explosions of increasing K_{St} value (see Figure 6.11).

Detection sensitivity — achieved by systematic tests against a worst case explosion using increasing detection threshold values (see Figure 6.12).

Suppressant deployment — achieved by systematic tests against a worst case explosion using reducing quantities of suppressors/suppressant (see Figure 6.13).

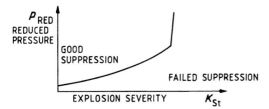

Figure 6.11 The effect of explosion severity (K_{St}) on reduced pressure of the suppressed explosion

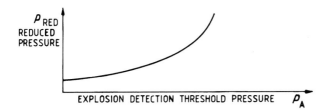

Figure 6.12 The effect of explosion detection threshold pressure on the reduced pressure of the suppressed explosion

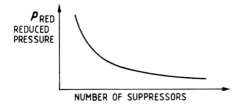

Figure 6.13 The effect of number of suppressors on the reduced pressure of the suppressed explosion

Provided that a sufficient quantity of suppressant is deployed sufficiently quickly into the enveloping fireball the explosion is suppressed and the resultant reduced explosion pressure (P_{red}) is measured. If this reduced (suppressed) explosion pressure is less than the maximum acceptable internal pressure in the plant component, then a successful suppression is achieved. If not then plant component damage must be expected. In extreme cases a suppression system can fail to suppress an explosion — see Figures 6.14 to 6.16. In these cases the explosion is not suppressed and explosion pressures approaching those of the unsuppressed explosion must be anticipated.

6.7.2 Design methodologies

The draft European standard[10] will enable the efficacy of an explosion suppression system to be ascribed, i.e., the effectiveness of the overall combination of explosion suppression hardware. To address system efficacy the draft standard reduces a process plant to its elements:

- Compact Vessels (aspect ratio < 2:1)
- Elongated Vessels (2:1 < aspect ratio < 10:1)
- Pipes (Ducts) (Aspect Ratio > 10:1)

It requires that system efficacy is quantified against defined explosions in each of the three elements.

The draft standard sets out a test methodology and criteria for system validation and interpolation. It provides for the validation of specific design guidance — nomograms, mathematical models, design equations etc.

Such validation is undertaken in test vessels of various volumes such that extrapolations between volume datum points is restricted to the volume range 0.75V to 4V — see Figure 6.17.

Design nomograms

Validation of design nomograms must be carried out for each nomogram (or equation) using a minimum of 2 compact vessels having different volumes.

For dust explosion design nomograms the draft European standard specifies a minimum of 2 tests at optimum concentration for each dust selected. The minimum number of dusts required for the validation is dependent upon the intended range of applicability of the design guidance:

Range 1: $K_{St,max} < 200\,\mathrm{m\,bar\,s^{-1}}$	5 different dusts having at least three completely different chemical compositions, e.g., natural, plastics, and dyestuff.
Range 2: $200 < K_{St,max} \leqslant 300\,\mathrm{m\,bar\,s^{-1}}$	3 different dusts.
Range 3: $K_{St,max} = 300\,\mathrm{m\,bar\,s^{-1}}$	2 different dusts.

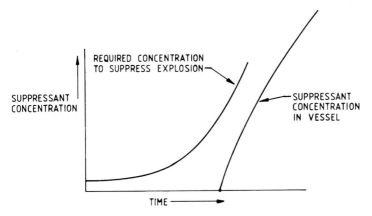

Figure 6.14 Suppressant concentration during a failed suppression — explosion detected too late

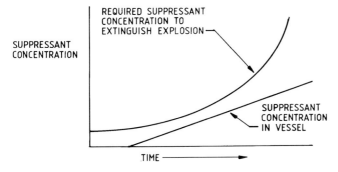

Figure 6.15 Suppressant concentration during a failed suppression — suppressant injected too slowly

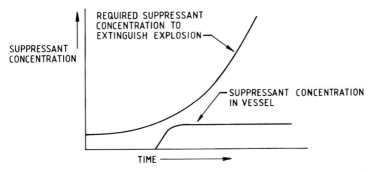

Figure 6.16 Suppressant concentration during a failed suppression — insufficient suppressant

93

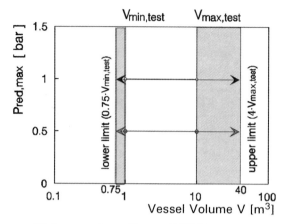

Minimum volume $V_{min} = 0.75 \cdot V_{min,test}$
Maximum volume $V_{max} = 4.00 \cdot V_{max,test}$

Figure 6.17 Example of extrapolation limits for design nomograms or equations

It is acceptable to reduce the number of dusts and simulate the variation of $K_{St,max}$ values by varying the ignition delay time, t_v and dust concentration, C.

Such design nomograms, and their equations, can only be considered valid within the volume boundaries and scope of parameters under which they have been validated (dust or gas type, P_{max}, $K_{St,max}$, MIT, activation pressure P_a, $P = P_{red,max}$).

Mathematical models

A mathematical model can be used for the design of explosion suppression systems. Such a model should describe the course of the explosion as a pressure time function and the interaction of the suppression system with the explosion. For the application of such a model the behaviour of the different components of the suppression system has to be quantified. This includes as a minimum the response characteristic of the detection system, the temporal and spatial distribution of the suppressant, and the suppression efficiency of the suppressant.

For this quantification, performance testing of the different components is required. The model has to be validated with explosion testing. Each dependent parameter used in the model shall be tested to validate the model's applicability. Dependent factors need to be tested at the extremes of their range. The draft European standard defines the following acceptance criteria for such models.

Model acceptance criteria:

For $P_{red,max} \leq 0.5$ bar the draft European standard sets an acceptance criterion for such models provided that it can be shown that a minimum 95% of all calculated reduced (suppressed) explosion pressures are equal to or higher than those measured by experimental tests (Figure 6.18). For $P_{red,max} > 0.5$ bar the acceptance criterion requires that a minimum of 90% of all calculated reduced (suppressed) explosion pressures are equal to or higher than those determined through experiment (Figure 6.19).

Such validated models can only be considered valid within the volume boundaries (see Figure 6.17) and scope of parameters under which they have been validated (dust or gas type, P_{max}, K_{max}, MIT, P_a etc.). The draft European standard further requires that the calculated maximum P_{red} must be, on average, at least 5% higher than those measured, demonstrating that the model calculation errs on the side of safety.

Representative test to validate system efficacy

The draft European standard also provides for system validation using a single specific test configuration. For such validation, the selected test must be representative of the specific worst case explosion challenge against which the system efficacy is to be validated. System validation will be specific to the tested explosible fuel, the tested explosion suppression system hardware and configuration, and the test vessel volume. Volume extrapolation is admissible within the boundary limit $0.75 V_{test}$ to $4 V_{test}$ using only the specific hardware that has been validated.

6.8 Applications

When installing a suppression system, consideration should be given to the application of the system with regard to zoning. If the process system to be protected by explosion suppression requires a number of vessels to be protected, it is not commercially viable to activate the complete suppression system.

To restrict the number of suppressors that are activated, the suppression system is divided into individual zones working independently of each other with their own detectors, control unit and suppressors. These suppression zones depend upon the process configuration and should be defined by the supplier of the suppression system and process designers.

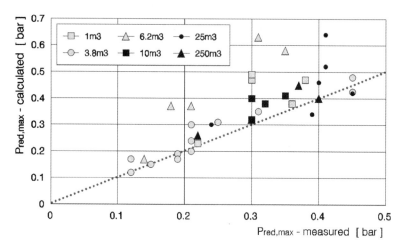

Figure 6.18 Typical validation criterion for explosion suppression system for $P_{red,max} < 0.5\,bar$

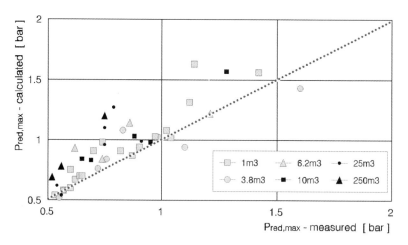

Figure 6.19 Typical validation criterion for explosion suppression system for $P_{red,max} > 0.5\,bar$

The photographs in Figures 6.20–6.24 illustrate a typical range of explosion suppression applications, and some examples are discussed in detail below. Industrial practice has demonstrated that the systems are of proven reliability, and that the incidence of false alarms is very low.

Figure 6.20 A spray dryer protected by HRD suppressors
Reproduced courtesy of Ciba

Figure 6.21 A bucket elevator protected by hemispherical and HRD suppressors
Reproduced courtesy of Tate and Lyle

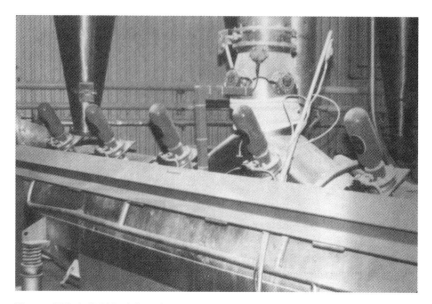

Figure 6.22 A fluid bed dryer in a creamery protected by HRD suppressors
Reproduced courtesy of Kerry Coop

Figure 6.23 A cyclone handling a milk product protected by HRD suppressors
Reproduced courtesy of Kerry Coop

Figure 6.24 Batch fluid bed dryer for agglomeration of powder protected by PHRD
suppressors
Reproduced courtesy of Custom Powders Ltd, Crewe

6.8.1 Sulphur mill and bucket elevator

Figure 6.25 shows a sulphur mill and bucket elevator. The two plant items are
isolated from each other by means of advanced inerting. Hemispherical
suppressors installed in the legs of the elevator are sufficient to protect it in
the event of explosion. The mill/hopper combination is similarly protected.
Explosions are again prevented from propagating beyond the hopper by means
of advanced inerting.

6.8.2 Two leg belt and bucket elevator

Figure 6.26 shows a typical explosion protection system for a two-leg belt and
bucket elevator. In most such applications the highest probability of an ignition
is in the boot or head. Therefore, explosion protection by suppression is
provided in both the boot and the head. Here detection is by a pair of pressure
detectors set to trigger at typically 0.035 bar — both are required to operate to
trigger the system. The 4 kg 75 mm HRD suppressor acts to suppress the
explosion and 3 kg advanced inerting suppressors eliminate any flame propa-

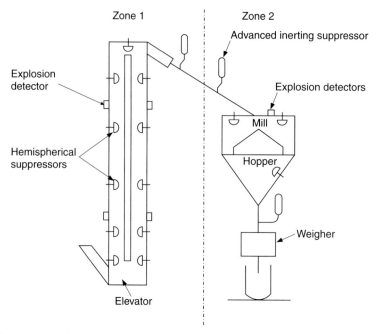

Figure 6.25 Sulphur mill

gation up/down the legs. The dust extraction and feed ducts are also protected by advanced inerting suppressors to ensure the explosion is contained.

Should an ignition occur away from the head or boot an explosion could propagate in the elevator legs — although usually much attenuated by the clutter in the legs. Extinguishing barriers are set as explosion isolation systems — preventing the build up of destructive pressures from such an incident. In this example an extinguishing barrier is located half way up the elevator legs. Single pressure-threshold detectors, set at typically 0.07 bar, trigger the HRD suppressors. For St1 material a single barrier provides adequate protection for an ∼40 m elevator — in larger elevators more than one barrier is deployed.

Although the design concept is a combination of explosion suppression (head and boot) and explosion isolation (legs) it would be normal practice to treat it as one zone and trigger all the suppressors — irrespective of which of the detectors trigger the system. For larger elevators, where at least two barriers are located in the legs the system may be divided into two discrete zones of protection.

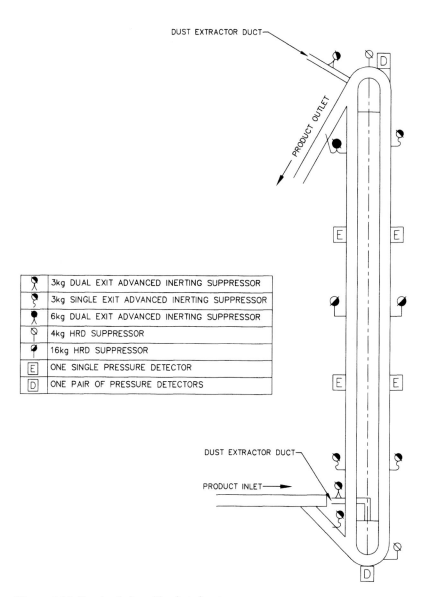

Figure 6.26 Two-leg belt and bucket elevator

101

6.8.3 Bucket elevator protected by a combination of suppression and venting

Figure 6.27 shows a sugar elevator protected by means of a combination of venting and suppression. The boot and legs of the elevator are protected by hemispherical suppressors leaving the head volume alone to be protected by venting. Elevator legs are often protected by suppression since they would require the installation of a large number of vent panels.

6.8.4 Spray drying plant

Figure 6.28 shows a spray drying plant. The spray dryer and the two product cyclones are each separately protected by suppression so that the suppressors are activated only if an increase in pressure is detected in the protected equipment. Actuation of any of the protective systems initiates the complete shutdown of the whole installation. A rapid action valve or extinguishing barrier prevents an explosion propagating between the spray dryer and the fines cyclone. Rotary valves, which are stopped immediately on shutdown, are also used to prevent the spread of the explosion. The spray dryer is also isolated

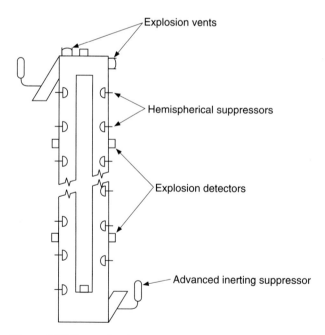

Figure 6.27 Sugar elevator

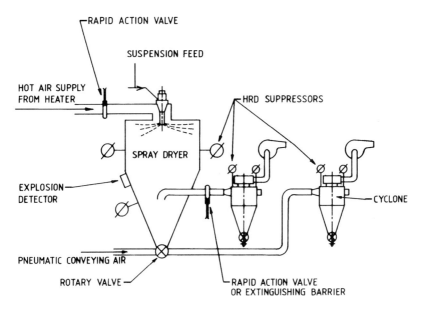

Figure 6.28 Spray dryer

from the hot air supply heater by means of a rapid action valve. In many plants this valve is not required because a suppressor is installed in the dryer close to the air inlet.

6.8.5 In-line hopper/collector

Figure 6.29 shows a typical in line hopper/collector, handling a St2 fine chemical dust, protected by explosion suppression. Material collects in the lower hopper and is fed onwards into a conditioning hopper as part of the process. Cartridge filters clean the air. Explosion detection is by a pair of pressure detectors. Primary suppression is by three HRD suppressors deployed to discharge suppressant into the lower unobstructed hopper segment. Two dual exit HRDs are used in the upper part of the unit. These are located to deploy suppressant between the cartridge elements of the filter assembly and are necessary to attain a low P_{red} for this component. This is a typical feature for the protection of an obstructed volume. If suppressant is not deployed into the voids in the obstructed part of the volume an explosion is free to propagate into these voids and thus increase the resultant suppressed explosion pressure. This technique of suppression system design eliminates this problem.

103

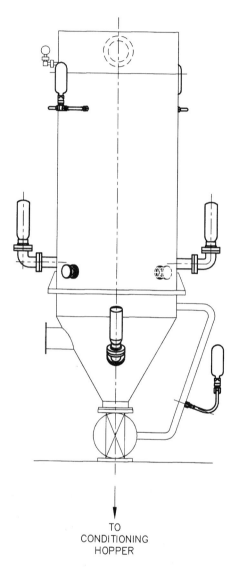

Figure 6.29 In line hopper/collector

6.8.6 Product feed, classification and collection system

Figure 6.30 shows a typical product feed, classification and collection system protected by explosion suppression. Each of the four components — receiving hopper, classifier, product hopper and filter are separately protected by explosion suppression hardware. In this example the system operates as two discrete zones — the dual-exit explosion-isolation suppressor represents the boundary

104

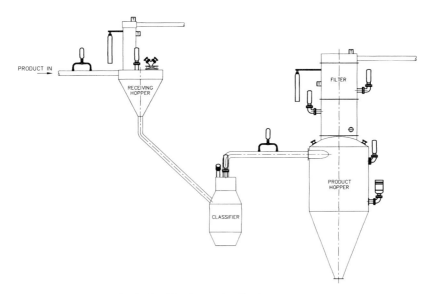

Figure 6.30 Product feed, classification and collection system

between the zones and provides isolation at the boundary. For each component the explosion suppression system hardware is selected to ensure that the resultant suppressed explosion pressure (P_{red}) for a worst case explosion incident is set below the corresponding plant component pressure-shock resistance.

In this example the product may evolve residual flammable solvent. The explosion protection system is coupled to a fire extinguishing system which is independently triggered by temperature sensors and deploys carbon dioxide extinguishing agent into the process in the event of any overheat detection. It is also normal practice to trigger the fire extinguishing system in the event of any explosion detection — this ensures that there is no risk of a subsequent fire from any flammable vapours after the explosion has been suppressed and the plant automatically shut down.

6.8.7 Bag filter unit

Figure 6.31 shows a basic explosion suppression system used on a bag filter unit. Detection is by a dynamic pressure sensor or a multi-sensor (fire and explosion) as appropriate. Here suppressant is deployed below the filter elements. Since no suppressant is deployed into the interstices between the filter bags it is necessary to allow for the additive pressure that may result from an explosion in specifying P_{red}. Of course the flame will be extinguished as the

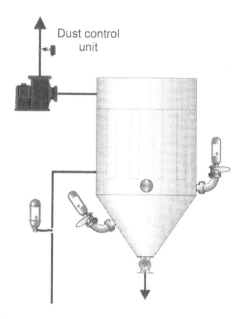

Figure 6.31 Bag filter unit suppression system

suppressant is pulled into these interstices so there is no risk of a post explosion fire from this safety solution. Since no protection is provided on the clean side of this filter installation, a dust concentration monitor in the downstream airflow is advised to detect and alarm to any bag break occurrence.

6.8.8 Vent-suppression combination system

Figure 6.32 shows a concept system that demonstrates the application of explosion isolation by a fast shutting gate valve, explosion isolation by an extinguishing barrier, explosion relief venting and explosion suppression all in one montage.

In this example explosion vent doors protect the feed hopper. A threshold pressure detector triggers explosion isolation in both the air return line (fast shutting gate valve) and product feed line (extinguishing barrier). Detection of an explosion in the hopper/filter unit is by a multi-sensor (see Figure 6.6). The use of the dynamic pressure detection of the multi-sensor provides the earliest possible detection of an explosion incident and triggers the electro-mechanically operated HRD suppressors. The multi-sensor also provides for detection of any fire in the unit and will trigger the suppressors to extinguish it.

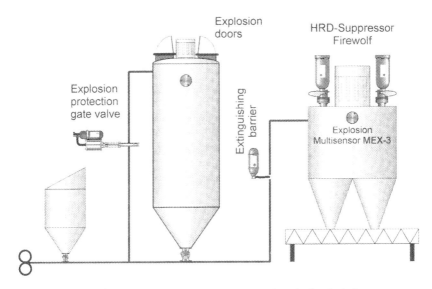

Figure 6.32 Vent-suppression combination system and explosion isolation

Figure 6.33 Sludge dryer
Reproduced courtesy of Stuvex

107

6.8.9 Waste sludge drying system

A particular waste sludge drying system generally comprises a four-zone suppression system, protecting a Rovactor, an inclined cooling screw, a pellet elevator and a filter unit. The Rovactor and cooling screw are protected by rate of rise detectors linked via a control unit to gas generator suppressors. The lower and middle sections of the pellet elevator's suppression system is protected by a pair of static threshold detectors linked via a control unit to a number of gas generator suppressors. Along the top section of the elevator is an explosion relief vent panel. The filter unit's primary protection is relief venting and the filter air inlet duct is protected by a chemical isolation system. The isolation system has a pair of threshold detectors mounted on the side of the filter and linked via a control unit to the gas generated isolation suppressor.

References in Chapter 6

1. Siwek, R., *Explosion suppression in very small volumes*, Proc. Europex World Seminar, Brussels, 1992.
2. Moore, P.E., and Bartknecht, W., 1986, Proceedings of the International Loss Prevention Symposium, Cannes, September 1986.
3. Moore, P.E., 1986, *Suppression of dust explosions*, IMechE/IChemE Seminar, Westminster, 15 December 1986.
4. Moore, P.E., and Siwek, R., 1998, *Explosion suppression overview*, 9th Symposium on Loss Prevention and Safety Promotion in the Process Industries, 4–7 May 1998, Barcelona, Spain.
5. Moore, P.E., 1996, *Fluorocarbon halon alternatives*, Fire Safety Engineering, 3(6): 20–22.
6. Loss Prevention Council, LPR6, July 1996, *Halon alternatives.*
7. Moore, P.E., *Explosion suppression trials*, The Chemical Engineer, December 1984, (IChemE).
8. Bartknecht W., 1981, *Explosions: Course, prevention, protection*, (Springer-Verlag, ISBN 0 387 10216 7).
9. ISO 6814/4, 1985, International Standards Organization, Explosion protection systems — Part 4: Determination of the efficacy of explosion suppression systems, 1985.
10. Moore, P.E., and Siwek, R., *Explosion suppression in accordance with the draft European standard*, Proc. Europex World Seminar, Gent 1999.
11. Moore, P.E., and Cooke, P.L., *The suppression of metal dust explosions*, British Materials Handling Board Report 88.36, 1988.

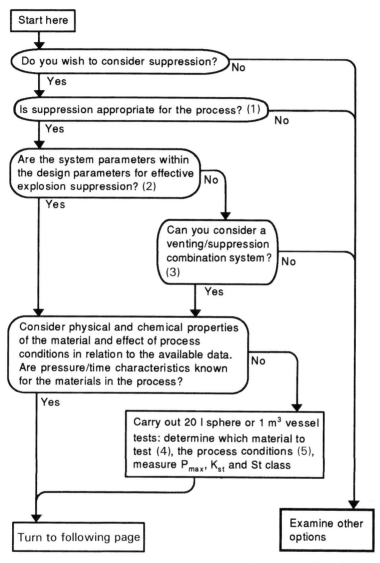

Logic Diagram 6a Suppression (the numbers in brackets relate to those in the notes on the following pages).

109

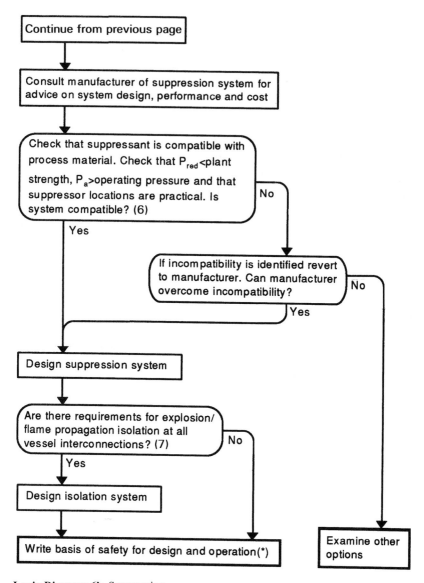

Logic Diagram 6b Suppression

                 * It is strongly recommended that the basis of safety for the design
should be formally recorded.

(1) Suppression as a basis of safety

(1.1) Applicability of a suppression system

Industrial explosion suppression systems are active systems consisting of explosion detector(s), high-rate discharge explosion suppressor(s) and a central control unit. The detector(s) and suppressor(s) are mounted onto the plant component and are wired to the central control unit. Explosion suppression relies on the fact that there is a finite time between detection of the incipient explosion and the development of destructive pressure in the plant component. This time must be sufficient to allow effective deployment of a suppressant material throughout the volume that is to be protected — typically 20–200 ms. To determine the effectiveness of a suppression system it is necessary to know the explosibility characteristics of the process material. As a general guide explosion suppression can normally be applied to most flammable gases, stable organic dusts, and flammable vapour/dust mixtures, but not to metal dusts, or pyrotechnic or explosive materials. Before deciding on this route for explosion safety the manufacturers of such systems should be consulted to confirm applicability.

(1.2) Compatibility of suppressant with process materials

Suppressants deployed in suppression systems include liquids such as water, vaporising fluorinated hydrocarbons[d] and dry extinguishing powders. The compatibility of the suppressant with the process must be considered. It may be necessary to trade suppression effectiveness to a degree with suppressant compatibility — where for example a non-toxic suppressant or a vaporizing suppressant is a process requirement. As a generalization dry powder suppressants are more effective than most liquid and vaporizing liquid suppressants against dust explosion incidents. Water with chemical additives, and super-heated water deployed from heated explosion suppressors also has a wide spectrum of suppression effectiveness.

(1.3) Shape and size of equipment

Since automatic explosion suppression systems operate by the injection of an extinguishing agent from a pressurized container into the process equipment there are upper and lower limits of vessel size that can be effectively protected

---

[d] Prior to 1995 halogenated hydrocarbons (Halons) were widely used as an explosion suppressant. These chlorinated and brominated alkanes are ozone depleting substances, and are now not admissible under the terms of the Montreal Protocol ["The Montreal Protocol on Substances that Deplete the Ozone Layer", Final Act, United Nations Environmental Program, September 1987 (HMSO, CM977)]

because of limitations in suppressant deployment. For most materials the lower limit of process equipment volume is $0.25\,m^3$, and the upper limit of process equipment volume is $1000\,m^3$. This upper limit can be extended provided explosion suppressors can be deployed within the volume to be protected. Larger silos can be protected by suppression provided the silo radius is within the throw limit of the selected suppression system hardware.

(1.4) Plant pressure shock resistance

The maximum pressure attained in a suppressed dust explosion event depends on factors such as the explosion intensity (this is dependent not only on the explosion characteristics of the process dust but also on the process conditions– e.g., the operating temperature and pressure, the homogeneity of the explosible cloud and its turbulence); explosion detection parameters; type of suppressant; and the number, type and deployment of high rate discharge explosion suppressors. In a typical system with an activation pressure set at 0.05– 0.1 bar the suppressed explosion pressure transient would be $\sim$0.2–0.4 bar overpressure. Release of suppressant alone will result in a small pressure transient — typically $\sim$0.05 bar when the suppressant is expelled by stored pressure. This may be higher for vaporizing liquid and superheated water suppressants — defined by the thermodynamic vapour pressure in the vessel after suppressant deployment, and lower for some explosive or gas generating activated explosion suppressors. Equipment that is to be protected by suppression must be capable of withstanding the resultant suppressed explosion overpressure transient.

(1.5) Equipment location

Suppression equipment manufacturers will advise on equipment location. It is normal practice to locate explosion detectors away from the main product flow to minimise damage and attrition of the sensor element. Explosion suppressors are located to attain most efficient suppressant deployment, and to reduce the risk of combustion wave propagation beyond the vessel boundaries through inlets/outlets. Manufacturers will advise on how alternative detector and explosion suppressor locations affect the projected worst case suppressed explosion pressure. Equipment must be located where it can be accessed for periodic checks and service.

(1.6) Operating costs

Automatic explosion suppression systems, like all other explosion safety systems, must be maintained in good working order. Such installations require regular inspections by trained engineers, and the periodic change of any 'lifed' components to maintain system reliability. The cost consequences of this maintenance should be considered at the system design stage. Maintenance will also require an occasional plant shut down — typically annually for about 4 hours — to allow for full inspection of critical components.

(2) Suppression system design parameters

(2.1) Applicability

For most applications suppression systems are appropriate provided the explosible dust is an St 1 or St 2 classified organic material, and mixtures thereof. Some St 3 materials can be protected effectively but higher suppressed explosion pressures must be allowed for in the design.

(2.2) Reduced explosion pressure, P_{red}

Manufacturers of explosion suppression systems will define the worst case reduced (suppressed) explosion pressure (P_{red}) for an explosion event resulting from an ignition in the protected vessels based on the defined explosion intensity (K_{st} value) of the process dust. It is important to verify that the plant strength is sufficient to accommodate this pressure transient.

WARNING: This basis of safety assumes that an ignition occurs within the protected vessel. For the cases where an explosion may propagate from another plant component different design criteria must be taken — analogous to the requirement for explosion venting.

(2.3) Activation pressure, P_a

Most automatic explosion suppression systems are triggered by an accurately calibrated pressure sensor that is either set to operate at a predetermined pressure threshold or a predetermined rate of rise of pressure. The set detection point(s) must be above the process induced pressure fluctuations and be independent of process temperature. Explosion detection by the flame signature can be used for flammable gas explosion hazards, but for most dust explosion hazards they are to be avoided because it is difficult to ensure that the detectors' line of sight has not become obscured by layers or clouds of the explosible dust. Some types of process plant may not be suitable for threshold pressure detection because the process conditions involve significant pressure excursions.

(2.4) Prevention of emissions

Explosion suppression is often selected as the safety means when the plant component cannot be safely vented because of the risk of flame emissions, or where the process materials are toxic, or could contaminate the environment if released. In such applications it is essential to remove any explosion relief vent from the protected plant component(s).

(2.5) Reliability

System reliability is both the assurance that the system will operate effectively in the event of an explosion incident, and the prevention of any nuisance activation of the system.

Nuisance activations of automatic explosion suppression systems are prevented by appropriate system design. They occur when process conditions have caused the explosion detectors to exceed their detection criterion. Care in setting the system explosion detection design parameters can essentially eliminate such events. Regular maintenance of such systems is essential to maintain system reliability. Manufacturers' recommendations for maintenance and service must be adhered to. Some explosion suppressors are operated by means of the release of stored pressure, or by an electromechanical device, or a piston actuator. Pyrotechnic or explosive devices operate other explosion suppressors.

In the UK it is necessary for the plant operator to obtain an explosives licence, which is granted by the local police, if the suppression system uses any classified pyrotechnic or explosive actuator device. This is the case even though only the suppression system supplier would normally carry out handling of the explosive devices. These explosive devices must be changed at set intervals to ensure system reliability.

As far as is known there are no instances where an automatic explosion suppression system that was properly installed and maintained has failed to mitigate against the consequence of an explosion.

(3) Venting/suppression combination system

A combination of explosion venting and explosion suppression can sometimes reduce the explosion pressure to the required P_{red} value in circumstances where each technique used separately would be inadequate. Deployment of certain explosion suppressants shortly after ignition will reduce the explosion violence such that a lower vented (reduced) explosion pressure can be attained from a vented explosion incident. Alternatively, the use of a small vent closure in conjunction with an explosion suppression system will reduce the resultant suppressed (reduced) explosion pressure.

Injecting suppressant into the flame front near the vent opening will minimise and in many cases prevent flame ejection from the vent closure. Specialist help is required to design these combination systems.

(4) Which test to use

The pressure-time characteristic of the material under test can be measured using the 20 litre sphere or $1\,m^3$ bomb ISO standard test procedures (see Chapter 2 section 2.2 and Appendix 3).

(5) Which material to use for the pressure time test

Often tests are done on samples as received. If the sample does not ignite it should be re-tested under conditions of dryness and fineness appropriate to the process. Materials classified as Group B (non-explosible) at ambient temperature may be explosible when the process temperatures are higher than ambient, or larger ignition sources are present. See Chapter 2 section 2.1.

Warning: The addition of any flammable vapour to an explosible dust will significantly influence the resultant ignition and explosibility characteristics of the dust.

(6) System compatability

It is necessary to verify that the value of the activation pressure (or other criterion) chosen for explosion detection is higher than the values for the chosen parameter (e.g., pressure) exhibited by the process under normal and abnormal conditions. It is further necessary to determine that the plant component can withstand the projected P_{red} that may arise from a worst case suppressed explosion incident. It is also necessary to check that it is practicable to fit the required number and type of explosion detector(s) and explosion suppressor(s) to the plant component.

(7) Explosion isolation

Prevention of combustion wave propagation down interconnecting pipelines must be considered for all containment, venting or suppression explosion protection systems. Explosion isolation can be by passive means such as rotary gate valves or explosion chokes, or by active means such as advanced inerting, triggered chemical barriers or slam shut valves (see Chapter 14).

Provided that appropriate explosion isolation measures are taken, the design of explosion venting or explosion suppression systems can assume that ignition can occur only within the confines of the protected vessel. Without appropriate explosion isolation the prospect of flame jet ignition down an interconnected pipeline into the vessel must be assumed and the consequential requirements for more rigorous explosion safety implemented.

Explosion venting

7

7.1 Introduction

Explosion venting is a protective measure that prevents unacceptably high explosion pressures by ensuring that most of the explosion takes place in a safe, open area and not inside a building or dust handling enclosure.

Weak areas in the walls of the enclosure are designed to open at an early stage in the explosion. The burning material and products of combustion are released, and the overpressure inside the enclosure is reduced. The residual overpressure from a vented explosion is known as the reduced explosion pressure, P_{red}. Figure 7.1 shows typical pressure-time traces from contained and vented explosions. Curve A is from a contained explosion, and the pressure rises to a maximum of 10 bar or greater — higher than most plant can withstand. In vented explosions, the maximum pressure is reduced, as in curve (C). The value of P_{red} depends on the size and location of the vent, the opening pressure of the vent closure and other factors. A properly designed venting system should ensure that P_{red} is brought down to a level below the design strength of the enclosure. All parts of the enclosure, e.g., access doors, slide valves, which are exposed to the explosion pressure, should be considered when estimating the design strength. The design strength of the weakest part should be used as the enclosure strength.

Quanitifying the strength of weak plant, especially when it is old and has been in service for some time is not easy. IChemE guidance on the estimation of the strength of weak components of plant is available[1]. The guidance is based on a finite element analysis of selected constructional features typical of those found in weak process vessels. The analysis was justified by comparison with results from a series of validation tests on a specially designed rig. From this, simple formulae were derived with which to calculate the pressure capability of each constructional feature of a 'weak' process vessel. Each section or feature is to be examined separately and given a feature pressure rating P_f. The pressure rating for the whole vessel or structure is then the pressure rating of the weakest feature (i.e., the lowest P_f value). This is taken as the value needed for P_{red}.

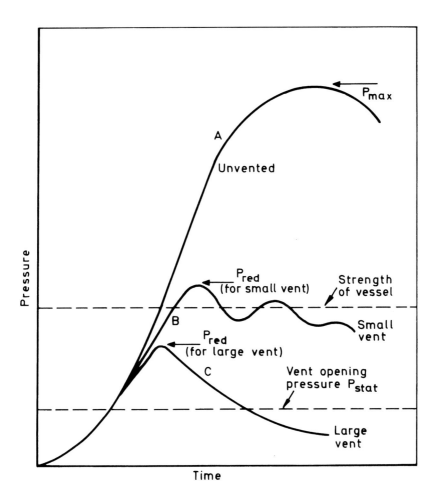

Figure 7.1 Typical pressure-time history of a vented and unvented explosion

The area of the vent is the most important factor that determines the value of P_{red} in a vented explosion. Methods are available for calculating vent areas, and the following information is necessary to apply them:

- P_{red}. This pressure should not be exceeded; its value depends on the strength of the enclosure and has units of bar. If the strength of the enclosure is not known accurately, or cannot be estimated reliably, this lack of information must be an important consideration when applying vent area calculations.
- The explosion characteristics of the dust, i.e., the K_{St} value and the maximum explosion pressure, P_{max}, measured in a confined explosion.

117

Both are measured by standard tests using either the 1 m³ explosion vessel or the 20 litre sphere (see Chapter 2, Section 2.2, and Appendix 3). The K_{St} value is a volume-independent parameter that characterises the explosibility of a dust. It has the units $bar\,m\,s^{-1}$, and is calculated from the Equation:

$$K_{St} = (dP/dt)_{max}.V^{1/3} \tag{7.1}$$

where V is the vessel volume (m³) and $(dP/dt)_{max}$ is the maximum rate of pressure rise measured in the standard tests.

- The characteristics of the enclosure, V and L/D. V is the volume of the enclosure. Generally, it is the open volume that is used in the calculations, e.g., in a dust collector the volume of the filter bags would not be included. L/D is the height to diameter ratio of the enclosure. In compact enclosures the movement of the flame is unaffected by axial flow, the flame speed remains low and the maximum overpressure in an enclosed explosion is, for most dusts, in the region of ten times the initial pressure. In elongated enclosures, the axial flow can cause the flame to accelerate to high speeds. High explosion pressures can then develop, especially when the L/D ratio is large. The L/D ratio can have a significant effect on vent area calculations.
- The characteristics of the vent cover. The vent cover bursting pressure, P_{stat}, in bar, is required for vent area calculations. The maximum value of the tolerance range of P_{stat} should be used when applying calculation methods. The inertia of the vent cover, $kg\,m^{-2}$, can have an influence on the necessary size of the vent and an efficiency factor, Ef, determined either by explosion testing or calculation, may need to be included in the calculations.

Explosion venting limits the explosion pressure, but does not prevent or limit the explosion itself. Fires inside the enclosure and flame and pressure effects outside should be anticipated when drawing up a basis of safety.

7.2 Venting as a basis of safety

The considerations necessary before explosion venting can be accepted as a basis of safety are shown in Logic diagram 7 at the end of this chapter. Explanatory notes are given with the diagram; the bracketed figures relate to those on the logic diagram.

7.3 Sizing of vents for single enclosures

The vent sizing methods described in this section apply to isolated enclosures only and should not be used if the explosion can be propagated from one enclosure to another through connecting pipelines. Isolating techniques include fast-acting cut-off valves and are described in Chapter 14.

Until fairly recently, the preferred method for calculating the vent area was the K_{St}-Nomograph approach, an easy to use graphical technique which gave vent areas which were conservative and have, in practice, never been known to be inadequate. This method has been superseded by a new calculation technique described in Section 7.3.1. This new method is included in a European Standard currently being drafted by CENTC 305[2]. The new method gives a vent area which is lower than that produced, for the same conditions, by the K_{St}-Nomograph approach (see Appendix 5).

It is recommended that for vent areas in isolated enclosures, the methods given in Sections 7.3.1 and 7.3.2 be used. There are circumstances, however, when it may be necessary to use the K_{St}-Nomograph approach, and these have to do with the fitting of vent ducts and the increase in reduced explosion pressures they produce. The guidance on vent ducts applicable to the vent sizing methods given in 7.3.1 caters for straight ducts only. The only freely available guidance for ducts with bends is that in Appendix 6 of this book. This guidance requires vent areas calculated by the K_{St}-Nomograph approach if it is to be valid. The effects of vent ducts and the recommended calculation methods for these effects are discussed in Chapter 9, Section 9.4.

7.3.1 Enclosures with $P_{red} \geqslant 0.1$ bar

The draft European standard Equation[2] recommended for calculating the required vent area, A_V, is based on experimental data and has been derived for German regulations, VDI 3673[3].

The Equation is an empirical fit to explosion test measurements, and is not the result of a theoretical analysis:

$$A_V = [3.264 \times 10^{-5}.P_{max}.K_{St}.P_{red,max}^{-0.569} + 0.27(P_{stat} - 0.1)P_{red,max}^{-0.5}]V^{0.753}$$
$$\times [1 + (-4.305.\log P_{red,max} + 0.758).\log(L/D)] \qquad (7.2)$$

Worked Example:

A powder with a K_{St} value of 175 bar m s^{-1} and a P_{max} value of 9 bar is handled in an enclosure of 128 m^3 volume. The height to diameter (L/D) ratio of the enclosure is 6, and the explosion pressure should not exceed 0.5 bar. The vent closure has a static bursting pressure, P_{stat}, of 0.1 bar. Calculate the required vent area for an explosion vent fitted in the roof.

$$A_V = [3.264 \times 10^{-5} \times 9 \times 175 \times 0.5^{-0.569}$$
$$+ 0.27(0.1 - 0.1)0.5^{-0.5}]128^{0.753}$$
$$\times [1 + (-4.305 \log_{10} 0.5 + 0.758) \times \log_{10}(6)]$$
$$= [0.076]38.6 \times [2.60]$$
$$= \underline{7.65\,m^2}$$

Equation (7.2) is valid for:

(1) Vessel sizes $0.1\,m^3 \le V \le 10{,}000\,m^3$;
(2) static activation gauge pressure (P_{stat}) of the venting device $0.1\,bar \le P_{stat} \le 1\,bar$;
(3) maximum reduced explosion gauge pressure ($P_{red,max}$) $P_{stat} < P_{red,max} \le 2\,bar$. For a maximum reduced explosion pressure $1.5\,bar < P_{red} \le 2\,bar$, the factor following the multiplication sign in Equation (7.2) can be ignored;
(4) maximum explosion gauge pressure (P_{max}) $5\,bar \le P_{max} \le 10\,bar$ for a dust specific parameter $K_{St} \le 300\,bar\,m\,s^{-1}$;
(5) maximum explosion gauge pressure $5\,bar \le P_{max} \le 12\,bar$ for a dust specific parameter $300\,bar\,m\,s^{-1} < K_{St} \le 800\,bar\,m\,s^{-1}$;
(6) homogeneous dust cloud;
(7) atmospheric conditions.
(8) L/D ratio not greater than 20, or minimum vent area greater than the cross-sectional area of the vessel for end venting.

The explosion characteristics of the dust are measured by a test methodology that establishes representative conditions of fuel concentrations, dust cloud homogeneity and turbulence that are considered to encompass those in the majority of practical applications (see Chapter 2).

From these standard determinations it is possible to quantify the worst case explosion for most situations in a compact volume, and for most practical applications this serves as a basis for assessing the requirements of explosion venting.

In conditions of low turbulence, and in conditions where a non-homogeneous fuel-air mixture or low dust concentration is the norm, the standard procedure is likely to overstate the explosion hazard. In such circumstances a reduced vent area can be based on either published or experimental data, that have been obtained from representative explosion venting trials.

In conditions of particularly severe turbulence there is a possibility that the explosion intensity is understated by the standard test methodology. In some plants there can be conditions that may generate severe turbulence, and in these cases Equation (7.2) can underestimate the necessary vent area. In such circumstances a vent area can be based on either published or experimental data that has been obtained from representative explosion venting trials.

Application of Equation (7.2) is straightforward when the enclosure has a simple shape, such as cylindrical. In other circumstances, however, the calculation of the L/D ratio is more complicated.

Estimating the L/D ratio when calculating vent areas for elongated enclosures
The length to diameter ratio (L/D) of an elongated enclosure is needed if Equation (7.2) is to be applied. This value of (L/D) depends on the shape of the enclosure and the position of the vent, and need not necessarily equal the physical value of L/D evident from the design of the enclosure.

The worst case condition to which Equation (7.2) can be applied is an enclosure with a vent at one end, because then the flame can travel the entire length of the enclosure before it vents. If, in such a case, the enclosure is cylindrical, for example, then the value of L/D can be calculated directly from physical dimensions. If the enclosure does not have a simple shape, however, or the vent is not at one end, the appropriate value of L/D has to be estimated. The estimate is based on the enclosure design, the maximum distance inside the enclosure that a flame can travel before it vents, and the volume through which the flame travels.

A simple procedure has been devised for estimating L/D ratios for any shape of elongated enclosure and for any vent position:

- Estimate the maximum possible flame path along which the flame can travel before reaching the vent, H.
- Calculate the volume of that part of the enclosure through which the flame can pass as it travels along the maximum flame path, V_{eff}.
- Divide V_{eff} by H to produce an effective enclosure area, A_{eff}.
- Calculate, from A_{eff}, an effective enclosure diameter, D_{eff}.
- L/D equals H/D_{eff}.

Examples of L/D calculations are given in Figures 7.2 to 7.8.

7.3.2 Buildings
Internal dust explosions can endanger buildings or parts of buildings and venting may be applied to protect the integrity of the building. Buildings are weak when compared to most process equipment.

There may be several reasons for a dust explosion inside a building:

(a) a controlled vented explosion into the building from process equipment;
(b) an uncontrolled explosion into the building emerging from process equipment;
(c) either (a) or (b) followed by a secondary explosion in the building;
(d) an explosion starting in the building itself.

The course of the explosion will be affected by several parameters including the shape of the building (elongated enclosures); the presence of equipment and structural elements; the possibility of propagation from room to room; and the presence of explosible dust left to lie on surfaces such as sills, pipework, etc. The dust explosion may be limited to a small part of the total volume. Pressure development will vary according to circumstances and a wide range of dust explosion loads can be expected.

Where a room is much greater in volume than the vessel which is situated in it (for example, 50 times), a primary explosion venting into the room will cause only marginal pressure increases in the room. If the vent is close to a wall or roof panel, however, significant local overpressures may result.

Where a vented vessel occupies a substantial proportion of the room, as in some large spray drying installations, an explosion venting from the enclosure may cause a significant pressure rise in the room as a whole.

One option may be to fit flame-limiting devices to the vents (see Chapter 9) or apply combinations of venting and suppression (see Chapters 6 and 9). Alternatively, it may be possible to segregate the hazardous operations in a specially constructed cubicle into which the operation may vent[4]. This is common for some types of milling operation. The door between the cubicle and the general workspace should be strong, open inwards and overlap the walls so that these support the door in the event of an explosion. The door must also be interlocked with the operation to prevent access whilst the plant is operating.

The walls of the cubicle inside the factory should be of suitably strong construction and the cubicle vented to outdoors. The outer wall of the cubicle should be constructed of a fragile material to act as an explosion relief and access to the region of the outer wall should be prohibited. Figure 7.9 shows such a cubicle.

The primary requirement is that an explosion inside a building should not cause progressive collapse of the building by displacement of load bearing walls. A second objective should be that the consequences of venting from a building should cause the least risk to persons outside the building. Both these objectives imply a strong preference for steel framed buildings with lightweight panel walls, rather than masonry construction.

A simple venting equation published in NFPA68[5] can be applied to low strength enclosures with $P_{red} < 0.1$ bar. This method applies principally to buildings, but also to low strength dust-handling plant and similar enclosures. The Equation from NFPA68 is:

$$A_V = C_1 A_S / (P_{red})^{0.5} \qquad (7.3)$$

where A_S is the total internal surface area of the enclosure and C_1 is a factor with units of $(bar)^{0.5}$, and a value dependent on the explosibility classification of the dust:

$$
\begin{aligned}
K_{St} &< 200 \, \text{bar m s}^{-1} & &: C_1 = 0.026 \\
200 &< K_{St} \leq 300 \, \text{bar m s}^{-1} & &: C_1 = 0.03 \\
300 &< K_{St} \leq 600 \, \text{bar m s}^{-1} & &: C_1 = 0.051
\end{aligned}
$$

The degree of venting should be sufficient to prevent unacceptable structural damage, and the weakest structural element should be identified. The vent area should be distributed as symmetrically and as evenly as possible. There are no dimensional constraints to the shape of the enclosure, but if the vent area is restricted to one end of an elongated enclosure, the L/D ratio should not exceed 3. For rectangular enclosures:

$$L_3 < 6(L_1 L_2 / (L_1 + L_2)) \qquad (7.4)$$

where L_i denotes the length of the vessel sides, and $L_3 > L_2 > L_1$.

The internal surface area, A_S, includes external walls, floors and roof, but not internal partitions that cannot withstand the reduced explosion pressure. The internal surface area of adjoining enclosures should be included if the partition cannot withstand the reduced explosion pressure. The surface area of equipment and contained structures is not included.

Irregularly shaped buildings can be squared off to a more easily calculated shape. When parts of the wall or roof area are not available for the fitting of vents, e.g., because of fitments, the presence of personnel, or the close proximity to other buildings, the building that is to be vented must be strengthened, so that the explosion pressure that it can withstand matches the available vent area according to Equation (7.3). The required vent area can be reduced by installation of internal walls that will withstand explosion pressures and confine the explosion to a part of the enclosure.

Reduced vent areas can be determined directly from representative explosion venting trials if they demonstrate that a smaller value of constant C_1 can be used in Equation (7.3).

Worked example:

A building with a volume of 250 m^3 is used to house dust handling equipment (Figure 7.10). The dust has a K_{St} value of 250 bar m s^{-1}. The reduced explosion pressure must not exceed 0.09 bar. Calculate the vent area necessary to limit the reduced explosion pressure to this value.

In order to demonstrate the application of Equation (7.3), the 250 m^3 vessel has been divided into 3 volumes:

> Volume I — 100 m^3, with dimensions 2.5 × 4 × 10 m;
> Volume II — 100 m^3 , with dimensions 2.5 × 5 × 8 m;
> Volume III — 50 m^3, with dimensions 2 × 5 × 5 m. And:
> Volume I — $A_s = 4 \times 2.5 \times 2 + 4 \times 10 \times 2 + 2.5 \times 10 + 2.5 \times 5$
> $= 137.5\,\text{m}^2$;
> Volume II — $A_s = 8 \times 2.5 \times 2 + 8 \times 5 \times 2 + 0.5 \times 5 = 122.5\,\text{m}^2$;
> Volume III — $A_s = 5 \times 2 \times 3 + 5 \times 5 \times 2 = 80\,\text{m}^2$.
> Total $A_s = 340\,\text{m}^2$

For St 2 dust the recommended value of C_1 is 0.03 (bar)$^{1/2}$.

Substituting the appropriate values into the equation gives:

$$A_V = 0.03 \times 340/(0.09)^{1/2} = 10.2/0.3 = 34\,\text{m}^2.$$

Answer: Vent area = 34 m^2

The vent areas calculated by this equation are essentially for a situation where there is a substantial dust cloud undergoing combustion inside the building. Vent areas are likely to be oversized if the dust explosion is limited to one vented from an enclosure. The importance of good housekeeping to avoid secondary explosions cannot be over-stressed. A minor explosion can quickly develop into a major event if dust is left to lie on surfaces such as windowsills, pipework and so on. A layer only one millimetre thick, when dispersed, is quite capable of forming an explosible dust cloud in a building 3 m or so in height.

There remains, also, the possibility of an accidental release of large quantities of dust into the workplace through process failure, the subsequent ignition of which may cause much damage. One example of such an incident is the explosion at General Foods, Banbury[6]. The acceptability of a particular building design may be influenced by such considerations.

If buildings do not need to be totally enclosed, open vents such as louvered openings can be used, although the obstruction and decreased vent area due to the louvers must be taken into account in sizing the vent opening. Otherwise, the use of profiled lightweight panels attached to a steel frame is normally the preferred option for vent closures where building relief is required. The inertia of the panels should be as low as is practicable after considerations of the forces likely from wind and snow loads, but should not exceed $12\,\mathrm{kg\,m^{-2}}$.

NFPA 68[5] recommends shear-type and pull-through fasteners as suitable for very large vent areas such as the entire wall of a room.

Information about vent panels and appropriate fasteners is given in Chapter 11. These panels should not be made out of brittle material, which can shatter during explosion venting. Often in buildings, however, a part of the wall or roof may be designed to fail at a low overpressure. Lightweight panels are positioned between strong partition walls or may make up the entire roof. These panels must be suitably anchored to prevent wind lift. Suitable fastenings to prevent large panels acting as missiles are described in NFPA68[5].

Windows can act as explosion vents, but shards of glass are dangerous missiles and it is best to substitute either plastic glazing or types of safety glass, which will fracture into pellets. An example of a vented building is shown in Figure 7.11 and an explosion in such a building shown in Figure 7.12.

The maximum value of the tolerance range of the static activation pressure shall be used. For weak enclosures (< 0.1 bar) the static activation pressure shall not exceed 50% of the design pressure.

7.3.3 The Factory Mutual Research Corporation (FMRC) Method of Vent Sizing

A method for sizing of vents for dust explosions has been developed by the Factory Mutual Research Corporation and reported by Tamanini[7]. This method is based on a model of the venting process, with some fitting to published experimental results.

The method is not generally available at the moment, but discussions have been held with a view to incorporating it in a new edition of NFPA 68.

The FMRC method has some advantages over the draft European standard method — it accommodates values of P_{red} from zero upwards and does not, therefore, require a change of method at P_{red} equal to 0.1 bar; it accurately describes the behaviour of P_{red} as vent areas decrease i.e. P_{red} approaches P_{max} as the vent area becomes vanishingly small. The calculation method has been extended to take account of the effect of vent ducts, including straight vent ducts and ducts with bends (see Chapter 9).

Comparisons of the draft European standard method and the FMRC method show:

- At P_{stat} values of 0.1 bar, the FMRC method nearly always predicts greater vent areas than does the draft European standard method.

- At P_{stat} values of 0.2 bar, the FMRC vent area predictions are sometimes less than those from the draft European standard method, and sometimes greater.
- At P_{stat} values of 0.5 bar, the FMRC vent area predictions are less than those from the draft European standard method.

7.4 Conclusions

The vent sizing methods given in 7.3.1 and 7.3.2 are recommended for isolated enclosures.

If vent ducts with bends are to be fitted to the enclosure, however, the only available guidance requires that the vent area is calculated by the K_{St} Nomograph approach, which is described in Chapter 9.

The FMRC method has several advantages over the methods in 7.3.1 and 7.3.2, but is not generally available.

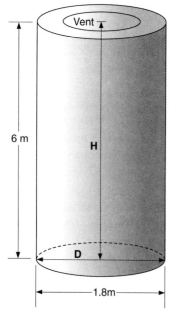

(a) H equals the vertical height of the enclosure

(b) $V_{eff} = (\pi D^2/4) \times H = \frac{\pi(1.8)^2}{4} \times 6 = 15.27\,\mathrm{m^3}$

(c) $A_{eff} = V_{eff}/H = 15.27/6 = 2.545\,\mathrm{m^2}$

(d) $D_{eff} = (4A_{eff}/\pi)^{1/2} = (4 \times 2.545/3.142)^{1/2}$
$= 1.8\,\mathrm{m}$

(e) $L/D = H/D_{eff} = 6/1.8 = 3.33$

In this example, L/D equals the physical length to diameter ratio of the enclosure.

Figure 7.2 Calculating L/D ratio for a cylindrical vessel with a top vent

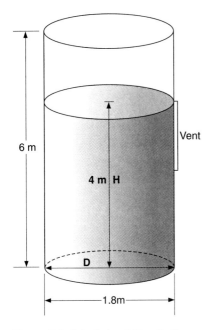

(a) H equals the distance from the enclosure floor to the top of the vent $= 4\,\text{m}$

(b) $V_{\text{eff}} = (\pi D^2/4) \times H = (\pi(1.8)^2/4)4 = 10.18\,\text{m}^3$. V_{eff} is the shaded region in the diagram

(c) $A_{\text{eff}} = V_{\text{eff}}/H = 10.18/4 = 2.545\,\text{m}^2$

(d) $D_{\text{eff}} = (4A_{\text{eff}}/\pi)^{1/2} = (4 \times 2.545/3.142)^{1/2} = 1.8\,\text{m}$

(e) $L/D = H/D_{\text{eff}} = 4/1.8 = 2.22$

In this example, L/D does not equal the physical length to diameter ratio of the enclosure.

Figure 7.3 Calculating L/D ratio for a cylindrical vessel with a side vent

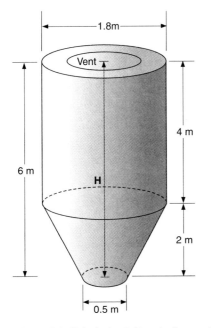

(a) H equals the vertical height of the enclosure $= 6\,\text{m}$

(b) $V_{\text{eff}} =$ the total free volume of the enclosure. The volume of the cylindrical part $= (\pi(1.8)^2/4)4 = 10.18\,\text{m}^3$; The volume of the hopper $= \pi.2/12 (1.8^2 + 1.8 \times 0.5 + 0.5^2) = 2.3\,\text{m}^3$; $V_{\text{eff}} = 2.3 + 10.18 = 12.48\,\text{m}^3$

(c) $A_{\text{eff}} = V_{\text{eff}}/H = 12.48/6 = 2.08\,\text{m}^2$

(d) $D_{\text{eff}} = (4A_{\text{eff}}/\pi)^{1/2} = 1.627\,\text{m}$

(e) $L/D = H/D_{\text{eff}} = 6/1.627 = 3.69$

In this example, D_{eff} will be less than the diameter of the cylindrical portion of the enclosure, and so L/D will be greater than if it had been calculated by taking actual physical dimensions

Figure 7.4 Calculating L/D ratio for a cylindrical vessel with a hopper and a top vent

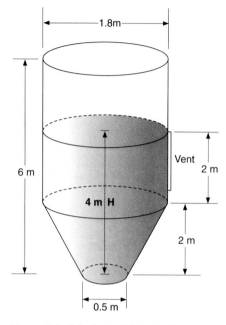

(a) H equals the vertical distance from the bottom of the hopper to the top of the vent $= 4\,\text{m}$

(b) $V_{\text{eff}} =$ the volume of the hopper plus the volume of the cylinder to the top of the vent
The volume of the cylindrical part $= (\pi(1.8)^2/4)2 = 5.09\,\text{m}^3$
The volume of the hopper $=$
$\pi.2/12\,(1.8^2 + 1.8 \times 0.5 + 0.5^3)$
$= 2.30\,\text{m}^3$
$V_{\text{eff}} = 5.09 + 2.30 = 7.39\,\text{m}^3$
V_{eff} is the shaded region in the diagram

(c) $A_{\text{eff}} = V_{\text{eff}}/H = 7.39/4 = 1.85\,\text{m}^2$

(d) $D_{\text{eff}} = (4A_{\text{eff}}/\pi)^{1/2} = 1.534\,\text{m}$

(e) $L/D = H/D_{\text{eff}} = 4/1.534 = 2.61$

Figure 7.5 Calculating L/D ratio for a cylindrical vessel with a hopper and a side vent

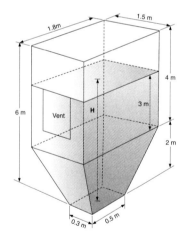

(a) H equals the vertical distance from the bottom of the hopper to the top of the vent $= 5\,\text{m}$

(b) $V_{\text{eff}} =$ the volume of the hopper plus the volume of the rectangular vessel to the top of the vent
The volume of the rectangular part
$= 1.8 \times 1.5 \times 3 = 8.1\,\text{m}^3$
The volume of the hopper $=$
$0.5 \times 2 \times (1.5 - 0.3)/2 + 0.3 \times 2 \times$
$(1.8 - 0.5)/2 + 2(1.8 - 0.5) \times$
$(1.5 - 0.3)/3 + 0.5 \times 0.3 \times 2 = 2.33\,\text{m}^3$
$V_{\text{eff}} = 8.1 \times 2.33 = 10.43\,\text{m}^3$
A general formula for calculating the volume for a rectangular hopper is given with Figure 7.8

(c) $A_{\text{eff}} = V_{\text{eff}}/H = 10.43/5 = 2.09\,\text{m}^2$

(d) $D_{\text{eff}} =$ the hydraulic diameter of area A_{eff} assuming A_{eff} is square $= (2.09)^{0.5} = 1.44\,\text{m}$

(e) $L/D = H/D_{\text{eff}} = 5/1.44 = 3.47$

Figure 7.6 Calculating L/D ratio for a rectangular vessel with a hopper and a side vent

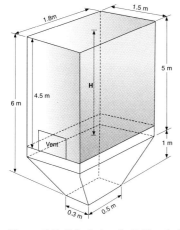

(a) H equals the vertical distance from the top of the rectangular vessel to the bottom of the vent. H is the longest flame path possible because the vent is closer to the hopper bottom than it is the vessel top $= 4.5\,\text{m}$

(b) $V_{\text{eff}} =$ the volume from the top of the rectangular vessel to the bottom of the vent $= 4.5 \times 1.8 \times 1.5 = 12.15\,\text{m}^3$
V_{eff} is the shaded region of the figure

(c) $A_{\text{eff}} = V_{\text{eff}}/H = 12.15/4.5 = 2.7\,\text{m}^2$

(d) $D_{\text{eff}} =$ the hydraulic diameter of area $= (0.5 \times (1.8 + 1.5)) = 1.65\,\text{m}$

(e) $L/D = H/D_{\text{eff}} = 4.5/1.65 = 2.73$

Figure 7.7 Calculating the L/D ratio for a rectangular vessel with a hopper and a side vent

a) Rectangular hopper

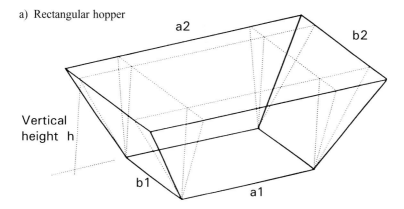

$$V = (a1)(h)(b2 - b1)/2 + (b1)(h)(a2 - a1)/2 + h(a2 - a1)(b2 - b1)/3 + (a1)(b1)h$$

b) Conical hopper
$$V = \pi(h)(D_1^2 + D_1 D_2 + D_2^2)/12$$ where D_1 is the diameter of the base, and D_2 is the diameter of the top

Figure 7.8 Methods for calculating the volume of a hopper

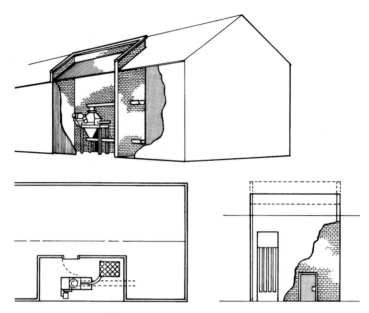

Figure 7.9 A strong cubicle designed for the grinding of particularly hazardous materials or for explosion-prone plant which cannot be situated in a safe place. (Reprinted with permission from *Dust Explosions in Factories*, Copyright 1972, HSE)

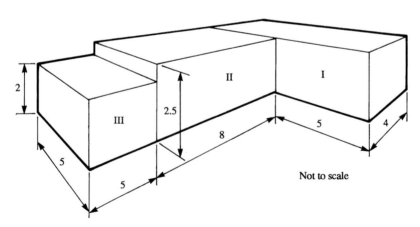

Figure 7.10 Worked example: venting of a building

Figure 7.11 Vented building. Almost 100% of the wall area of this building is explosion vent area. Each of the lightweight aluminium wall panels is secured by shear pins designed to release the panel at 30 psi. A chain at the top of each panel prevents it from being blown any distance if blown out by an explosion (Kodak Park Industrial Photo)

Figure 7.12 Explosion in vented building venting an explosion of starch dust through hinged windows and hinged doors in a building of light construction

References in Chapter 7

1. IChemE (2000), *Process vessels subject to explosion risk: design guidelines for the pressure rating of weak vessels subject to explosion risk*, Pilkington, S. (Ed.), (ISBN 0 8529 5428X).
2. Siwek, R., *New findings on explosion venting*, Paper to the Loss Prevention Symposium, Barcelona (1998).
3. VDI, 1999, *Pressure release of dust explosions* (VDI 3673), Verein Deutsche Ingenieure — Kommission Reinhaltung der Luft, Germany (Green Paper).
4. HSE 1992, (HS(G)103) *Safe handling of combustible dusts*, HMSO.
5. NFPA 1988 *Guide for venting of deflagrations* (NFPA 68), National Fire Protection Association, Quincy, USA.
6. HSE, 1983, *Cornstarch dust explosion at General Goods Limited, Banbury, Oxfordshire, 18 November 1981*, Report by HM Factory Inspectorate (HMSO).
7. Tamanini, F., and Valiulis, J.V., Improved guidelines for the sizing of vents, in *Dust Explosions*, J. Loss Prev. Process Ind. 9, 105, (1998).

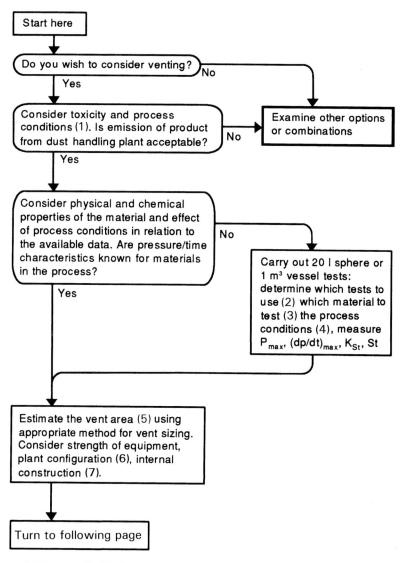

Logic Diagram 7a Venting.

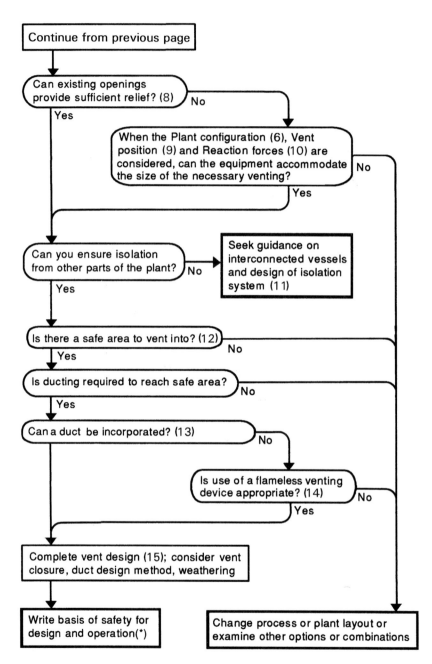

Logic Diagram 7b Venting (the numbers in brackets relate to those in the notes on the following pages)

*It is strongly recommended that the basis of safety for the design should be formally recorded.

(1) Venting – guidelines for assessment

If venting is to be considered as a basis for safety it must be in relation to its suitability for the process; for example, a toxic emission through a vent may be unacceptable. Containment or suppression could be better for toxic materials where the danger from an emission could be serious.

There are other circumstances also where venting is an altogether inappropriate technique, either because it is unreliable, is not adequately researched, or is itself dangerous. Venting is inappropriate and should not be used when:

1. The dust and/or its combustion products are excessively toxic or corrosive or both.
2. The dust is violently explosible — that is, outside the range over which vent estimation techniques can be applied.
3. The dust is a detonating or deflagrating explosive — that is, will explode in the absence of atmospheric oxygen. Where detonations occur there is insufficient time for the vent to open to reduce the pressure.

In these circumstances, alternative precautions should be used and if necessary specialist advice sought.

A further consideration is that there may be circumstances where, although there are no objections to the venting technique, per se, it is nevertheless difficult to employ. There are often going to be borderline cases where, although venting may be an attractive option, its implementation is not easy. One example of this is a relatively small vessel such as a storage bin positioned inside a building but too far from an external wall for explosion products to be ducted to a safe place.

(2) Which test to use

The pressure-time characteristic of the material under test can be measured using the 20 litre sphere or $1\,m^3$ vessel (see Chapter 2, Section 2.2, and Appendix 3).

(3) Which material to use for the pressure time test

Often tests are done on samples as received. If the sample does not ignite it should be tested under conditions of dryness and fineness appropriate to the process. Materials classified as Group B at ambient temperature may be explosible when process temperatures are higher than ambient or larger ignition sources are potentially present.

(4) Rate of pressure rise – effect of process conditions

(4.1) Temperature
The rate of pressure rise, dP/dt, may change significantly when the process temperature exceeds 50°C. Under these conditions dP/dt can be measured at the elevated temperature, if considered necessary.

(4.2) Pressure
It is unusual to convey dusts at pressures greater than 2–3 bar and below this the effect of pressure on the rate of pressure rise is minimal.

(4.3) Concentration
Tests are normally carried out using a range of concentrations. The rate of pressure rise, dP/dt, increases with concentration and reaches a maximum in the 20 litre sphere at an optimum concentration somewhat higher than the stoichiometric concentration. At higher concentrations, dP/dt reduces, or stays roughly constant.

(4.4) Turbulence
Dust clouds are usually turbulent to some degree because there must be some air movement if the dust is to remain dispersed. At low levels of turbulence the explosion violence of a dust cloud may be relatively mild, but at high states of turbulence, when the flame front is broken up and its effective area much increased, the explosion will propagate much more rapidly and the explosion violence will reach high values. This effect is very important in explosions moving through ducts and pipework because the confinement channels the air movement ahead of the explosion, generating high turbulence and driving the explosion to ever more rapid propagation. Constrictions and obstructions influence the development of turbulent explosions.

The level of turbulence can affect the venting requirements strongly; the greater the turbulence the faster the combustion rate, the faster the rate of pressure rise and thus the greater the area required to successfully vent the volume production caused by the explosion.

The rate of pressure rise is the important explosion parameter when determining the venting requirements of compact vessels. Standard methods for its determination and how it relates to the methods for estimating venting requirements are discussed in Chapter 2, section 2.2, and Appendix 3. The turbulent state of the dust cloud can, however, have a significant effect on the rate of pressure rise.

The standard tests, which form the basis for methods for vent sizing are usually done at a level of turbulence that simulates on the small scale that met with on the large scale in most industrial applications. It is well known that vent areas calculated using this data are generally satisfactory in all but the very worst cases.

When the turbulence level is less than that simulated in these standard tests then some reduction in vent area can, in principle, be made, although great care must be taken in the application of any methods which rely on a presumed lower turbulence. A thorough knowledge of the details of both the industrial process and the limitations of the vent sizing method are crucial.

Assessing turbulence levels in industrial plant is difficult and there are many problems associated with the application of any such measurements. Under normal working, turbulence levels may be relatively low, but an explosion elsewhere in the plant or an incipient explosion in the particular item of equipment may generate turbulence levels (possibly due to internal obstructions, flow through pipes and ducts, etc.) that are well above those met normally. These complications can be important for venting in real life situations.

The rate of pressure rise, dP/dt, can vary by a factor of ten when changing from static to turbulent conditions. Turbulence can only be studied in detail if full-scale test facilities are available.

A secondary influence on the rate of pressure rise and the consequent venting requirements is the strength of the ignition source. The most used standard test uses a strong, localized, ignition source made up of two 5 kJ chemical igniters (Chapter 2, section 2.2, and Appendix 3). In practice many likely ignition sources will have much lower energies. There may, however, be circumstances, for example, a flame entering a vessel as a jet from a conduit connection, where the ignition source can be very large, can result in a very rapid rate of combustion, and can have an important effect on the venting requirements. These particulars need to be considered before a decision to employ explosion venting is made, and when the venting requirements are being estimated. As much information as possible about the process, likely ignition sources and state of the dust cloud inside the plant must be collected if an effective calculation of vent area is to be made.

(4.5) Moisture content

The explosion violence falls as the moisture content of a dust increases. Eventually the dust is no longer explosible.

Guidelines for the effect of moisture content are as follows:

0–5%: little effect;
5–10%: decrease in sensitivity;
>25%: the dust is unlikely to be held in suspension and even if it is there will be a further decrease in sensitivity.

To avoid the sample being classified unrealistically, it is important that tests are not carried out on over-dried materials, i.e. on samples containing less than the minimum moisture content found under normal process conditions.

In processes where the minimum moisture content can be closely defined, explosibility testing to determine the sensitivity under process conditions should be carried out using a sample containing the minimum moisture content found in the process.

(4.6) Scale of the vessel and size of dust cloud

The violence of a dust explosion — as indicated by the rate of pressure rise — depends on the size of the vessel. The larger the vessel the slower the rate of pressure rise, although the potential for destruction will be greater because of the increased scale of the explosion. One of the simplest scaling laws is the cubic law which relates the rate of pressure rise in an explosion to the cube root of the vessel volume, and is used to calculate the K_{St} value from measurements of $(dP/dt)_{max}$ in the 20 litre sphere apparatus.

The size of vents required to limit the pressure rise to a prescribed level depends upon the volume of the vessel.

In the simplest situation it is assumed that the dust cloud is uniformly distributed throughout the vessel, i.e., the volume of the explosible dust cloud is equal to the volume of the vessel. Indeed, in some of the test equipment described in Chapter 2 and Appendix 3 the procedure is designed to ensure that this is the case. In practice the volume of the explosible dust cloud may be significantly less than the volume of the vessel. If so, the pressure rise will be less than for the case of uniform dust dispersion, provided the ignition is not in such a position that the dust cloud expands to fill the vessel before the flame arrives at the vent. However, work has shown that reduced pressures in vessels where the dust cloud only partially filled the vessel were similar to those where the dust cloud totally filled the vessel.

Where the provision of sufficient vent area (based on the vessel volume) may be practically difficult or expensive and where there may be good reason for suspecting that the explosible dust cloud may be smaller than the vessel volume, the possibility of basing the vent design on the supposed dust cloud volume, rather than the vessel volume, appears attractive. However, it is recommended that in methods for assessing venting requirements the actual volume of the vessel should be used rather than the dust cloud volume, unless specialist knowledge indicates otherwise. In some applications such as in certain types of spray drier the volume of an explosible dust cloud, in normal operation, will be significantly smaller than the volume of the vessel. However, there may also be quantities of dust deposited on either the walls of the vessel or other internal structures, or held in the base. In the event of an explosion the initial size of the dust cloud could be rapidly increased because of the entrainment of deposited dust stirred up due to process upset or the effects of the initial explosion. Quite generally, as dust explosions quite often follow some sort of process upset, steady state operating conditions may not be a good guide to the nature of dust clouds that could explode. Unless a great deal is known about the processes involved there can be little certainty in determining the size of dust clouds smaller than the containing vessels. The whole volume should be used in assessing venting requirements.

(5) Vent area calculation

This is the subject of this Chapter and Chapters 8, 9 and 10.

(6) Plant configuration

Pressure effects can be markedly enhanced as the length to diameter ratio of an enclosure increases. These effects are taken into account in the methods for vent sizing described in this Chapter.

(7) Internal construction

In some applications, usually involving relatively small vessels, it may be impractical to provide the vessel with explosion vents and the vessel must be designed to withstand the maximum explosion pressure, P_{max}, without rupture. In some small enclosures the maximum explosion pressure is reduced below that measured in standard tests because of cooling caused by large internal areas provided by components — for example, mills.

When a vessel is not designed to pressure vessel codes, the difficulty of estimating its strength should not be underestimated. It is the strength of the weakest link that must be known, be it, e.g., a bolted joint, a riveted joint, or a door fastener etc., and this determines the explosion pressure that the vessel can withstand. Quantifying the strength of weak plant, especially when it is old and has been in service for some time, is not easy. IChemE guidance on the estimation of the strength of weak components of plant is available[1].

(8) Can existing openings provide sufficient relief?

In small compact vessels the process entry and exit ports may provide a satisfactory amount of venting, although due consideration must be paid to preventing propagation of an explosion into other items of plant and other parts of the process. With full information as to how the maximum explosion pressure is limited by internal components and on the enclosure's inherent venting it may be that small vessels especially can be designed so that no extra venting is required. A convincing case would need to be made, and the justification for this option would need to be well documented.

(9) Vent position

The flame front must have free and unimpeded access to the vent. This can be a problem with filters and bucket elevators.

(10) Reaction forces

The ejection of the explosion from a vent may produce reaction forces that may damage a vessel if the forces are too unbalanced.

(11) Explosion isolation

Prevention of combustion wave propagation down interconnected pipelines must be considered for all containment, venting or suppression explosion protection systems. Explosion isolation can be by passive means such as rotary gate valves or explosion chokes, or by active means such as advanced inerting, triggered chemical barriers or slam shut valves.

Provided that appropriate explosion isolation measures are taken the design of explosion venting or explosion suppression systems can assume that ignition occurs within the confines of the protected vessel. Without appropriate explosion isolation the prospect of flame-jet ignition down an interconnected pipeline into the vessel must be assumed and requirements for more rigorous explosion safety considered (see Chapters 6 and 8).

There is one other consideration in the practical application of venting. It is usually good practice to provide interlocks so that, in the event of an explosion and the bursting of a vent closure, all or parts of the process are automatically shut down. It is, for instance, vital for dust conveying to be stopped because smouldering or burning clumps of dust remaining after the explosion can be transferred into adjacent items of plant where they can act as ignition sources for further explosions (see Appendix 1). Screw conveyors and rotary locks are obvious examples of conveying equipment that should be stopped as rapidly as is possible.

(12) Hazardous discharge area

The vent must be sited to prevent injuries to personnel and to minimize the effects of fire and blast (see Chapter 12). Hazard analysis may provide guidance to define a hazard area. Exclusion of personnel from the discharge area is a relevant consideration.

The volume of flame ejected by a vented explosion can be large and although it is best practice to site vented plant in the open air, where this is impracticable the burning cloud should be ducted to a safe place outside the building. Flame, unburned dust that can then inflame outside the vent and explosion over-pressures are all ejected from the vent opening. Personnel must be excluded from the discharge areas of vents or vent ducts during normal operation. Deflectors can be installed to guide the vented explosion to a safe place (see Chapter 9, Section 9.3).

Explosion venting inside buildings is viable only when the vent discharges into an enclosed area from which personnel are completely excluded when the plant is operating. As well as procedures for excluding personnel from the vicinity of the vent, the strength of the building, its internal design and the dangers of secondary explosions must all be considered if venting into an enclosed area has to take place. Under no circumstances must secondary explosions be allowed to develop. The blast from the vented explosion will disturb dust layers and other accumulations that have collected in the work-place, dispersing them into the air and producing a cloud that will fuel an explosion of much more destructive potential than the original event. These secondary explosions can be extensive and good housekeeping must ensure that dust accumulations are not allowed to build up in any location. Explosible clouds can form from very thin layers of dust.

(13) Ducting design method

Design methods for vent ducting are discussed in Chapter 9.

(14) Flameless venting devices

Flameless venting devices (for example, the Q-pipe; see Chapter 14) quench the flame when it ejects from an explosion vent. Although experimentation has shown them to be promising devices in principle, their use should be validated at the full scale for any particular situation.

(15) Complete the vent design

Sufficient work has been published on vent closure design (see Chapter 11) to allow this to be done. The proper design of an explosion vent will result in the safe discharge of the explosion without otherwise splitting the vessel walls.

Explosion venting of linked vessels

8

8.1 Introduction

Most industrial dust handling plant consists of vessels linked by pipelines. The greatest hazard in a linked system is the behaviour of the explosion as it propagates from one vessel into another through the interconnecting pipe. The increased turbulence due to the fluid flow engendered by the oncoming explosion, the pre-compression of the explosible atmosphere that can occur in confined systems and the energetic nature of the flame jet leaving the pipe combine to produce conditions where the explosion violence can be increased. Figure 8.1 shows a dust explosion in a linked system.

If enclosures — for example, vessels — are not isolated, interconnected systems require explosion protection by containment, explosion suppression, or venting. Information is given in Chapter 5 on the protection of linked contained systems (Section 5.3) and in Chapter 14 on the protection of pipelines (Section 14.2). Chapter 6 gives information on explosion suppression. This chapter is about the protection of linked vessels by venting. Dust explosions in inter-connected systems have been the subject of experimental investigation over the past decade[1–3].

8.2 Guidance on explosion venting of linked vessels

8.2.1 Simple rules

VDI 3673

In systems of interconnected enclosures where only one of the vessels can be vented, states some simple rules:

142

Figure 8.1 Dust explosion in a linked vessel system

143

i. When the larger of the enclosures cannot be vented, then the entire system must be designed for full containment. [Note: In a system of fully contained interconnected enclosures, high explosion overpressures may result from pressure-piling effects (see Chapter 5) and this needs to be taken into account in their design].

ii. When the smaller of the enclosures cannot be vented, then it must be designed for containment and the vent area of the larger vessel determined directly from representative explosion trials or appropriate published data.

iii. When the enclosures are of equal size, and one enclosure cannot be vented, ii) applies.

Guidance based on the results of an experimental investigation

Guidance has been published on estimating the vent areas for some linked systems[4], and is based on the results of an experimental investigation. From this the following simple rules have been derived that can be applied up to vessel volumes of $20 \, m^3$:

- For K_{St} values of $150 \, bar \, m \, s^{-1}$ or less, a dimensionless vent area (A_D) in both vessels of greater than 0.25 will limit the reduced explosion pressure to 0.5 bar.
  $A_D = A_V/V^{2/3}$, where A_V is the vent area and V is the vessel volume.
- For K_{St} values between 150 and $250 \, bar \, ms^{-1}$, a value of A_D in both vessels of 0.4 will limit the reduced explosion pressure to 0.5 bar.

The venting area shall be divided between enclosures so that A_D is the same in both enclosures. When venting a system of linked enclosures, the venting devices shall be designed for a low static activation overpressure, $P_{stat} \leq 0.1$ bar.

8.2.2 More detailed guidance

The following more detailed guidance is based on the results of the experimental programme[4], using various vessel volumes, pipe lengths and diameters, and explosible dusts. The guidance has been developed from the results of several hundred explosion tests in which the total vent area in the linked system was divided so that each vessel had the same effective vent area:

$$A_{D_1} = A_{D_2} \tag{8.1}$$

where A_v is the vent area, V the vessel volume and the subscript numerals refer to the vessels. Primary ignition occurs in vessel 1 and the secondary explosion in vessel 2. As the vent area decreases, the relative effect of linking the vessels increases. The increase in pressure is greatest when primary ignition occurs in the larger of the linked vessels. Generally, the longer the pipe the less is the effect on the explosion pressure, but this is not always so.

The higher the explosibility of the dust, the higher the effect on the explosion pressures.

Estimating vent areas for linked vented vessels

The flow chart in Figure 8.2 indicates the conditions to which each part of the guidance applies.

Figures 8.3 to 8.15 show relationships between the maximum reduced explosion pressure (in bar) and A_D for the conditions listed in each graph. The graphs can be used in two ways: to estimate the maximum reduced explosion pressure in an interconnected system when the vent area is known; and to estimate the necessary vent area to limit the maximum reduced explosion pressure to a given value.

Limits of the guidance

- The L/D ratio of each vessel should not exceed 2.
- P_{stat} of vent closures should not exceed 0.1 bar.
- The larger of the vessels should not exceed $20 \, m^3$.
- The length of the interconnecting pipe must not exceed 15 m, and must not be less than 5 m.
- The pipe area to volume of the smaller vessel in the system must not exceed 0.1.
- The P_{max} of the dust should not exceed 10 bar a.
- The vent area is always divided between the vessels so that A_D is equal in each vessel.
- The volume ratio V_1/V_2, (R), is calculated by taking V_1 as the larger volume and V_2 as the smaller. The volume of the connecting pipeline is ignored.

8.3 Other considerations

The transmission of an explosion from one vessel to another is not a certainty. The flame may not propagate through the entire length of the pipe, and even if it does it may not ignite the dust cloud in the second vessel. The probability of transmission generally increases with increasing K_{St}-value.

The amount of flame produced in the primary explosion (in vessel 1) appears important in determining the probability of secondary ignition (in vessel 2).

An obstruction, such as a baffle plate, external to the pipe and a short distance from the outlet, increases the probability of secondary ignition. When the jet-flame impinges on the baffle, the structure of the jet-flame is disturbed. Distortion of the flame by the baffle distributes burning material over an extended area, and this increase in the size of the potential ignition source, along with an increase in its lifetime, increases the chance of a secondary explosion.

Introduction of an obstacle can result in a more violent secondary explosion. Furthermore the violence of the tertiary explosion outside the vent can be increased also.

Fast jet-flames leaving the outlet of the pipe will cause high dynamic loading on any impingement surfaces. An example, Figure 8.16, shows pressure-time traces from three positions in a vessel during a secondary explosion. At the location in the wall directly opposite the pipe outlet where the jet flame enters the vessel, a pressure spike has occurred, prior to the secondary explosion. The effect is localized and these high pressures are not registered elsewhere.

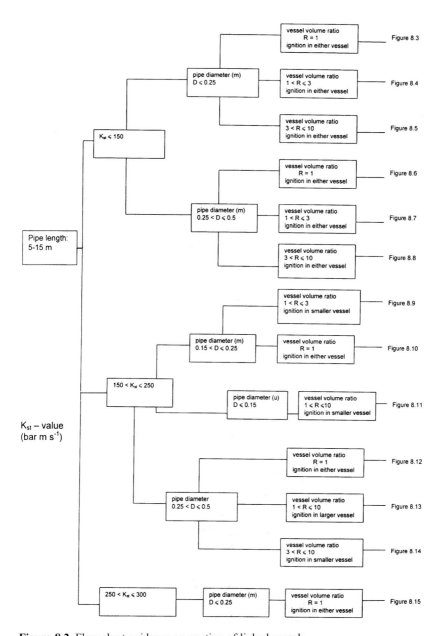

Figure 8.2 Flow chart guidance on venting of linked vessels

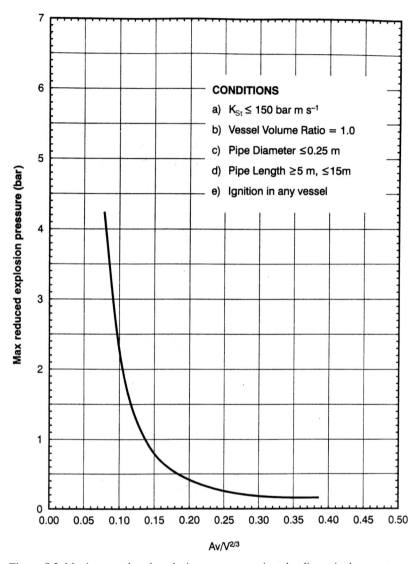

Figure 8.3 Maximum reduced explosion pressure against the dimensionless vent area $A_v/V^{2/3}$

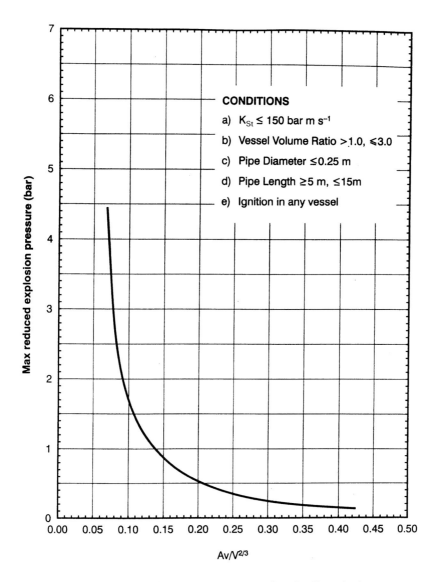

Figure 8.4 Maximum reduced explosion pressure against the dimensionless vent area $A_v/V^{2/3}$

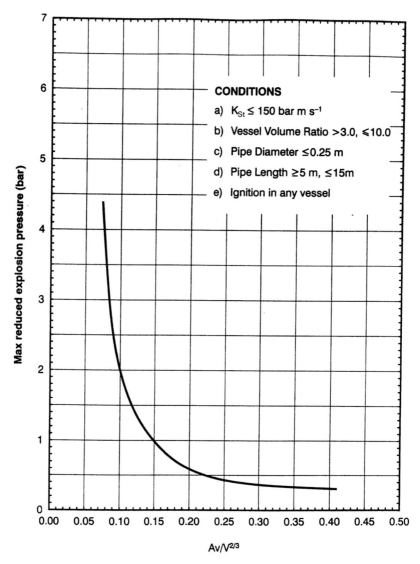

Figure 8.5 Maximum reduced explosion pressure against the dimensionless vent area $A_v/V^{2/3}$

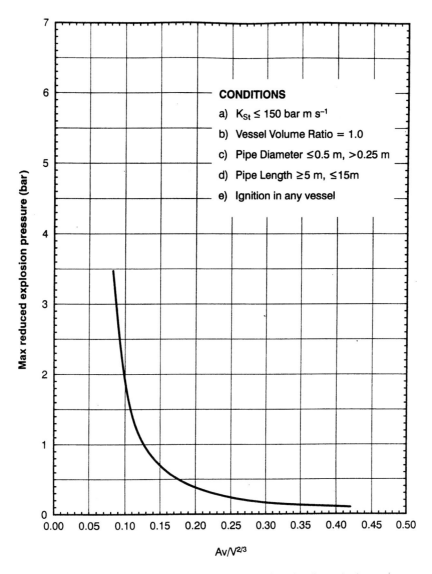

Figure 8.6 Maximum reduced explosion pressure against the dimensionless vent area $A_v/V^{2/3}$

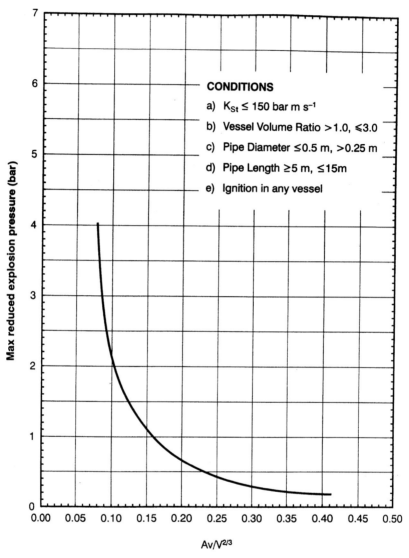

Figure 8.7 Maximum reduced explosion pressure against the dimensionless vent area $A_v/V^{2/3}$

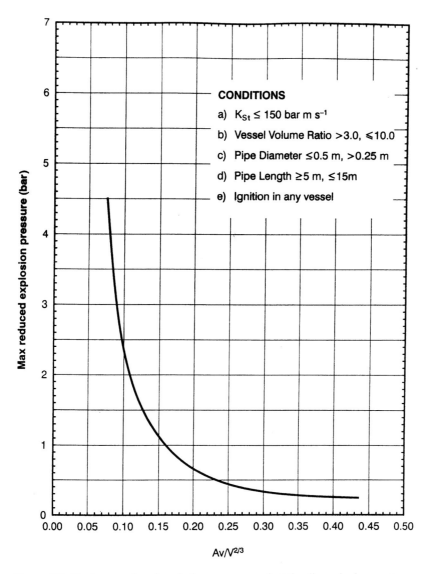

Figure 8.8 Maximum reduced explosion pressure against the dimensionless vent area $A_v/V^{2/3}$

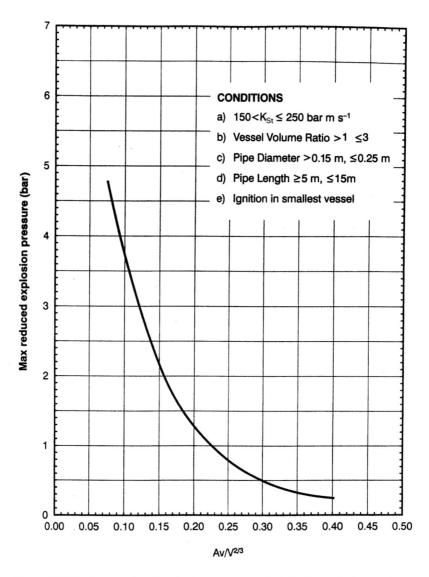

Figure 8.9 Maximum reduced explosion pressure against the dimensionless vent area $A_v/V^{2/3}$

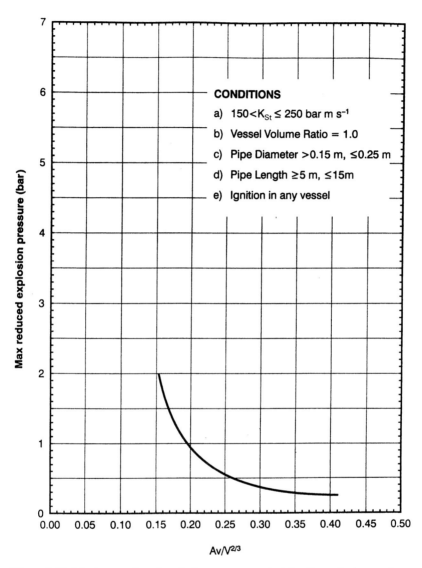

Figure 8.10 Maximum reduced explosion pressure against the dimensionless vent area $A_v/V^{2/3}$

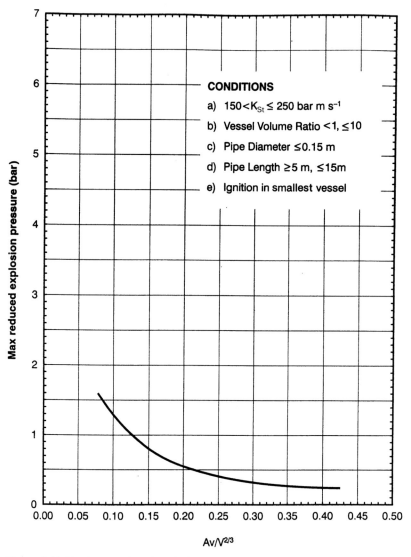

Figure 8.11 Maximum reduced explosion pressure against the dimensionless vent area $A_v/V^{2/3}$

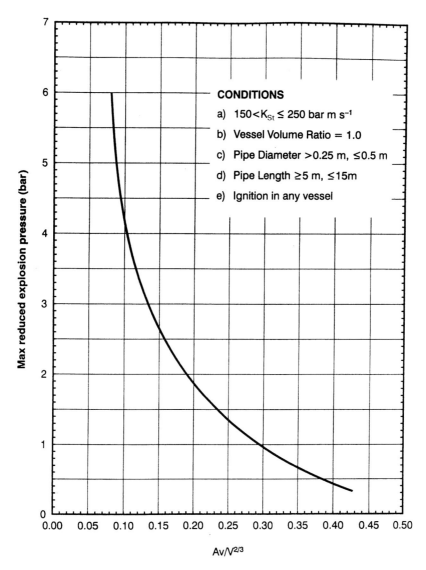

Figure 8.12 Maximum reduced explosion pressure against the dimensionless vent area $A_v/V^{2/3}$

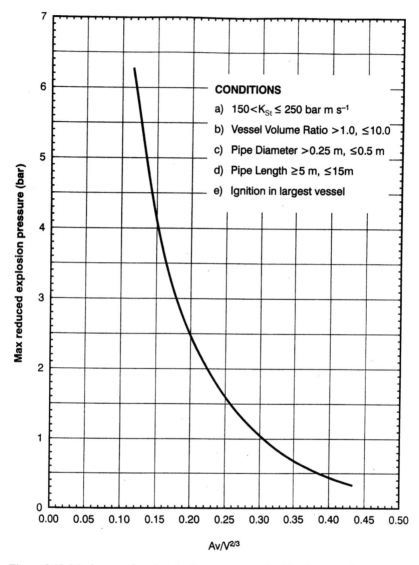

Figure 8.13 Maximum reduced explosion pressure against the dimensionless vent area $A_v/V^{2/3}$

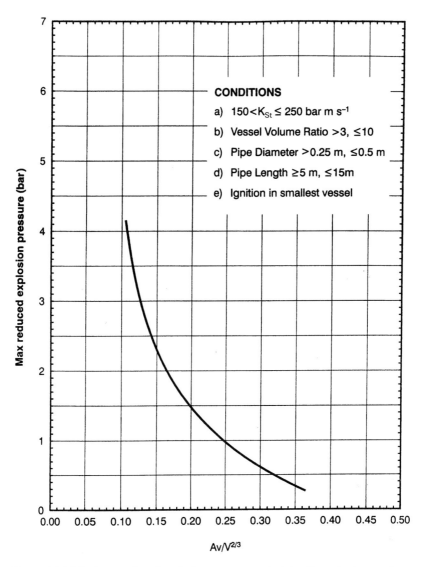

Figure 8.14 Maximum reduced explosion pressure against the dimensionless vent area $A_v/V^{2/3}$

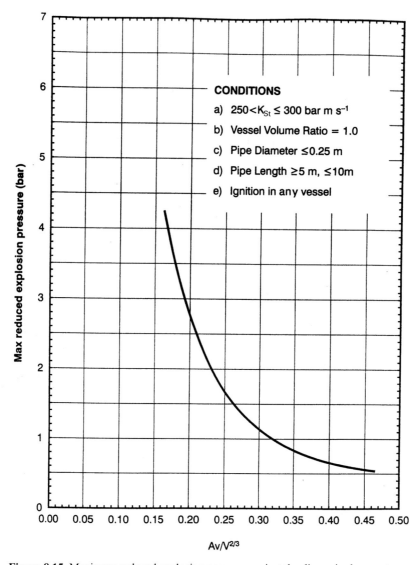

Figure 8.15 Maximum reduced explosion pressure against the dimensionless vent area $A_v/V^{2/3}$

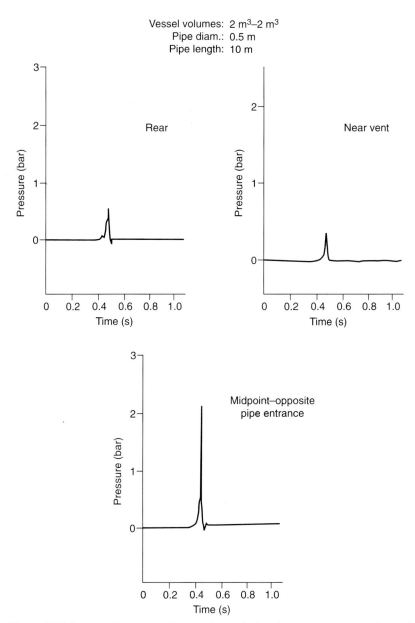

Figure 8.16 Pressure time traces in second vessel of an interconnected vented vessel system

References in Chapter 8

1. Van Wingerden, K. and Alfert, F., 1992, *Dust Explosion Propagation in Connected Vessels,* VDI, Berichte Nr. 975, p. 507.
2. Holbrow, P., Andrews, S. and Lunn, G.A., 1996, Dust Explosions in Interconnected Vented Vessels, *J. Loss Prev. Process Ind.* 9, pp. 91–103.
3. Vogl, A., 1996, *Explosionsubertragung aus Behaltern in Rohrleitungen pneumatischer Anlagen*, VDI, Berichte Nr. 1272, p. 215.
4. Holbrow, P., Lunn, G.A., and Tyldesley, A., 1999, Dust Explosion Protection in Linked Vessels: Containment and Venting, *J. Loss Prev. Process Ind.*, 12, pp. 227–234.

Explosion venting – supplementary design considerations

9

9.1 Introduction

Successful application of explosion venting is not only a matter of specifying a vent area of sufficient size, but also of dealing effectively with the hazards that arise from the venting process. These hazards are:

- external flame;
- external blast;
- dust and product emissions;
- recoil forces.

This Chapter gives some practical guidance on dealing with the effects from these.

9.2 Plant layout

Plant in which an explosible concentration of dust can exist should be clearly identified and whenever possible separated from other plant. It is best practice to ensure that different product streams are separated from each other so that the effects of an explosion in one product stream are not transferred to another.

Plant items protected by explosion venting will need to be sited so as to allow venting to a safe place (see Section 9.3). If this cannot be achieved it may be necessary to use alternative methods of protection.

A frame building with lightweight cladding is preferred for buildings handling explosible dusts in order to prevent severe damage or collapse from secondary explosions (see Chapter 7, Section 7.3.2).

9.3 Safe discharge area

As well as the pressure developed inside a vented vessel, a vented explosion generates secondary effects, due to blast and fire, outside the vented vessel. These secondary effects need to be considered so that appropriate protection can be provided for people or nearby installations and buildings.

In practice, venting is not simply a matter of allowing the dust cloud and flame to disperse anywhere. The dust cloud and flame ejected from a vented explosion can be extensive (see Figure 9.1, which shows the fireball from a vented dust explosion). Thus the area external to an explosion vent is hazardous and represents an obvious danger to personnel and equipment. Methods for estimating the extent of the hazardous area have been published (see Chapter 12).

Venting to a safe place is, therefore, very important and will have implications for plant layout and access. If the dust-handling equipment cannot be placed in the open air, then it is best practice to guide the burning cloud to a safe place through a vent duct fitted to the vent opening (see Section 9.4). Generally, upward facing vents or vent duct outlets passing through the roof of a factory are a preferred option, provided access to that part of the roof is strictly limited to those occasions when the plant is not operating. If equipment is located on a factory roof then side venting should be non-hazardous provided other roof mounted equipment and surrounding buildings are far enough away.

Figure 9.1 Example of flame from a vented dust explosion

Vents through side walls of a factory, or from equipment located outside a factory building should not be directed towards other equipment or towards any thoroughfare, either traffic or pedestrian, and access to the vicinity of the vent must be prevented during plant operation.

Vents should not discharge into the factory or any other building containing plant, or where personnel may be present. Flame and overpressure hazards are always a danger, and personnel must be totally excluded, during operation of the plant, from any enclosed space into which plant is vented. If there is no option but to vent inside a building, account must also be taken of the rise in pressure inside the building or room and its effect on the structure (see Chapter 7, Section 7.3.2, regarding the venting of buildings to limit overpressures). The avoidance of secondary explosions by good housekeeping and regular cleaning is of particular importance.

The requirement to vent to a safe place may sometimes be impossible to achieve without very expensive plant modifications. There are techniques, outlined below, i.e., deflector plates, shroud deflectors, combined venting/ suppression, and flameless venting devices, that can help to alleviate the problem. In the final analysis, however, there will be circumstances where venting is clearly unsuitable and alternative measures should be used.

9.3.1 Use of deflector plates

The use of deflector plates is an accepted way of reducing the extent of the hazardous area external to a vent.

A short test programme was carried out at the UK's Health and Safety Laboratory, Buxton, with the intention of producing results either confirming or indicating changes to custom and practice. A 6.3 m^3 explosion vessel was used. In summary, the tests showed that an increase in the area of the plate, and an increase in the angle of deflection both improved the effectiveness of the device. The plate had negligible effect on the reduced explosion pressure.

Some modifications have been made to established practice and a possible design of a deflector plate and its installation are shown in Figure 9.2.

The area of the plate should be at least three times the area of the vent, and its dimensions not less than 1.6 × the dimensions of the vent. The plate should be inclined at an angle of at least 45°(but 60° is better) to the horizontal, to deflect the ejected flame upwards. The plate should be installed at a sufficient distance from the vent to ensure that it does not act as an obstacle to the venting process and so cause an increase in the reduced explosion pressure inside the enclosure. However, the plate should not be installed at too great a distance from the vent. The distance of 1.5 D, given in Figure 9.2, where D is the diameter of the vent has been shown to be most satisfactory in the explosion trials, but may need to

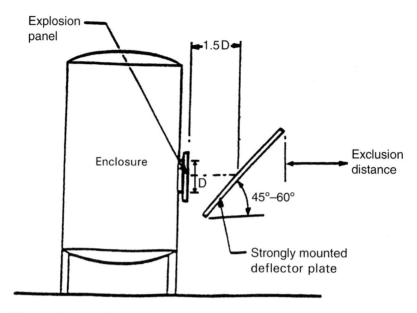

Figure 9.2 Design for an installation of a blast deflector plate

be modified in practice, depending on circumstances. The plate should be mounted so that it can withstand the force exerted by the vented explosion, which can be calculated by multiplying the reduced explosion pressure by the area of the plate.

The plate limits the horizontal extent of the flame and trials show that a deflector plate positioned as in Figure 9.2 approximately halves the length of the flame compared to when the plate is absent. Methods for estimating the length of flame from a vented explosion are given in Chapter 12. An exclusion distance beyond the deflector should be specified from which personnel are excluded while the plant is operating. The plate deflects flame sideways and the lateral extent of the exclusion zone should be sufficient to avoid harm from the sideways deflection. Deflectors should not be installed when the enclosure volume is greater than 20 m³.

9.3.2 Use of combined suppression/venting

The combination of venting the explosion and the injection of a suppressant into the flame front near to the vent opening will almost certainly help to reduce the hazardous area. Injection of suppressant material into the vessel shortly after ignition will reduce the rate of pressure rise developed inside the plant, thus allowing smaller vent sizes to be fitted. Specialist help is necessary to design such systems.

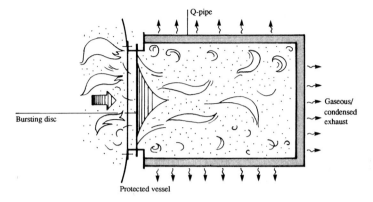

Figure 9.3 Q-pipe principle, combining filter and quenching effects without causing consideration flow resistance
Reproduced by permission of GexCon AS

9.3.3 Use of flameless venting devices

Flameless venting devices are designed to allow venting of explosions without the attendant risks of an external fireball.

Figures 9.3 and 9.4 show typical devices each comprising a proprietary vent panel, housing and flame arrester element. Flame propagation is stopped by energy dissipation in the arrester element, reducing the burning fuel below its ignition temperature.

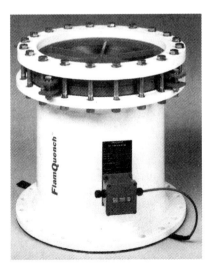

Figure 9.4 Flame-trap type flame-limiting device
Reproduced by permission of FIKE

167

Extensive explosion testing has validated flameless venting for volumes up to 1000 m^3 and dust classes including St 3, although there is some restriction on the applicability of the technique for dusts with low minimum ignition temperatures.

A breakwire installed on the vent panel provides means of automatic plant shutdown in the event of an explosion occurring.

9.4 The use of vent ducts

Vent ducts are used to direct a vented explosion to a safe area, usually from plant in a building to the open air. Ducts, however, obstruct the venting process, with the result that the reduced explosion pressure in the plant is increased. Whereas the venting requirement may be appropriate for a vessel standing on its own, once a vent duct is fitted the reduced explosion pressure may be increased above the design strength of the vessel.

There are three methods for estimating the effect of vent ducts, namely, the method included in a European standard currently being drafted (prEN)[1], the Institution of Chemical Engineers (IChemE) method[2], and the Factory Mutual Research Corporation (FMRC) method[3].

This guidance applies to vent ducts which do not contain any dust prior to the vented explosion. It is not applicable in any way to dust-carrying pipelines.

9.4.1 The draft European standard (prEN) method[1]

The method in prEN was developed for VDI 3673[5]. This method consists of a series of empirical equations fitted to explosion test data, and Equations (9.1) and (9.2) are included in the prEN. This guidance applies when the equation given in Chapter 7, Section 7.3.1 has been used for initial sizing of the vent before the vent duct is fitted. This method is recommended when a straight vent duct is fitted to an isolated enclosure. If the vent duct contains a bend, then the IChemE method given in Section 9.4.2 should be used.

For cubical vessels, and homogeneous dust air mixtures, the guidance is:

$$\frac{P'_{red,max}}{P'_{red,max}} = 1 + 17.3 \left[\frac{A}{V^{0.753}} \right]^{1.6} L \qquad (9.1)$$

where A is the vent area, m^2

L is the vent duct length to diameter ratio

V is the vessel volume, m^3

P$_{red,max}$ is the reduced explosion pressure, without a vent duct, bar

P'$_{red,max}$ is the reduced explosion pressure, with a vent duct, bar.

The length of the duct at which further increases in length have little or no effect on the reduced explosion pressure is given, empirically, by:

$$L_s = 4.564 \times P_{red,max}^{-0.37} \tag{9.2}$$

valid for the pressure range $0.1\,\text{bar} \leq P_{red,max} \leq 2\,\text{bar}$[4]. The value of P_{stat} is 0.1 bar.

VDI 3673 gives equations for the effect of vent ducts when fitted to elongated vessels and also for inhomogeneous dust clouds in compact enclosures, but these equations will not be included in the European standard.

9.4.2 The Institution of Chemical Engineers (IChemE) method[2]

If the vent duct contains a bend, the only freely available guidance is the IChemE method. For this method to be valid, however, the original vent area must be calculated by the K_{St} Nomograph approach and not by Equation 7.2 in Chapter 7, Section 7.3.1. The IChemE method is based on a set of experimental measurements[5]. A mathematical model of the physical behaviour of the explosion was used to derive guidance[2].

The IChemE guidance consists of calculated results presented as graphs which allow estimation of the new reduced explosion pressure when a vent duct of given L/D ratio is fitted. The guidance is specifically designed to fit with the K_{St} Nomograph approach to vent sizing, and D, the vent diameter, follows from use of the Nomograph approach.

The K_{St} Nomographs are given in Appendix 5. The limitations to their use are:

- Enclosure volume, $V \leq 1000\,\text{m}^3$
- Vent bursting pressure, $1.1\,\text{bar a} \leq P_{stat} \leq 1.5\,\text{bar a}$
- Reduced explosion pressure, $1.2\,\text{bar a} \leq P_{red} \leq 3.0\,\text{bar a}$
- K_{St} value, $10\,\text{bar m s}^{-1} \leq K_{St} \leq 600\,\text{bar m s}^{-1}$
- For K_{St} values $\leq 300\,\text{bar m s}^{-1}$, $P_{max} \leq 11\,\text{bar a}$
- For K_{St} values $> 300\,\text{bar m s}^{-1}$, $P_{max} \leq 13\,\text{bar a}$

Apart from the characteristics of the vent duct, the only information necessary to use the vent duct guidance is that required for the K_{St}-Nomograph approach.

The guidance comprises four sets of graphs given in Appendix 6:

A) The effects on the reduced explosion pressure of straight vent ducts.
B) The effect on the reduced explosion pressure of vent ducts containing a sharp 45° bend.
C) The effect on the reduced explosion pressure of vent ducts containing a sharp 90° bend.

D) The effect on the reduced explosion pressure of straight vent ducts for metal dusts such as aluminium in the St 3 group (300 bar m s^{-1} < K$_{St}$ ≤ 600 bar m s^{-1}).

The preliminary information required for using the graphs is the K$_{St}$ value of the dust (bar m s^{-1}) and the bursting pressure of the vent cover, P$_{stat}$ (bar a). Each set contains a graph applicable to the K$_{St}$ and P$_{stat}$ values used in the K$_{St}$ Nomographs. These are:

K$_{St}$ values (bar m s^{-1}): 10, 20, 30, 40, 50, 75, 100, 150, 200, 250, 300, 400, 500 and 600.
P$_{stat}$ (bar a): 1.1, 1.2 and 1.5.

The graphs are applicable to vent ducts less than 16 m in length of circular cross section, with the cross-sectional area equal to the area of the vent. Each graph shows the effect on the reduced explosion pressure of vent ducts characterised by the L/D ratio, beginning at L/D = 0. L is the length of the vent duct and D is the diameter. Methods for estimating L are shown diagramatically in Figure 9.5. The additional information required for this estimation is the vessel volume, V, and the area of the vent A$_v$.

When using the design guide it may be necessary to interpolate between graphs and between the lines on any particular graph.

An example of the guidance is given in Figure 9.6; the graph relates the reduced explosion pressure to the (L/D) ratio of the duct for a given value of K$_{St}$ and P$_{stat}$. Using the guidance to predict the effect of a duct on P$_{red}$ is straightforward and is demonstrated in Figure 9.7. When the enclosure volume and the vent area are known, as well as the K$_{St}$ and P$_{stat}$ values for which a particular graph is valid, the K$_{St}$ Nomographs are used to calculate (P$_{red}$)$_0$, the reduced explosion pressure when no vent duct is fitted. In Figure 9.7 (P$_{red}$)$_0$ is found on the vertical axis of the graph. The effect of the duct is estimated by following the appropriate line along the horizontal axis to the known value of L/D. The duct diameter, D, is calculated from the known vent area. In Figure 9.7 the duct has an L/D ratio of 7. The new value of reduced explosion pressure can then be read from the graph. In Figure 9.7, the new value of P$_{red}$ is 3.6 bar a. The length of the duct, L, is calculated as shown in Figure 9.6.

Worked Example
A vessel of 6 m^3 capacity is used to handle a dust with a K$_{St}$-value of 150 bar m s^{-1}. A vent with an area of 0.7 m^2 is fitted, closed with a vent panel having an opening pressure of 1.2 bar a. A vent duct 5 m long containing a

45° bend is to be attached to the vent opening. Estimate the reduced explosion pressure in the vessel.

Method:
From the K_{St} Nomograph in Appendix 5 find $(P_{red})_0$, the reduced explosion pressure with no vent duct fitted. $(P_{red})_0 = 1.38$ bar a (see Figure 9.7(a)). Assume 5 m is the length of the duct, L, as measured in the method given in Figure 9.5. The diameter of the duct, $D = (4 \times 0.7/3.142)^{1/2} = 0.944$ m

$$\therefore (L/D) \text{ ratio} = 5/0.944 = 5.33$$

From Appendix B, using the graph (Figure A6.58) for $K_{St} = 150$ bar m s^{-1} and $P_{stat} = 1.2$ bar a:

When $(P_{red})_0 = 138$ bar a and $L/D = 5.3$, the reduced explosion pressure = 2.1 bar a (see Figure 9.8(b)).
   Answer: The reduced explosion pressure = 2.1 bar a.

This example demonstrates the straightforward estimation of reduced explosion pressure when a vent duct is attached.

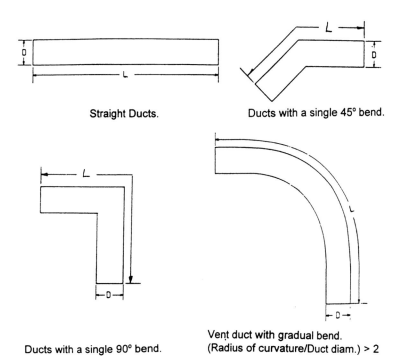

Straight Ducts.

Ducts with a single 45° bend.

Ducts with a single 90° bend.

Vent duct with gradual bend.
(Radius of curvature/Duct diam.) > 2

Figure 9.5 Measurement of the vent duct L/D ratio

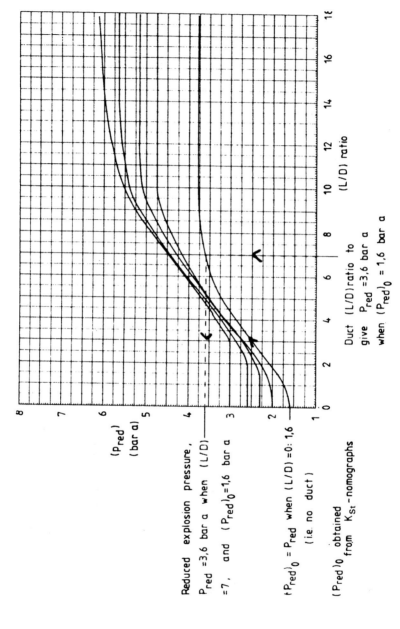

Figure 9.6 Example of IChemE Vent Duct Guidance. The length of the duct, L, is calculated as shown in Figure 9.5

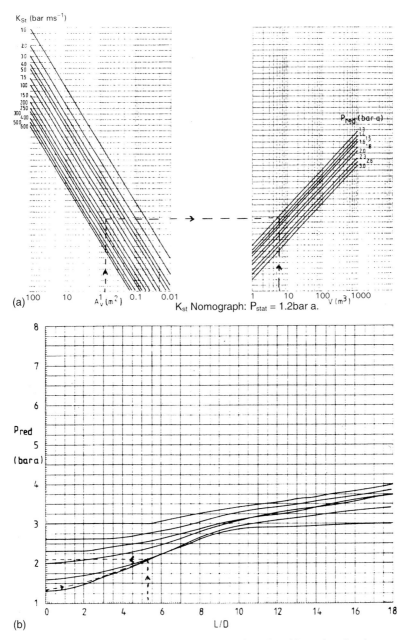

Figure 9.7 (a) Worked example – determination of $(P_{red})_0$ with no duct fitted.
(b) Worked example – determination of P_{red} with duct fitted. (From Appendix 6B Figure A6.58). $K_{St} = 150\,bar\,ms^{-1}$, $P_{stat} = 1.2\,bar\,a$. Duct configuration – simple sharp $45°$ bend.

9.4.3 The FMRC method[3,6]

This vent duct calculation method is an extension of the FMRC method described in Chapter 7 for calculating vent areas. (Section 7.3.3).

The FMRC analysis produces three parameters[8]:

1. Vent parameter, Γ

$$\Gamma = a_{cd} \frac{A_{v0}}{V_0^{2/3}} \frac{P_m - P_0}{K_0} \tag{9.3}$$

2. Duct inertia parameter, ϕ

$$\phi = \frac{L_D V_0}{A_d} \frac{M}{RT_0} \left(\frac{K_0}{P_m - P_0} \right)^2 \tag{9.4}$$

3. Friction loss parameter, Ψ_D

$$\Psi_D = \left[C_f \frac{P_d L_d}{A_d} + C_\alpha \right] \frac{V_0}{L_D A_d} \tag{9.5}$$

where a_{cd} constant
   A_{v0} vent area, m^2
   V_0 enclosure volume, m^3
   P_m maximum pressure in enclosed explosion, bar
   P_0 initial pressure in the enclosure, bar
   K_0 effective mixture reactivity, bar m s^{-1}
   L_d duct length, m
   A_d duct cross section, m^2
   M   molecular weight of air
   R   universal gas constant
   P_d duct perimeter, m
   C_f friction factor
   C_α head loss factor.

The factor K_0 is calculated from the K_{St} value[8].

This correlation was developed by using the data on which the IChemE guidance is based[4], and a relation between effective vent area and the above parameters obtained.

This method is not generally available.

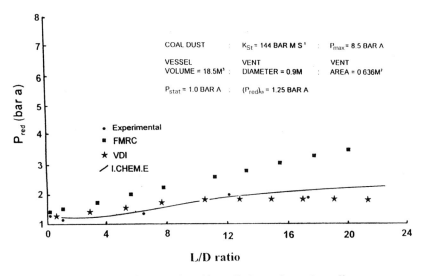

Figure 9.8 Comparison of test results with predictions of vent duct effect

9.4.4 Discussion

Figures 9.8 and 9.9 compare predictions from the three vent duct calculation methods (in Sections 9.1 to 9.3) with data from tests in an $18.5\,m^3$ vessel and a 20 litre sphere (respectively).

The IChemE method calculations are from the model, and not the guidance.

In Figure 9.9, while the IChemE calculation method passes through the experimental points the FMRC method envelops them. The prEN method predictions are close to experiment because of the cut-off point at a duct L/D ratio of 8.1. Had the cut-off point not been applied, the prEN (VDI) predictions would have continued to rise parallel to, but beneath, the FMRC predictions. The prEN and FMRC methods predict that there will always be an effect on the reduced explosion pressure, even for very short ducts, whereas the IChemE method does not.

In Figure 9.10, the agreement between predictions is good at low pressures, but not at high. Whereas the measured pressures and the IChemE calculations reach a plateau at an L/D ratio of 15 or so, the prEN method and FMRC predictions continue to rise. The prEN method cut-off point is well beyond the range of the graph.

An extensive series of comparison calculations has been performed. Some general conclusions, based on those comparisons are:

- At P_{stat} values of 0.1 bar, and K_{St} values up to $300\,bar\,m\,s^{-1}$, the prEN vent duct method generally predicts lower values of P'_{red} than does the FMRC method, but not always. This is certainly true, however, once the prEN cut-off length is exceeded; the prEN prediction then stays constant, while the FMRC prediction continues to rise.

- At P_{stat} values of 0.2 bar, the FMRC method usually predicts higher values of P'_{red} than the prEN method. The effect of the prEN method cut-off length is as described above.

- At P_{stat} values of 0.5 bar, the FMRC method predicts lower values of P'_{red} than does the prEN method, although once the prEN method cut-off length is exceeded, the reverse eventually occurs.

- Because of the circumstances described above, there is in the main, better agreement between the prEN method predictions and the IChemE predictions, than between FMRC and IChemE. The application of the prEN method cut-off point assists materially in this better agreement. There comes a point, however, in the majority of the comparisons, where, as the vent duct lengthens, the IChemE prediction exceeds the prEN method prediction.

- The IChemE and FMRC methods cater for bends in vent ducts, the prEn method does not.

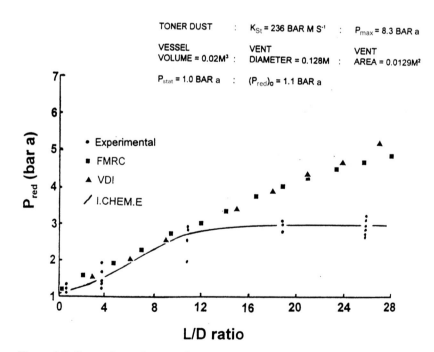

Figure 9.9 Comparison of test results with predictions of vent duct effects

In conclusion, it is recommended that when straight vent ducts are to be fitted, the prEN method described in Section 9.4.1 should be used. When the vent duct contains a bend, the IChemE method (Section 9.4.2) should be used in conjunction with the K_{St}-Nomograph method of vent sizing. If the FMRC method (Section 9.4.3) becomes available, this will be an option for both straight and bent ducts.

9.4.5 Allowed vent duct designs

Allowed vent duct designs are shown diagrammatically in Figure 9.10, as are some which are forbidden. The guidance that should be applied to a particular design is identified. Other designs are allowable if calculation of the reduced explosion pressure is based on appropriate explosion tests.

Other designs matters that should be taken into account are:

- Position of the bend along the duct.
  The experiments on which this design is based were mostly done with a bend one metre from the duct exit. The bend must not be close to the vent opening itself. It is recommended that the bend be at least 2 m from the vent opening.
- Effect of multiple bends.
  It is recommended that single bends only be incorporated in a vent duct. Experiments show that the effect of two bends on the reduced explosion pressure is greater than suggested by assuming that the contributions are additive.
- Strength of ducts.
  Explosion pressures in the vent duct can be as high as those measured in the explosion vessel. The ducting should thus be made strong enough to withstand the expected explosion pressures. Pressures in the vent duct can sometimes be higher than those measured in the explosion vessel. These, however, are short-lived pressure pulses.
- Gradual bends.
  Sharp bends have been used in this guidance because they represent the worst case. If a gradual bend is used the pressure will be lower than for a sharp bend, all other things being equal. It is recommended that the outer curve of the duct be used when calculating the L/D ratio of a gradual bend (see Figure 9.6 and Appendix 6). When the ratio (radius of curvature of the bend/duct diameter) is less than 2, however, the length should be measured in the same way but the bend is considered as sharp, and Appendix 6, Sections B or C used.
- Reaction forces.
  Both explosion vessels and ducting should be securely fixed to withstand

ALLOWED VENT DUCT DESIGNS

Use guidance for straight ducts.

Vent duct with gradual bend.
(Radius of curvature/Duct diam.) > 2

Use guidance for ducts with a single 45° bend.

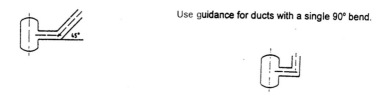

Use guidance for ducts with a single 90° bend.

FORBIDDEN VENT DUCT DESIGNS.

Vent duct area less
than vent area.

90° bend too close
to vent opening.

Vent duct area much
greater than vent area.

Figure 9.10 Allowed vent duct designs for the guidance

reaction forces. If the vent duct contains a bend, lateral reaction forces should also be catered for.

- Protecting the vent duct by an end grating.
  A grating over the end of a vent duct does not have a noticeable effect on the reduced explosion pressure, providing the mesh is not too small. The use of a light weight cover may increase the reduced explosion pressure.

9.4.6 Ducts with areas larger than the vent

It is always the recommended practice that the area of the vent duct should equal the area of the vent. Such a design essentially means that, if the vent is unobstructed, the explosion in the duct is a continuation of the primary explosion in the enclosure.

If the duct area is greater than the vent area, then circumstances arise where the explosion in the duct is essentially a separate event, ignited by the primary explosion. One example is when the vent area is much smaller than the duct area and the venting flame acts as a jet ignition source for the dust cloud ejected into the duct prior to the flame. The explosion in the duct is then disconnected from the conditions of the primary explosion[9].

A second example is when, because of a grid across the vent, the effective vent area is less than the total vent area over which the duct is fitted. In this example the flame is distributed across the duct cross-section, and, again, the explosion in the duct is disconnected from the conditions of the primary explosion[10].

In the first example, high explosion overpressures can occur when a combination of increased turbulence and a jet-flame ignition source produces an explosion of relatively high intensity in the duct. These conditions are most likely to occur when the reduced explosion pressure without a vent duct is high. Tests show, however, that if the reduced explosion pressure without a duct does not exceed 0.5 bar, and the ratio of duct area to vent area does not exceed 2, the final reduced explosion pressure can be lower than if the duct and vent have equal areas[9].

In the second example, the jet-flame ignition effect does not occur. Tests show that, at low reduced explosion pressures, the final reduced explosion pressure is less than predicted by published guidance[10].

It is recommended that even when the practical conditions are such as to produce reduced explosion pressures less than predicted by the guidance, the guidance should, nevertheless, be used, with the L/D ratio calculated using the vent diameter. Only when, in specific practical applications, lower reduced explosion pressures have been proven by explosion trials should ducts with areas greater than the vent area be used and a lower pressure than predicted by guidance anticipated.

9.4.7 Recoil forces

Recoil forces are generated during explosion venting when material is ejected from the opening of the vent.

The maximum recoil force can be calculated with the equation:

$$F_{R_i \, max} = \alpha \times A_v \times p_{red} \qquad (9.6)$$

where $F_{R_i \, max}$ is the recoil force, kN
A_v is the vent area, m^2
P_{red} is the reduced explosion pressure, bar.

Based on experimental work the recommended value of the factor α is 119.

The total thrust force can be considered as a force applied at the geometric centre of the vent. Installation of vents of equal area on opposite sides of a vessel may in some instances compensate for recoil forces, but this cannot be depended upon to prevent thrust in one direction, as one vent may open before another. These imbalances should be considered when designing the restraints for resisting thrust forces.

Knowing the duration of the recoil forces can aid in the design of certain support structures for vented vessels. The duration calculated by the following equation will be conservative:

$$t_R = (10^{-2})K_{St}V^{1/3}/A_v P_{red} \qquad (9.7)$$

where t_R is the duration of the pulse, seconds
K_{St} is the K_{St} dust explosibility measure, $bar\,m\,s^{-1}$
P_{red} is the reduced explosion pressure, bar, and
A_v is the vent area, m^2

The impulse transmitted by the recoil force can be approximated by a rectangular impulse equal in area to the recoil force-time variation. The height of this rectangular impulse is given by:

$$F_R = 0.25 \times A_v \times P_{red} \qquad (9.8)$$

The impulse transmitted by the recoil force is approximated by:

$$I_R = F_R \times t_R \qquad (9.9)$$

where I_R is the impulse, kN.s.

References in Chapter 9

1. Siwek, R., 1998, *New Findings on Explosion Venting*, Paper to the Loss Prevention Symposium, Barcelona.

2. Lunn, G.A., 1988, *Guide to Dust Explosion Prevention and Protection. Part 3 — Venting of Weak Explosions and the Effect of Vent Ducts* (Institution of Chemical Engineers, Rugby, U.K.).

3. Tamanini, F., 1995, *An Improved Correlation of Experimental Data on the Effects of Ducts in Vented Dust Explosions.* Loss Prevention and Safety Promotion in the Process Industries. Vol. 1. Eds. J.J. Mewis, H.J. Pasman and E.E. De Rademaeker. p. 243.

4. VDI, 1999, *Pressure Release of Dust Explosions*, VDI 3673, 1999 Green Paper, Verein Deutshcher Ingenreure Beuth-Verlag GmbH.

5. Lunn, G.A., Crowhurst, D., and Hey, M., 1988, The Effect of Vent Ducts on the Reduced Explosion Pressures of Vented Dust Explosions, *J. Loss Prev. Process Ind.*, *1*, p. 182.

6. Tamanini, F. and Valiulis, J.V., 1998, Improved Guidelines for the Sizing of Vents in Dust Explosions, *J. Loss Prev. Process Ind., 9*, 105.

7. Ural, E.A., 1993, A Simplified Method for Predicting the Effect of Ducts Connected to Explosion Vents, *J. Loss Prev. Process Ind., 6*, p. 3–10.

8. Tamanini, F., 1993, Characterisation of Mixture Reactivity in Vented Explosions, in *On the Dynamics of Explosions and Reactive Systems*, 14th Int. Coll., Coimbra, Portugal, 1–6 Aug.

9. Hey, M., 1991, *Pressure Relief of Dust Explosions through Large Diameter Ducts and Effect of Changing the Position of the Ignition Source*, *J. Loss Prev. Process Ind.*, *4*, p. 217.

10. Lunn, G.A., Nicol, A.M., Collins, P.D. and Hubbard, N.R., 1998, Effects of Vent Ducts on the Reduced Pressures from Explosions in Dust Collectors, *J. Loss Prev. Process Ind.*, *11*, p. 109.

Explosion venting – special dust cloud conditions

10

10.1 Introduction

Methods for calculating vent areas are described in Chapter 7. To apply the methods the explosion characteristics (principally the K_{St} value and the maximum explosion pressure, P_{max}) of the dust are measured by standard tests using either the 1 m^3 explosion vessel or the 20 litre sphere (see Chapter 2, Section 2.2, and Appendix 3). These tests take into account representative conditions of fuel concentrations, dust cloud homogeneity and turbulence that are considered to encompass those in the majority of practical applications.

However, in conditions of moderate and low turbulence, and in conditions where a non-homogeneous fuel–air mixture or low dust concentration is the norm, the standard tests are likely to overstate the explosion hazard, and thus the calculated vent area. Similarly, in conditions of high turbulence the standard tests may understate the explosion hazard, and thus the calculated vent area. In such circumstances the appropriate vent areas can be based on representative explosion venting trials, or, if available, published data appropriate to the circumstances.

As an example, Figure 10.1 shows explosion venting trials done under real conditions in a cyclone dust collector[1] compared to predictions from the draft European standard (prEN) calculation method given in Chapter 7, Section 7.3.1.

Information has been published on the venting of relatively low turbulence, inhomogeneous dust clouds, and of very high turbulence clouds. This information is reviewed in this Chapter.

It should be recognized that the guidance described in this chapter is not as well-founded as that in earlier chapters. It is based on limited data that has not been validated so substantially. The guidance should be used with caution, and the reasoning behind its application should be well formulated. If necessary, specialist advice should be sought.

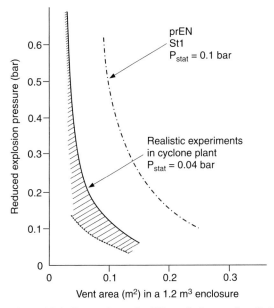

Figure 10.1 Comparison of prEN predictions and realistic explosions in a cyclone plant (data from reference 1)

10.2 Inhomogeneous dust clouds of relatively low turbulence

The pneumatic charging (filling) of vessels is a particular case in which the turbulence of the dust cloud is relatively low and the cloud is inhomogeneous, i.e., the state of the dust cloud is different from the one created by the method of dust injection in the standard tests (see Chapter 2, Section 2.2, and Appendix 3). The venting requirements are discussed in this Section.

10.2.1 Pneumatic filling of vented vessels

Equations for calculating vent areas with pneumatic filling
A set of equations has been developed[2] that allows calculations of vent area for vessels in which the dust cloud is produced by pneumatic filling.

For pneumatic filling of compact vessels (i.e. $L/D < 2$):

$$A_v = [(8.6 \log P_{red} - 6)/D_z - 5.5 \log P_{red} + 3.7]0.011\, K_{St}D_F \qquad (10.1)$$

where D_F is the diameter of the axial feed pipe into the vessel. The K_{St} value should not exceed $300 \, \text{bar m s}^{-1}$ and P_{max} should not exceed 9 bar. The

183

conveying velocity should not exceed $40 \, \text{m} \, \text{s}^{-1}$. D_z is calculated by the equation

$$D_z = (4V/\pi)^{1/3} \tag{10.2}$$

where V is the vessel volume, which should be between $5 \, \text{m}^3$ and $10 \, 000 \, \text{m}^3$. P_{red} should be between 0.1 bar and 2 bar, and P_{stat} should be 0.1 bar. The height of the vessel should not exceed 10 m.

When the height of the vessel exceeds 10 m:

$$A_v = [(8.96 \log P_{red} - 6)/D_z - 5.5 \log P_{red} + 3.7]0.0011 K_{St} LD_F \tag{10.3}$$

For elongated vessels (i.e. L/D ratio $\geq$ 2) an addition to the vent area is required:

$$A_{vl} = A_v + \Delta A \tag{10.4}$$

where A_v is the venting area for the cubical vessel with the same volume and ΔA the supplemental vent area when $L/D \geq 2$.

For inhomogeneous dust clouds:

$$\Delta A = A_v 1.0715 P_{red}^{-1.27} \log(L/D) \tag{10.5}$$

The pneumatic filling equations will only apply under a narrow range of conditions and should not be used to extrapolate beyond these conditions.

The equations given in this Section should be used, if at all, with extreme caution. They have little published validation and it is difficult to perceive a totally consistent picture.

Experimental trials for the venting of pneumatically filled containers

Pneumatic filling of vented containers has been the focus of large-scale experimental trials by Bartknecht, Siwek and Eckhoff[3–5] in silos and compact enclosures.

Eckhoff[5] introduced a jet of conveying air and intermixed dust vertically upward into a $500 \, \text{m}^3$ silo through a single pipe entry. Figure 10.2 shows vent area measurements made by Eckhoff compared to the prEN calculation method (Chapter 7, Section 7.3.1).

Siwek[4] introduced the air/dust mixture vertically downward through a 90 mm diameter pipe positioned axially in the head of compact containers ranging from $10 \, \text{m}^3$–$250 \, \text{m}^3$ capacity. The ignition source, positioned at the vessel centre, had an energy content of 10 K Joules. The ignition delay was defined as the time between the start of dust feed into the containers and activation of the ignition source. The delay was varied between 10 s to 30 s

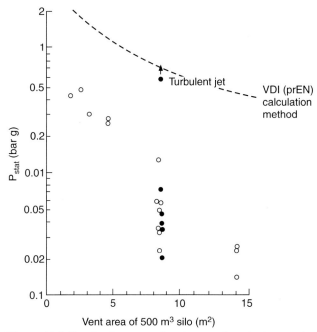

Figure 10.2 Results from vented maize starch and wheat grain dust explosions in a 500 m³ silo in Norway. Comparison with predicted P_{red}/vent area correlations. Data from Ekhoff and Fuhre[5]
○ data from 500 m³ silo, wheat grain dust
● data from 500 m³ silo, maize starch
(Adaptation taken from *Journal of Loss Prevention in the Process Industries*, 1990, Volume 3, p. 269, by permission of the publishers, Butterworth Heinemann Ltd.)

without any noticeable effect on the results. The dusts ranged in K_{St} value from 73 bar m s⁻¹ to 228 bar m s⁻¹.

The conclusions drawn from the Siwek pneumatic filling experiments can be applied to industrial practice only when the conditions match those of the investigation — that is:

- pneumatic conveying is used;
- the fall height H of the dust in relation to the vessel volume either conforms to or is less than the data given in Figure 10.3;
- the container is approximately cubical;
- the feed is axially downward;
- the diameter of the feed pipe is less than 90 mm.

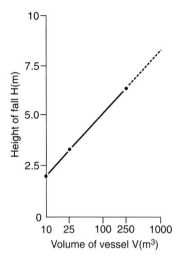

Figure 10.3 Pneumatic product feed into cubic containers: relationship between the container volume V and the fall height H employed (From reference 4, reproduced by permission of the author)

The maximum explosion effect is obtained at an optimum material-to-air loading of the dust stream. This is independent of vessel size and shape, size of the vent area and the air throughput, but it depends strongly on powder bulk density as shown in Figure 10.4. The experimental optimum material-to-air loadings were obtained from plots of reduced explosion pressures, P_{red}, and rates of pressure rise versus material-to-air loading under various experimental conditions. The curves were drawn through the maximum points obtained from a large number of experiments demonstrating a relatively large fluctuation for nominally identical conditions.

The air throughput Q $(m^3 \ min^{-1})$ is an important variable and has an effect on the relationship between P_{red} and the vent area, as Figure 10.5 demonstrates.

At low P_{red} values, however, the effect of the air throughput, Q, on the vent area is minimal, and the relationship between container volume and vent area for dusts of various K_{St} values and with $P_{red} = 0.25$ bar is independent of Q, as Figure 10.6 shows.

When P_{red} is relatively high, however, at 1 bar or 2 bar, a value for the air throughput, Q, has to be assigned. The data given in Figure 10.7 apply to values of $Q \leq 30 \ m^3 \ min^{-1}$, this being the maximum air throughput used in the tests.

Figure 10.8 shows a comparison between the results from the Siwek experiments and predictions from the prEN vent calculation method.

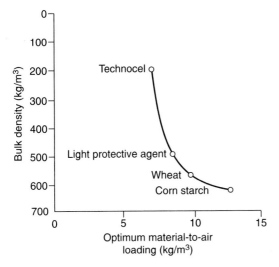

Figure 10.4 Pneumatic product feeding into cubic containers: relationship between bulk density and optimum material to air loading of the throughput (From reference 4, reproduced by permission of the author)

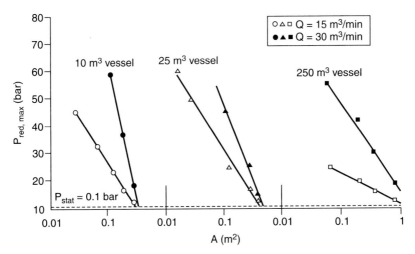

Figure 10.5 Cornstarch: reduced maximum explosion pressure P_{red} as a function of the venting area A, the air quantity Q and the influence of the container volume (From reference 4, reproduced by permission of the author)

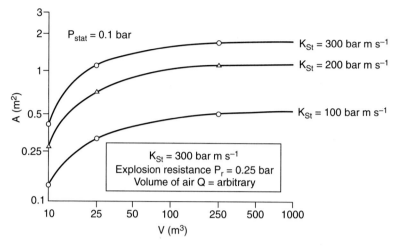

Figure 10.6 Direct pneumatic conveying of product into cubic containers: venting area A as a function of the container volume V for different dust-specific characteristics K_{St} P_{max} ≤ 9 bar (From reference 4, reproduced by permission of the author)

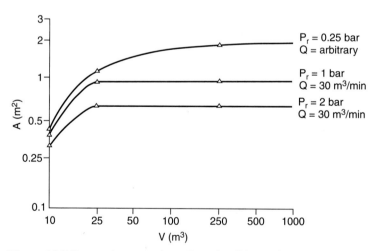

Figure 10.7 Pneumatic conveying of combustible products: venting area A as a function of the container volume V taking into account the container strength P, example: dust explosion class St 2 (From reference 4, reproduced by permission of the author)

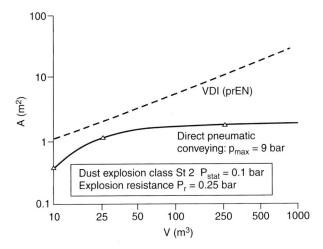

Figure 10.8 Explosion relief venting of combustible dusts: comparison of the area requirement in pneumatic conveying with the prEN predictions (From reference 4, reproduced by permission of the author)

The lower venting requirements, which Figure 10.8 demonstrates, are a result of lower turbulence than that on which the prEN method is based, inhomogeneity in the dust cloud and, especially when the vessel is of large volume, the volume of the cloud relative to the volume of the vessel. No attempt was made in these experiments to change either the diameter of the feed pipe or the ignition delay time as the vessel size increased. Increasing the throughput of air and maintaining the optimum material-to-air-loading by increasing the feed-pipe diameter would be expected to increase the size of the dust cloud in larger vessels and so produce higher P_{red} values for a given vent area. It is more than likely that such a change in the feed conditions would mean that instead of reaching a constant value of vent area as vessel volume increases, the pneumatic conveying data in Figure 10.8 would show a continual increase in vent area for increasing vessel volume. Furthermore, the L/D ratio of the vessel and the ignition position will both exert some influences on the reduced explosion pressure and venting requirements.

Explosion tests reported by Hauert[6] have shown how the ignition position and the method and direction of dust injection can influence P_{red} in an elongated silo. The vessel had a volume of 9.4 m³ and a length to diameter ratio of approximately 3. Dust injection through a ring system under pressure produced reduced explosion pressures that agreed well with prEN method predictions for homogeneous dust clouds (Figure 10.9).

189

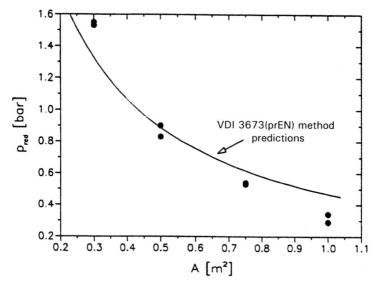

Figure 10.9 Reduced explosion-pressure measured as a function of the vent area for an ignition delay time of $t_v = 0.85\,s$ ($K_{St} = 200\,bar\,m\,s^{-1}$). The curve gives the results of the VDI 3673 (prEN) method predictions for a homogeneous dust/air mixture (From reference 6, reproduced by permision of the author)

Pneumatic filling, both vertically and tangentially, produced lower explosion pressures, however. Nevertheless, some of the measured pressures exceeded predictions from equations specifically for pneumatic filling, published by VDI. Figure 10.10 shows the comparison between the measured and predicted pressures. For ignition at the silo centre, the predictions generally exceed the measured values, but for ignition at the bottom of the silo, the measured values exceed the predicted.

Further experiments by Eckhoff, this time using a $236\,m^3$ silo[7], show the effect that changes in the position of the ignition source along the silo axis can have on the reduced explosion pressure. As Figure 10.11 shows, the effect has not been great in some experiments by Radandt in a $20\,m^3$ silo using pneumatic filling, but has been significant in Eckhoff's experiments. In Eckhoff's tests the dust cloud was ignited in essentially quiescent conditions; in Radandt's tests the ignition took place while the turbulent dust jet was still entering the silo.

Eckhoff's results can be explained if P_{red} is taken to be a function of the time taken to burst the vent closure. When ignition is at the silo bottom, the pressure rise necessary to burst the vent has to travel the length of the silo before venting can begin. As the ignition point is moved closer to the vent the localized pressure build-up is closer to the vent and it thus bursts earlier in the life of the

190

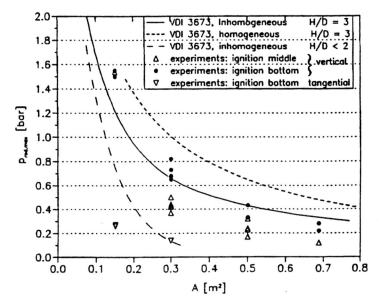

Figure 10.10 Comparison of the pressure-vent area course for the VDI 3673 guideline and experimental results. The VDI-curves are calculated for a K_{St} of a $140\,bar\,m\,s^{-1}$ and $P_{max} = 9\,bar$. The experimental data are only for a feeding rate of 3 and $5\,kg\,m^{-3}$ (maximum) (From reference 6, reproduced by permission of the author)

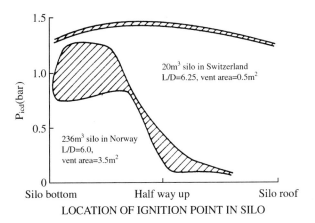

LOCATION OF IGNITION POINT IN SILO

Figure 10.11 Influence of location of the ignition point in the silo on maximum vented explosion pressure. Comparison of trends in a $20\,m^3$ silo and a $236\,m^3$ silo. (Reproduction from *Journal of Loss Prevention in the Process Industries*, 1990, Volume 3, p. 268, by permission of the publishers, Butterworth Heinemann Ltd.)

explosion. Furthermore, ignition at the silo base leads to propagation towards an open end, with all the consequences for flame acceleration that that entails. Ignition at the silo top leads to flame propagation away from an open end, a less serious case for flame acceleration as well as giving the added advantage of early venting of hot material. In Radandt's experiments, the relatively small size of the silo and the, presumably, greater turbulence in the dust cloud have meant that the more complicated behaviour has not developed.

The equations for pneumatic filling, assuming $P_{stat} = 0.1$ bar, gives predictions which produce a satisfactory envelope of Eckhoff's results for ignition at the silo centre, but underestimate reduced explosion pressures for ignition occurring at the silo base.

10.2.2 Filling of a silo by free fall from a cyclone
Free fall from a cyclone into a silo can result in even lower venting requirements than for pneumatic filling, as is illustrated in Figure 10.12.

10.2.3 Conclusion
Application of the information in Section 10.2 to practical installations is not easy. The conditions of dust feed, concentration of feed, point of feed, rate of feed, likely ignition sources and point of ignition need to be considered before

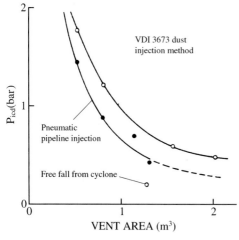

Figure 10.12 Results from vented maize starch explosions in a $20\,\mathrm{m}^3$ silo, demonstrating the marked influence of the mode of dust cloud generation on the maximum pressure. Data from Bartnecht. $K_{St} = 226\,\mathrm{bar\,m\,s^{-1}}$; $P_{stat} = 0.1$ bar. (Reproduction from *Journal of Loss Prevention in the Process Industries*, 1990, Volume 3, p. 268, by permission of the publishers, Butterworth Heinemann Ltd.)

an adequate assessment of vent sizes can be made. It bears repeating that the results for pneumatic conveying are applicable as guidance only when practical conditions do not fall outside the range of experimental conditions used in the tests.

10.3 The effects of high turbulence

As already stated the effect of cloud turbulence on P_{red} can be marked and the standard tests for measuring dust explosibility (see Chapter 2, Section 2.2, and Appendix 3) are conducted in conditions of turbulence designed to simulate on the small scale the conditions likely to be met with in industrial plant.

If plant conditions are highly turbulent, however, the standard test, and vent area calculations based on it, may underestimate the strength of the explosion and the venting requirements.

In these circumstances, effective vent sizing can be based only on explosion tests, or published information.

10.3.1 The AFNOR Nomographs

A set of Nomographs has been published by the French Standards Authority, AFNOR[8,9], that specify a vent area in some highly turbulent conditions. Dusts are characterized by a parameter $K_{max,t}$, essentially similar to the K_{St} value but measured under different conditions. The test vessel, developed by French Safety Laboratories, INERIS, has a volume of $1 m^3$ and a length to diameter ratio of approximately 4. The vessel is shown diagrammatically in Figure

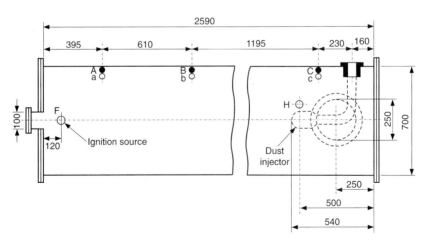

Figure 10.13 $1 m^3$ explosion vessel (INERIS)
ABC: pressure transducers
abc: flame detectors

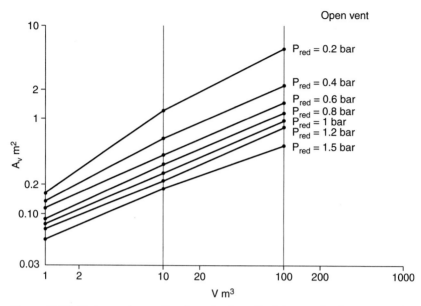

Figure 10.14 Vent area A_V as a function of volume V of the vessel to be protected for different reduced explosion pressures P_{red} with $P_{stat} = 0.2$ bar, $K_{max,t} = 100$ bar m s^{-1}

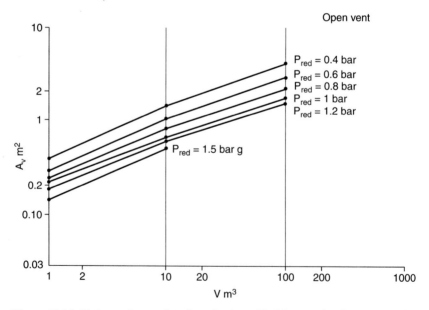

Figure 10.15 Vent area A_V as a function of volume V of the vessel to be protected for different reduced explosion pressures P_{red} with $P_{stat} = 0.2$ bar, $K_{max,t} = 400$ bar m s^{-1}

10.13. The dust is injected through a nozzle close to one end, while the ignition source is close to the other end. The ignition delay after the start of injection is 0.1 s, which contrasts with the delay of 0.6 s in the standard test in the 1 m^3 vessel (see Chapter 2, Section 2.2, and Appendix 3). The short delay means that conditions at the time of ignition are more turbulent than in a K_{St} measurement, and the explosion correspondingly more violent.

The AFNOR Nomographs are reproduced in Figures 10.14 to 10.16.

It is difficult to compare the AFNOR Nomographs with other vent sizing techniques because the relationship between $K_{max,t}$ and K_{St} is not well defined,

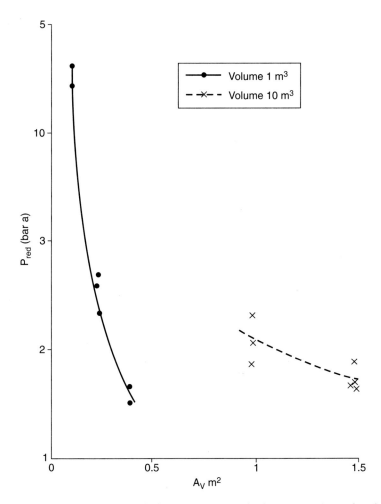

Figure 10.16 Reduced explosion pressure P_{red} (absolute pressure) as a function of the vent area, A_V, with $P_{stat} = 1.2$ bar a, $K_{max,t} = 600$ bar m s^{-1}

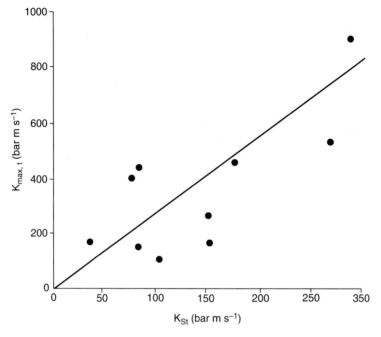

Figure 10.17 Relation between K_{St} and $K_{max,t}$

as Figure 10.17 demonstrates. The situation is complicated because the optimum dust concentration for a particular dust may not be the same for the $K_{max,t}$ as for the K_{St} measurement. Generally, the concentration at which the highest rate of pressure rise is measured is lower in the French test vessel, for a given dust, and closer to the stoichiometric concentration.

Pineau[8] has, however, published the following Table (10.1) that compares the St groups to P groups that have as their basis the $K_{max,t}$ values.

Table10.1 Comparison of St and P groups

Low and Medium Turbulence	High Turbulence
group St1: $0 < K_{St} \leq 200\,\mathrm{bar\,m\,s^{-1}}$	group P1: $0 < K_{max,t} \leq 100\,\mathrm{bar\,m\,s^{-1}}$
group St2: $200 < K_{St} \leq 300\,\mathrm{bar\,m\,s^{-1}}$	group P2: $100 < K_{max,t} \leq 400\,\mathrm{bar\,m\,s^{-1}}$
group St3: $300 < K_{St} \leq 600\,\mathrm{bar\,m\,s^{-1}}$	group P3: $400 < K_{max,t} \leq 600\,\mathrm{bar\,m\,s^{-1}}$

10.3.2 The Proust Nomograph

A Nomograph for use with high turbulence has also been published by Proust[10] and is reproduced in Figure 10.18.

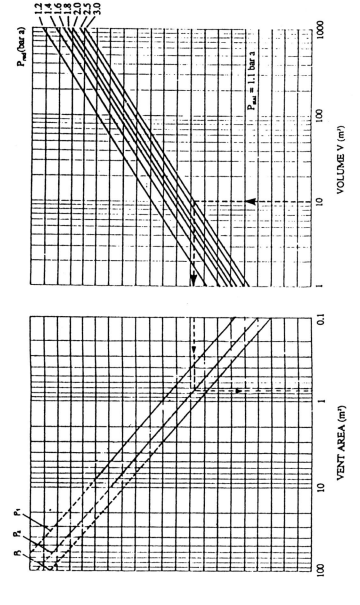

Figure 10.18 Venting Nomograph for high turbulence (From reference 10, reproduced by permission of the author)

References in Chapter 10

1. Tonkin, P.S. and Berlemont, F.J., 1972, *Dust Explosions in a Large-Scale Cyclone Plant.* Fire Research Note 942 (FRS, Building Research Establishment, Ltd.).

2. Scholl, E., 1992, The Technique of Explosion Venting, Much More than Just a Set of Nomographs, Paper presented at the *First World Seminar on Explosion Phenomenon and Practical Application of Protection Techniques*, Brussels, Europex.

3. Bartknecht, W., 1986, *Massnahmen gegen gefahrliche Auswirkungen von Staubexplosion in Silos und behaltern*, Jahresberichte 1985 zum BMF/had-Forschungsvorhaben vom Februar 1986.

4. Siwek, R., 1989, Dust Explosion Venting for Dusts Pneumatically Conveyed into Vessels, *Plant/Operations Progress*, 8, P. 129.

5. Eckhoff, R.K. and Fuhre, K., 1984, Dust Explosion Experiments in a Vented 500 m^3 Silo Cell, *J. Occupational Accidents 6*, p. 229.

6. Hauert, F., 1996, Influence of Particle Movement and Dust Concentration on the Explosion Characteristics in the Food Industry. Paper to *2nd World Seminar on the Explosion Phenomenon and on the Application of Explosion Protection Techniques in Practice*, Ghent, Belgium, 4th–8th March.

7. Eckhoff, R. K. and Fuhre, K., 1987, Dust Explosion Experiments in a 236 m^3 Silo Cell, *J. Occupational Accidents, 9*, p. 161.

8. Pineau, J.P., et al., 1986, Influence on Gas and Dust Explosion Development of Lengthening and Presence of Obstacles in Closed or Vented Vessels, Paper to the *5th International Symposium on Loss Prevention and Safety Promotion in the Process Industries*, Cannes, 15–19 September.

9. AFNOR U54-540, *Farming Buildings and Storage Equipment — Silo Safety-Attenuation of Explosion Effects by Discharge Vents — Calculation of the Vent Areas* (Association Francaise de Normalisation) (1986).

10. Proust, C., 1999, Le Dimensionnement des Events d'Explosion: Examen Critique des Methodes Existantes, European seminar on '*Dust Explosions*', Metz, France, 13th–15th April.

Explosion venting – design of vent closures

11

11.1 Introduction

Once the appropriate calculations have been made (Chapter 7) to determine the correct size of an explosion vent, consideration must be given to the best type of vent closure for a particular application. Relevant factors are shape, opening pressure, inertia, disposition, location, cost and maintenance requirements.

Vent closures may take the form of panels or doors; they may be reusable following an explosion, or they may have to be replaced whenever they open.

Vent closures are considered as autonomous protective devices under the ATEX product directive, and as such they must comply with the relevant essential safety requirements and be tested. Some closures are provided by specialist suppliers, and after 2003 will have to be properly marked and certified. In other cases, an item of plant may come with a panel or door as an integral part of the equipment. In such cases, it seems likely that testing and certification of the equipment as a whole will be acceptable.

In the past, there have been many examples of 'home-made' vent panels and doors, some of most dubious effectiveness. After 2003, panels and doors made and fitted at the user's premises need to meet the same standards and be tested in the same way as panels and doors sold as explosion protection devices. A draft European standard (prEN) is being prepared by TC305, which will describe the various types of vent closure and the test procedures.

11.2 Vent closures

11.2.1 Criteria

The main requirements for a vent closure device are:

- It must begin to open at a reasonably low, predictable pressure. This pressure should not be greatly affected by changes in ambient temperature.
- It must not open inadvertently, or leak substantial amounts of dust.

- It needs to open quickly, and that effectively means its mass must be limited.

Secondary considerations are:

- Is it a requirement that the device be capable of reuse after it has operated (e.g., a door), or is it acceptable that a replacement be purchased (e.g., a bursting panel)?
- It may need to fit smoothly on the inside to prevent dead areas where dust could collect, if this could create a problem, e.g., a health risk with food products.
- It may be advantageous if it re-closes after an explosion, as restricting the air supply can help extinguish residual burning.
- It may need to remain in place even if the outside pressure exceeds the inside pressure, for instance, it should be capable of withstanding wind forces.

11.2.2 Type

The prEN will describe various designs. The most commonly used devices are spring-loaded doors (see Figure 11.1) and pre-scored metal panels (bursting

Figure 11.1 Explosion door (720 × 370 mm) with resilient buffer (From Bartnecht, W., *Explosions: Course, prevention and protection* (Springer-Verlag) by permission of the author and publisher)

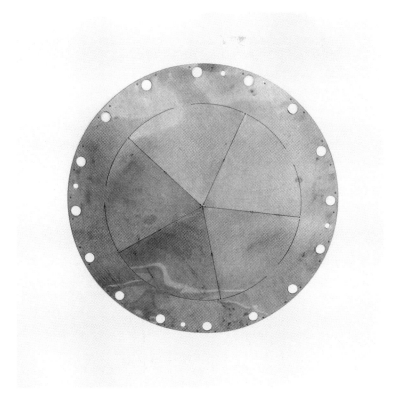

Figure 11.2 Example of a bursting disc

discs) (see Figure 11.2). Depending on the type of device chosen it may be necessary to take into account its inertia, which affects its venting efficiency (see Section 11.3). It is common practice for vent closures to incorporate an electrical detection device, interlocked to stop the operation of the plant if the vent opens, whether an explosion or premature failure causes this.

11.2.3 Shape
Calculations of vent area make no distinction between circular or rectangular vent openings. Generally, the effects of vent shape will not be great and there is probably enough of a safety factor to make any deviations due to vent shape unimportant.

11.2.4 Disposition
The required vent area can be made up of a number of smaller vents provided the total area is adequate and the vent opening pressures are suitable.

11.2.5 Location

The location of the vent is important. It should be such that the flame front is unimpeded in its movement from ignition source towards the vent, and the passage to the vent should never be such that the flame is constrained to an area less than the area of the vent.

Furthermore, the cloud of unburned dust and combustion products that is ejected from an explosion vent must discharge to a safe place. This too will determine the vent position, depending on the location of other equipment, occupied areas and proximity to an outside wall.

11.2.6 Installation and maintenance of vent covers

Correctly designed vent closures will only operate satisfactorily and thus guarantee safety if they are installed properly and maintained to a high standard. The manufacturers instructions should be followed. Important factors that must be considered:

- Access to the vent by personnel should be prevented, while the plant is operating.
- Vent covers should be clearly identified as such.
- Vents should not be used as inspection or access ports, whilst the plant is operating.
- Vent covers should never be fixed closed or covered whilst the plant is operating.
- Inspection and maintenance of vents should not be carried out whilst the process is operating.
- When necessary snow should be removed from vent covers.
- Icing around seals and hinges should be expected in some circumstances and it may be necessary to provide trace heating.
- The condition of vent closures should be checked frequently and closures replaced as necessary.

In some circumstances routine replacement may be more appropriate:

- Check freedom of hinges; clean and lubricate as appropriate.
- Check latches and spring clips.
- Check for corrosion around panels and doors.
- Check condition of gaskets and seals.
- Check for dust build-up on the inside of vents, and outside if a vent duct is fitted.
- Check integrity of panel restraints.
- Remove debris from covers and ducts.

Other ports or hatches on the plant must be securely closed and must not open in the event of an explosion.

11.3 Testing of vent closures

Vent closures are tested both for their mechanical strength and opening pressure, P_{stat}. A European Standard is in preparation by TC305 that will give the necessary testing requirements.

The venting process is, however, also influenced by the inertia of the vent closure, expressed as $kg\,m^{-2}$. As this increases, the venting process is progressively impeded (i.e., it is less efficient), and, for a specified vent area, the reduced explosion pressure, P_{red}, will rise.

11.3.1 Venting efficiency

The effect of inertia is determined by comparing the venting effectiveness of a given vent closure with one that is essentially inertia free and so has a venting efficiency of 100%; for example, a bursting diaphragm.

The venting efficiency is often obtained by explosion testing, but calculation techniques are available. The recommended method for estimating the venting efficiency by explosion testing is demonstrated in Figures 11.3 and 11.4. The venting efficiency is given by $(A_e \times 100/A_d)\%$, where A_d is the geometrical vent area of the vent closure and A_e is the effective vent area. Thus, in practice, the geometric vent area necessary to give safe venting of a given enclosure would be greater than the vent area estimated by the vent sizing methods given in Chapter 7 to an extent depending on the venting efficiency. As a simple example, if the estimated vent area necessary to protect a given enclosure was $2\,m^2$, then a geometric area of $4\,m^2$ would be necessary if the vent closures had a venting efficiency of 50%. Information from manufacturers of venting devices should quote both a geometric area and an effective area, or venting efficiency, for the device.

It is often the practice to introduce a limiting value of the inertia below which a closure can be considered to have an efficiency of 100%, i.e., the effects are minimal and not sufficient to be taken into account in calculating the vent area. Several experimental studies of the effects of inertia on the reduced explosion pressure have been carried out[1-7]. Analysis of the data indicates that, except at very small volumes, the effect of panel inertia up to $10\,kg\,m^{-2}$ is negligible. Thus, for closures with inertia of $\leq 10\,kg\,m^{-2}$, 100% efficiency can be assumed in vent area calculations.

References in Chapter 11

1. Buckland, I.G. and Tonkin, P.S., 1982, *The Use of Wall Mounted Inertia Vents to Mitigate Explosion Pressure*, Building Research Establishment Note N72/82.

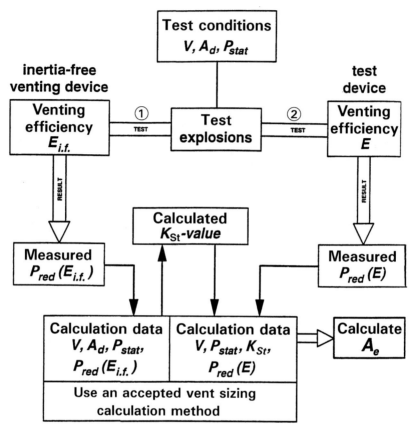

Figure 11.3 Direct comparison method for determining vent closure efficiency. V = volume of the test aparatus; A_d = area of the explosion venting device; P_{red} = reduced explosion pressure; A_e = effective vent area; P_{stat} = vent opening pressure. Test scheme ① produces a K_{St} value that characterizes the test explosion using an inertia free venting device. Test scheme ②, using the same test conditions as ① except for the test vent closure, uses this K_{St} value to calculate the effective vent area, A_e.

2. Harmanny, A., 1993, *Effect of Inertia on Effectiveness of Explosion Venting*, Europex Newsletter No. 21, p. 7 (April).
3. Brookes, D.E. and Nicol, A.M., 1996, *Inertia Effect of Vent Closure Design on Gas and Dust Explosions*, Health & Safety Laboratory Internal Report, DE/96/92.
4. DeGood, R. and Chatrathi, K., 1991, Comparative Analysis of Test Work Studying Factors Influencing Pressures Developed in Vented Deflagrations, *J. Loss Prev. Process Ind.*, *4*, p. 297.

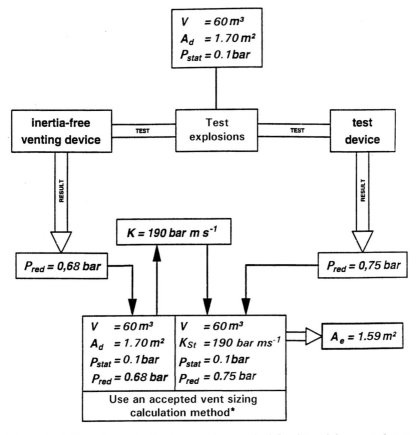

Figure 11.4 Example of the direct comparison method for determining vent closure efficiency.

V = volume of the test aparatus; A_d = area of the explosion venting device; P_{red} = reduced explosion pressure; A_e = effective vent area; P_{stat} = vent opening pressure. *Equation 7.2 has been used in this example, with L/D = 1 and P_{max} = 10 bar.

5. Siwek, R., and Skov, O., 1988, *Modellberechnung zur dimensionierung von explosionsklappen auf der basis von praxisnahen explosionsversuchen*, VDI Berichte, Nr. 701, p. 569.

6. Tamanini, F., 1996, Modelling of Panel Inertia Effects in Vented Dust Explosions, *Process Safety Progress*, *15* (4), p. 247.

7. Cooper, S., 1998, Explosion Venting — the Predicted Effects of Inertia, Paper to *Hazards XIV: Cost Effective Safety*, Symposium Series No. 114, Institution of Chemical Engineers.

Explosion venting – safe discharge area

12

This chapter seeks to provide some practical guidance on the external effects of vented dust explosions. The guidance is based on the results of explosion studies undertaken across Europe, in particular the foundational work of Battelle[1,2] and Christian Michelson Research[3], together with further studies which formed part of the EU sponsored CREDIT project[4].

12.1 Introduction

As well as the pressure developed inside a vessel, a vented explosion generates secondary effects, due to blast and fire, outside the vented vessel. These secondary effects need to be considered so that appropriate protection can be provided for people or nearby installations and buildings. There is very little published guidance relating to these secondary effects, how their magnitude can be estimated and what measures should be taken to minimise them.

The development of a dust explosion is described in Chapter 1. If explosion relief venting is used as a means of protection (see Chapter 7) the bursting of the relief vent results in the creation of an explosible turbulent dust cloud outside the vessel. The flame emerging from the vent ignites this external dust cloud, creating a secondary explosion. There are two mechanisms by which the secondary explosion is created:

- ignition of material that has accumulated outside the vented vessel before the explosion and which is dispersed and ignited as a result of the event, or
- through the ignition of unburned material ejected from the vessel during the course of the explosion.

Historically, guidance on venting dust explosions has recognised the importance of the former mechanism and considered its prevention through regular cleaning and good maintenance practices. Only comparatively recently has attention been paid to the latter mechanism and the consequences of the external blast and fire effects that may be generated as an inherent function of the venting process.

12.2 Relationships for determining the pressure and flame effects outside vents

12.2.1 Venting to an open area

A study of the external effects of vented dust explosions has been undertaken through the EU Environment Programme CREDIT project[4], building upon earlier work by Hattwig[5], Battelle[1] and Christian Michelson Research[3]. As part of this project vented dust explosions were carried out by three organisations:

FRS, Building Research Establishment Ltd., UK
Battelle, Germany, and
IBExU, Germany.

FRS carried out maize starch and coal dust explosions in $20\,m^3$ and $40\,m^3$ vessels. The principal parameters measured were the vent area, vent opening pressure and ignition location. Measurements were made of the internal pressure, external pressure and flame effects in the absence and presence of structural targets placed at various distances in front of the vent.

Battelle examined the influence of turbulence, by control of the ignition time delay, on the magnitude of the external blast and flame. This work was carried out in a closed and vented $1\,m^3$ chamber using maize starch and coal dust to provide some information on scaling effects.

At IBExU, vented explosions of lignite and wheat flour were carried out in a $324\,m^3$ vented chamber. IBExU investigated the influence of relief vent failure pressure P_{stat}, vent area and in some tests, targets were situated at various distances in front of the vent.

12.2.2 Guidance on maximum flame length

The results from the previous Battelle[1] studies indicated that the maximum flame length emitted from a vent was up to 8 times the cube root of the vessel volume. The results of the FRS study showed that, under certain circumstances such as horizontal venting, the maximum flame length could be 10 times the cube root of the vessel volume. The reason for this could be due to the effects of the ground extending the distance of the emitted flame.

The volume of the fireball, generally, was found to be of the order of 10 times that of the vessel and, in the absence of any obstruction, the maximum width of the flame was approximately the cube root of its volume.

On the basis of the results of the studies it is recommended that to estimate the maximum flame length ($x_{fl,max}$) emitted from a vent, the following equation be used:

$$X_{fl,max} = Q \cdot V^{1/3} \qquad (12.1)$$

where Q is a dimensionless constant which is used to take account of the direction of the venting. Therefore,

$Q = 8$ (for vertically discharging vents), or
$Q = 10$ (for horizontally discharging vents).

In practice, no flame length greater than 30 m has been measured, even for large volumes. This figure should be taken as the upper limit for any estimations of $X_{fl,max}$.

A reasonable estimate of the maximum width, $W_{fl,max}$, attained by the flame in the absence of any obstruction can be made using Equation (12.1a),

$$W_{fl,max} \approx 1.3 \cdot (10V)^{1/3} \qquad (12.1a)$$

The following restrictions apply to Equations (12.1), (12.1a) and all the equations in this chapter:

vessel volumes:	$0.1\,m^3 \le V \le 1000\,m^3$
relief vent static bursting pressures:	$0.1\,bar \le P_{stat} \le 0.2\,bar$
reduced maximum explosion pressures:	$0.1\,bar \le P_{red,max} \le 2\,bar$
maximum material explosion pressure:	$5\,bar \le P_{max} \le 10\,bar$
K_{St} value of material:	$10\,bar\,m\,s^{-1} \le K_{St} \le 200\,bar\,m\,s^{-1}$

12.2.3 Guidance on maximum explosion pressure

As part of the CREDIT project the results of the Battelle, FRS and IBExU studies were analysed, comparing the experimentally recorded maximum external (secondary) overpressure ($P_{s,max}$), with those predicted by the Wirkner–Bott Equation (12.2) derived from Battelle's earlier work[1].

From these studies it was found that the maximum external pressure, $P_{s,max}$, from a dust explosion can be estimated using the following equation:

$$P_{s,max} = 0.2 \cdot P_{red,max} \cdot A^{0.1} \cdot V^{0.18} \qquad (12.2)$$

where $P_{s,max}$ is the maximum secondary (external) explosion pressure from the vent,

$P_{red,max}$ is the maximum overpressure inside the chamber,
A is the vent area, and
V is the volume of the vessel.

The value of $P_{red,max}$ should either be determined experimentally for the particular system, or estimated from the K_{St} Nomographs in Appendix 5.

Preliminary indications are that for powders such as aluminium, with a $K_{St} \geq 300 \, \text{bar} \, \text{m} \, \text{s}^{-1}$, a safety factor of 2 should be applied to Equation (12.2) for the estimation of the maximum external pressure.

12.2.4 Pressure decay with distance

The maximum external pressure, $P_{s,max}$ was generally found to occur at a distance X_s from the vent, where X_s is determined by Equation (12.3) for venting directed vertically upwards or Equation (12.4) for venting directed horizontally:

$$X_s = 0.25 \cdot X_{fl,max} \tag{12.3}$$
$$X_s = 0.2 \cdot X_{fl,max} \tag{12.4}$$

For a dust explosion vented into an open area Equation (12.5) should be used to estimate the external pressure maximum, $P_{r,max}$ at any given distance r, provided r is greater than the distance X_s. X_s is the distance from the vent at which the maximum external explosion pressure, $P_{s,max}$, occurs, and is determined by Equations (12.3) or (12.4).

$$P_{r,max} = (X_s/r) \cdot P_{s,max} \tag{12.5}$$

12.3 Venting towards an obstruction

12.3.1 Pressure

Within the CREDIT project the studies of FRS and IBExU both examined the effects of placing an obstruction in the direct line of venting. The obstructions used by FRS were buildings with target areas 3.9 m × 2.4 m and 6 m × 3 m, respectively. IBExU used a large concrete wall 18 m × 6 m. These targets were placed at various distances between 10 m and 21 m from the vented chamber. The positioning of the targets at these locations had little effect on the pressure recorded inside the explosion chambers. However, the pressure at the location of the target could be up to twice that observed when the explosion vented into an unobstructed area.

When estimating the maximum pressure which might be exerted upon a structure at a distance, r_{obs}, from a vented vessel, a factor of 2 should be applied to Equation (12.5), giving the following Equation (12.6):

$$P_{r,max} = 2 \cdot (X_s/r_{obs}) \cdot P_{s,max} \tag{12.6}$$

12.3.2 Flame effects

The presence of the smallest obstruction (3.9 m × 2.4 m) had little influence on the flame emitted from the vent, the flame tending to flow around and over the target with only a small reduction in flame length. For the larger obstruction (6 m × 3 m), when the structure was closest to the vessel, the flame tended to divert upwards and to the sides, filling the area between the structure and the vessel.

The diameter of the fireball was dependent upon the size and location of the vents and the vessel volume. Generally, the volume of the flame emitted from the vent was in the order of 10 times the vessel volume, while the width of the flame was up to 2.5 times the height.

It should be assumed that the fireball generated by the vented explosion will occupy a volume at least 10 times the volume of the vessel and that this will fill the volume between the vessel and the obstruction. A reasonable estimate of the extent of lateral flame spread from a single vent, $W_{fl,max}$, when an obstruction is positioned in front of the vent can be made using Equation (12.7) or (12.1a), whichever gives the larger value.

$$W_{fl,max} = 2.5 \cdot \sqrt{10V/r_{obs}} \tag{12.7}$$

12.3.3 Pressure effects on buildings

The effects of pressure on structures were also investigated in the FRS study[6]. The structural targets examined were:

- single leaf masonry walls; dimensions 2.4 m × 2.4 m;
- small single storey building of external masonry and internal blockwork cavity wall construction, with a flat roof; dimensions (l) 3.9 m × (w) 1.4 m × (h) 2.4 m; and
- a cladded steel frame building with a 10° pitched roof, typical of a UK light factory/warehouse unit, dimensions (l) 6.0 m × (w) 3.0 m × (h) 4.0 m (front wall area 6 × 3 m²).

From the results of the study it was recommended that structures incorporating masonry and/or brickwork should not be sited within a distance where the maximum pressure exerted on them is estimated to exceed 4 kPa. At this pressure some cracking of masonry may still occur and damage to roofing is possible due to dynamic wind effects caused as the explosion wave traverses the building.

Steel frame metal clad structures, not of a specifically blast resistant construction, should not be sited within a distance where the maximum pressure that may be exerted on them is estimated to exceed 6 kPa. At this pressure, although serious structural damage is unlikely, significant deflections in the walls may occur which could result in damage to internal fixtures sited on or adjacent to the walls. Loose or poorly fitted flashing along corners or other edges may become detached.

12.4 Alternative approaches when predicted safe areas are impractical

It is realised that in some actual situations the equations above may give impractical safety distances for the particular vented plant item. In these cases there are some practical measures that may be used to overcome this problem.

A deflector plate is placed outside the vent to divert the explosion away from a sensitive area and into a safe area. Care should be taken not to place the deflector plate so close to the vent that the blast is deflected back into the vessel. The area of the deflector plate should be sufficient to encompass the width of the fire ball emitted from the vent and be strong enough to withstand the pressure generated by the explosion (see Chapter 9, Section 9.3.1).

Consider venting in a different direction, e.g. vertically instead of horizontally. Consider moving the vent to a different location, by use of vent ducts if necessary, (see Chapter 9, Section 9.4). Use other means of explosion protection such as inerting (Chapter 4), containment (Chapter 5) or suppression (Chapter 6).

References in Chapter 12

1. Schumann, St. and Wirkner-Bott, I., 1993, *Dust Explosion Venting: Secondary Explosion for Vessel Volumes up to 250 m³*, Europex News Letters 22, September.
2. Wirkner-Bott, I., Schumann, St. and Stock, M., 1992, *Dust Explosion Venting: Investigation of the Secondary Explosion*, 7th Int. Symp. on Loss Prevention and Safety Promotion in the Process Industries, Taormina, Italy, 4th–8th May.
3. van Wingerden, K., 1993, Prediction of Pressure and Flame Effects in the Direct Surroundings of Installations Protected by Dust Explosion Venting, *J. Loss Prev. Process Ind.,* 6(4), p. 241–249.
4. CREDIT Project (Final Report), Paper presented at *Dust Explosions*, IBC Conference, London, October 1995.
5. Hattwig, M., 1980, *Auswirkung von Drunckentlastungsvorgangen auf die Umgebung*, Forschungsbericht 66, Bundesantstalt fur Material Prufung, Berlin. (In German).
6. Crowhurst, D., Colwell, S., et al. *Dust Explosions — Flame and Pressure Effects Outside Vents: Guidance for Industry,* Fire Note 7, FRS, Building Research Establishment Ltd.

Explosion venting in industrial plant

13

13.1 Introduction

This chapter contains some examples of the way explosion venting, in particular, has been applied in practice on actual dust-handling plant and specific plant items. Browsing through Chapters 7 to 12 shows that the derivation of a basis for safety founded principally on venting can be a complicated procedure if the configuration of the plant departs from a single vessel and the connections between one unit and another have to be considered.

The discussions and the precautions recommended here are for illustration purposes only and refer specifically to the examples considered. Generally, as will be apparent from earlier chapters, a range of safety options is available to the designer of a whole plant or individual plant items and the ones chosen will depend on various factors, like relative cost, constraints or practicality.

13.2 Examples of explosion venting applied to industrial plant

13.2.1 Spray dryer system

The spray dryer system is shown schematically in Figure 13.1. The plant comprises a spray dryer connected to a cyclone followed by a dust collector. The spray dryer has a length to diameter ratio of 5; it is directly fired by natural gas and the hot air is supplied to the dryer co-currently with the spray. The spray is produced by means of a rotating disc atomiser at the top of the dryer, and dry powder product is collected at the base of the cyclone separator and at the base of the dust collection unit. The following considerations apply in deciding on the precautions to be taken.

Product
- Any product processed in the dryer should be screened to check for detonation or deflagration properties (see Chapter 1, Section 1.3). Materials

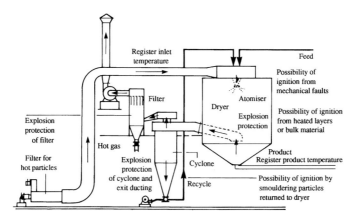

Figure 13.1 Spray dryer installation (schematic)

with these properties should be excluded. They exhibit the behaviour of explosives and are not manufactured in general chemical plant.

The dryer is not suitable for materials that could produce flammable vapour atmospheres in the dryer, or containing flammable solvents thus giving rise to a hybrid mixture.

The material assumed for this example is not an explosive, but has typical flammability and explosibility characteristics as measured by the standard tests (see Chapter 2, Section 2.1). It is sensitive to ignition by electrostatic discharges.

Heating system

- Atmospheres containing flammable gas must be prevented in the dryer system during burner ignition or if the burner malfunctions during normal operation. Flame failure protection, a pre-purge sequence, and control of the gas supply and combustion air by proving devices, are some of the techniques and procedures used to guard against this risk (see Chapter 3, Section 3.2.1).
- Hot particles from directly fired systems can act as an ignition source of an explosible dust cloud if they enter the dryer chamber in the inlet air supply. Incandescent particles of a size less than 3–5 mm will not normally ignite a dust cloud and a mesh screen with apertures of 3 mm or less across the hot air inlet to the dryer will adequately guard against this risk. The mesh should be cleaned regularly.

Spray dryer (see also section 13.3)

Ignition sources

Various ignition sources can be identified in the dryer chamber. Exclusion of all ignition sources is not possible and explosion protection methods need to be applied since the dust is explosible as a cloud.

213

- The material is sensitive to ignition by static electricity discharges (see Chapter 3, Section 3.2.7). All conducting plant should be earthed; non-conducting plastic material should be avoided especially in the vicinity of the product, and most especially where explosive atmospheres occur with minimum ignition energies less than 25 mJ; process personnel should be earthed by means of suitable footwear and floors when material with minimum ignition energies less than 50 mJ are being handled. Unintended build-up of bulk powder at the base of the dryer should be prevented. Such accumulations can be detected using a level sensor.
- The spray mechanism contains parts that may cause frictional heating (see Chapter 3, Section 3.2.5). The rotor mechanism may be a source of oil contamination that can result in a marked decrease in the thermal stability of the product.
- An explosible dust cloud will ignite spontaneously if the temperature is high enough. The minimum ignition temperature (MIT) of a dust cloud is measured in the Godbert–Greenwald furnace test (see Chapter 2, Section 2.3.3 and Appendix 3). Ignition of the cloud will be prevented if the inlet air temperature is limited to a value 50°C below the measured MIT[1].
- Material can be deposited on roofs or walls of dryers and exposed to temperatures high enough to cause self-ignition. If this progresses to red heat, burning material that breaks away can act as an ignition source in downstream units. Dryers should be operated so that layers do not form in zones where they are subjected to high temperatures[1]. For layers of powder not exposed for long periods, a safety margin of 20°C (see Chapter 3, Section 3.2.2) below the measured minimum ignition temperature of a dust layer (see Chapter 2, Section 2.4.3) is usually satisfactory[1].
- Material should not be allowed to form bulky deposits in the dryer chamber. However, bulking may happen in the cyclone, filter or in packages. Spontaneous heating (see Chapter 3, Section 3.2.3) leading to self-ignition may occur if the initial temperature is above a product- and size-dependent value. The maximum safe discharge temperature of material from the dryer is governed by the temperature measured in tests (see Chapter 3, Section 3.2.3) that assess the capability of bulk powders to undergo spontaneous heating[1,2] and the size of any container that will be filled by warm product.
- In order to prevent ignition by 'thermite' sparks (see Chapter 3, Section 3.2.4), aluminium, magnesium, titanium and light alloys containing these metals should not be used, unless rust can be excluded from the plant.
- All electrical equipment should be compatible with the materials used and the methods for handling them (see Chapter 3, Section 3.2.6).

Explosion protection of the dryer

Explosion protection of the dryer is provided by venting. Alternatively it could be protected by inerting or explosion suppression, and there may be situations where these options would be preferred. Typical explosion venting precautions are:

- The reduced explosion pressure, P_{red}, that the dryer chamber can withstand should be known; typical values are 0.2–0.7 bar.
- Explosion panels should occupy as much of the top area of the dryer chamber as is found necessary by using a vent calculation method (see Chapter 7). The area beneath the hot air inlet should not be used as a vent so as to prevent damage to the air inlet if an explosion takes place. There should be no structures that obstruct the venting area. The vent opening pressure, P_{stat}, should be known — for example, 0.1 bar. The total volume of the dryer must be used in the vent sizing procedure. An acceptable and detailed case must be made if a volume less than the total volume is used for the vent sizing method.
- Vent closures should be securely tethered to the main structure if they are capable of acting as missiles — for example, panels in a T-section frame.
- The forces holding the closure, including its mass, should be as low as is practicable (preferably $<10\,kg\,m^{-2}$) (see Chapter 11, Section 11.3). Any snow, corrosion or contamination should be prevented from interfering with the action of the vent.
- It is recommended practice for vents to be fitted with sensors interlocked such that the lifting of vents causes the airflow, and the rotary valve at the dryer product outlet, to be stopped.
- It is best practice to fit water sprays in the dryer chamber to control smouldering and fires.

Cyclone (see also Section 13.3)

Dust entrained in the hot exhaust from the dryer is separated out in the cyclone. Burning material from the dryer can be transported into the cyclone and ignite an explosible dust cloud there. Explosion venting is the option used (alternatively the cyclone could have been protected by inerting or explosion suppression, and there may be situations where these options would be preferred).

- The reduced explosion pressure that the cyclone and all connecting ductwork can withstand must be known — for example, 0.2–0.7 bar. In this example the cyclone outlet duct is strong enough to withstand an explosion (see Chapter 14, Section 14.2).

215

- Vents should be fitted to surfaces in the cyclone to which the flame has ready access — for example, the shoulder of the cyclone or the top. Sometimes vents can be positioned on top of the vortex tube, but explosion pressures will, as a consequence, be higher and the vortex tube must be strong enough to withstand the explosion. The area obstructed by the air outlet duct should not be used as part of the vent.
- The opening requirements of the vent closure are as discussed for the spray dryer chamber. Lifting of the explosion vent should stop all rotary valves to prevent passage of burning or smouldering material to the product collection point.
- If there is a long pipe between the cyclone and the dryer consideration must be given to isolating the cyclone from the dryer in the event of an explosion (see Chapter 14).

Dust collector (see also Section 13.3)

The dust collector (filter) removes final traces of product from the exhaust air and passes clean air to the atmosphere. Hot particles and sparks from the dryer can ignite a dust cloud in the collector. In this example, the dust enters near the top of the tapered section at the base of the collector, and it is in this area that high concentrations of dust are most likely to be found. Internal fitments such as filter bags should not obstruct the explosion vent, so that the explosion has unimpeded access to the vent.

- The reduced explosion pressure that the collector and all connected parts, including door latches, can withstand should be known — for example, 0.4–0.7 bar.
- The vent should be fitted at the top of the shaped section of the collector where the explosible dust cloud is most likely to be localized and where ignition is most likely to take place. The nearer the vent can be positioned to the ignition point the lower the explosion pressure inside the collector will be. The vent area should be calculated by a suitable method when the vent bursting pressure, P_{stat}, is known — for example, 0.1 bar — and the free volume of the collector is known.
- If the clean-side volume is greater than half the dirty-side volume, it is prudent to provide the clean side with vents in case dust deposits build up over time and are capable of being stirred up by an explosion.
- The vent closure can be of any appropriate type, e.g., a proprietary bursting panel.
- The vent should be positioned to direct the explosion to a safe place (see Chapter 9, Section 9.2).
- A deflector plate can be fitted at the vent discharge point (see Chapter 9, Section 9.3.1).

216

13.2.2 Milling system

The milling system is shown schematically in Figure 13.2. The unit is in five parts:

- charge hopper and kibbler;
- mill;
- cyclone and dust bag;
- blender;
- drum filling point.

Charge hopper and kibbler

There is a significant risk of ignition in the kibbler and the possibility of a dust cloud in the charge hopper. As well as taking the precautions necessary to avoid

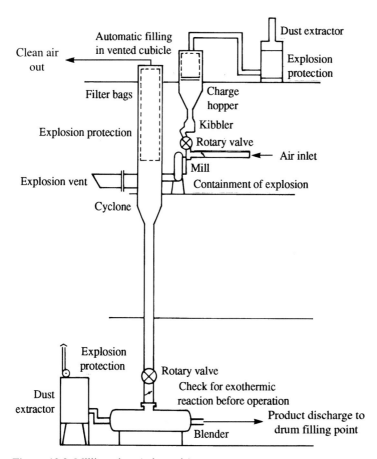

Figure 13.2 Milling plant (schematic)

ignition by static electricity (see Chapter 3, Section 3.2.7), safety will need to be based on provision of an explosion-protected charging cubicle. The charge hopper should be fitted with doors that are closed after loading and interlocked with the kibbler drive to prevent the unit from running until the doors are closed.

- Material should be emptied into the charging hopper inside a closed charging cubicle using a drum tipping device that cannot operate until the cubicle doors are closed. The cubicle should be fitted with an appropriate explosion vent. The reduced explosion pressure that can be withstood must be known, as must the bursting pressure of the vent closure. The vent closure should be as light as is practicable.
- A rotary valve below the kibbler will prevent an explosion inside the mill propagating into the charging hopper.
- The dust collector in the dust extraction system attached to the charging cubicle will require explosion venting. Keeping the dust concentration below 10 g m^{-3} may be a satisfactory basis for safety in the ducting, as long as the duct is kept free of powder deposits that could be raised into a dust cloud.

The mill (see also Section 13.3)

In this example, safety is based on explosion venting of the small volume of the mill into the cyclone and filter volumes. The vent on the cyclone should be directly opposite the entry pipe from the mill. Alternatively, explosion containment could be used, as long as explosions are prevented from propagating from the mill into adjacent plant. For containment the mill should be capable of withstanding the maximum explosion pressure, P_{max} (for example, 7 bar).

Because of their grinding tools, mills have a large inner surface area, and the explosion pressure and rate of pressure rise are often reduced compared to the values in an empty vessel.

Cyclone and dust collector (see also Section 13.3)

In this example the cyclone and collector are connected and must be treated as one unit. If explosion venting is a valid option for explosion protection, then either a vent large enough to accommodate the entire vessel can be fitted in the cyclone or two vents can be used, one in the cyclone and one close to the filter bags and venting on the dirty side. The reduced explosion pressure, P_{red}, that the unit can withstand — for example, 0.4–0.7 bar — and the opening pressure of the vent closure, P_{stat} — for example, 0.1 bar — must be known. An appropriate vent sizing technique is used to calculate the vent area based on the free volume of the vessel. Venting of dust collectors is discussed in Sections 13.2.1 and 13.3.

Explosion precautions in a cyclone are discussed in Section 13.2.1 and 13.3.

Blender

Material from the cyclone is fed by a rotary valve through a duct into the top of the blender. Dust clouds can be generated inside a blender. Possible ignition sources include spontaneous heating of the bulk powder and incandescent particles from upstream units. It is difficult to avoid these ignition sources with total effectiveness. The blender should be checked for signs of spontaneous heating before operation.

Explosion venting of blenders is generally not satisfactory because of the large amount of material inside them. In the event of a dust cloud explosion much of this inventory can be entrained in the gas movement and ejected into the open where it can be ignited by the initial vented explosion, producing extensive flame. Voluminous dust clouds are theoretically possible in these circumstances. Venting into a confining vented room is particularly not recommended because the dust cloud ejected from the blender would be turbulent, possibly pressurized to above ambient and subject to ignition by a large jet flame.

If ignition sources cannot be excluded in the blender then, since venting is not a practical option, an alternative basis of safety must be identified — for example, explosion suppression, containment, or inerting.

The dust extraction system from the blender will require explosion venting of the duct and the collector — see Section 13.2.1.

Drum filling point

Operatives at drum filling points should be protected against the danger of fire or explosion. Anti-static precautions should be taken (see Section 13.1.1) and a dust extraction system employed.

Storage bins can be vented (see Section 13.2.1), with the vent area estimated by the usual sizing techniques.

13.2.3 Spin flash dryer

The system is shown schematically in Figure 13.3.

The drying chamber

The product is dried by a flow of hot air passed through the bed of paste. At the same time the product is agitated in the drying chamber. As the paste dries the

219

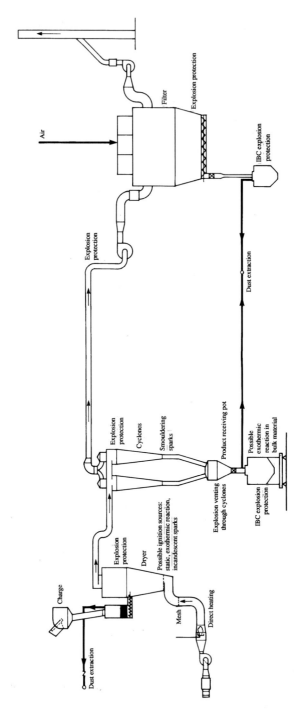

Figure 13.3 Spin Flash Dryer system (schematic)

agitation breaks the product into small pieces and when it is sufficiently dry it is carried in the air stream to a cyclone and then a dust collector.

Some of the ignition sources in the drying chamber are as discussed in Section 13.2.1:

- Danger of fuel from the natural gas burners collecting in the drying chamber.
- Spontaneous heating of the product due to too high a drying temperature. Temperatures measured in appropriate tests will limit the practical temperature after subtraction of an adequate safety margin (see Chapter 3, Section 3.2.3).
- Frictional ignition from contact between the rotary agitator and other parts of the equipment or tramp metal.
- Electrostatic discharges from charge accumulation due to movement of the powder.

Total exclusion of ignition sources is not possible and explosion protection is necessary. The vent area in the drying chamber can be calculated by any appropriate method (see Chapter 7). If an explosion door is fitted this should be as light as is practicable — for example, <10 kg m^{-2}. If heavier doors are fitted then the vent area will need enlarging (see Chapter 11, Section 11.3). The door should be positioned above the level of the agitator. The opening pressure of the vent door should be known, and the reduced explosion pressure that the dryer chamber will withstand — for example, 1.8 bar.

Opening of the door should cause automatic shutdown of the plant. The explosion should be vented to a safe place.

The cyclone

The main risk is the appearance of burning material from the dryer; venting is a suitable precaution, as discussed in Sections 13.2.1 and 13.3. The reduced explosion pressure that the cyclone can withstand should be the same as the drying chamber, as should that of the intervening ductwork — for example, 1.8 bar.

The opening pressure of the vent closure should be known and the vent sized by an appropriate method. The vent closure should be supported internally, to guard against vacuum inside the unit, by a 15×15 mesh. The process should shut down automatically if the vent opens.

Dust collector

Venting of the dust collector is as described in Sections 13.2.1 and 13.3.

221

Product-receiving pot

This vessel receives product directly from the cyclones and feeds it to the IBC via a rotary valve. It is impossible to guarantee the absence of burning products in this unit, and thus ignition sources cannot be avoided. Safety can be based on venting or containment.

In this case the volume of the pot is small and it is a relatively strong vessel, capable of containing an explosion if the feed lines from the cyclone become partially blocked. The volume of the cyclones and connecting ducts is relatively large, and thus the powder delivery ducts from the cyclones can act as explosion vents. In this case the cyclone can be regarded as a duct fitted to an explosion vent. The vent on the cyclone is fitted on the top. This approach is considered to be satisfactory because every attempt is made to keep the vents — that is, delivery ducts — open all the time. Powder blockage in the cyclone and ducting must be minimized, although the vessel is strong enough to contain an explosion. The strength of the receiving pot should be high.

Rigid intermediate bulk containers (RIBCs) and flexible intermediate bulk containers (FIBCs)

Intermediate bulk containers (IBCs), particularly flexible intermediate bulk containers (FIBCs) are being used increasingly by industry for the storage and transport of powders. The increase in container volume from about 0.2 m^3 for drums and sacks to 1.5–2.0 m^3 for an IBC can markedly change the dust dispersion characteristics in the container and increase the possibility of an explosion in the package should an ignition source be present.

RIBCs have been successfully protected by explosion suppression and inerting. Explosion venting can also be used but the maximum vent area is that of the RIBC fill hole. This limits the use of venting to powders of low K_{St}.

The use of suppression and venting for the protection of FIBCs (essentially large woven plastic bags) are rarely practical because of the low and uncertain strength of the container.

Inerting can be used for non-porous fabrics but care must be taken to contain the inert gas within the system to avoid asphyxiation hazards. Options to reduce the risk of a dust explosion are (a) filling a collapsed bag to reduce the volume of the ullage space or (b) by control of ignition sources. The latter requires that antistatic FIBCs are used and that the FIBCs are not filled directly from plant containing friction or heat ignition sources.

A risk assessment should be carried out before IBCs are introduced into plants handling powders capable of forming explosible dust clouds.

13.3 Venting of specific plant items

The guidance in this section refers to explosions ignited within the plant item itself and not from flame propagation into the unit. The venting of interconnected units is discussed in Chapter 8. Precautions against the transmission of explosion from one item of plant to another must be taken in all the following units.

13.3.1 Bucket elevators

Most bucket elevators are of a twin-leg design, with buckets attached to a belt that travels up one leg and down the other. The clearance between the buckets and casing is small. However, some elevators are of a single leg design with the buckets circulating inside one casing only, and there is a substantial open space down the centre in which a dust cloud may form.

Recent research has provided data that allows the number and location of vents required to be linked to the properties of the dust, the static bursting pressure of the vent closure and the strength of the elevator[3]. The whole structure of the elevator will need to be assessed in order to identify the weakest point.

Single leg Elevators

Vent openings should have an area equal to the cross-sectional area of the elevator leg and the least requirement is that vents should be fitted in the head and as close as is practicable to the boot. This generally means a vent within 6 m of the boot or within the recommended spacing, whichever is the lesser. The spacing between vents along the elevator is listed as a function of the dust K_{St} value, the vent burst pressure and the reduced explosion pressure in Table 13.1.

For dusts with K_{St} values of 150 bar m s^{-1}, a vent spacing of 6 m will limit the reduced explosion pressure to 300 mbar, when the vent static burst pressure is 0.1 bar.

For dusts with a K_{St} value of 80 bar m s^{-1}, a vent spacing of 20 m will limit the reduced explosion pressure to 250 mbar.

Twin-leg Elevators

Vent openings should have an area at least equal to the cross-section of the elevator leg; larger vents are preferred, as this will reduce the risk that a vent will be shielded from the pressure wave by a bucket, and fail to open when required. The least requirement is that vents should be fitted in the head and as close as is practicable to the boot. This generally means within 6 m of the boot or within the recommended vent spacing, whichever is the lesser. The static burst pressure of the vent closure should not exceed 0.1 bar.

Table 13.1 Spacing of vents in single leg elevators

K_{St} (bar m s^{-1})	P_{stat} (bar)	P_{red} (bar)	Vent spacing (m)
150	0.05	1	19
		0.5	10
	0.1	1	14
		0.5	7
175	0.05	1	7
		0.5	4
	0.1	1	5
		0.5	4
200	0.05	1	5
		0.5	3
	0.1	1	4
		0.5	3

The spacing of additional vents depends on the K_{St} value of the dust.

- Although explosions are possible with dusts of low K_{St}, generally the pressures developed by dusts with K_{St} values below 100 bar m s^{-1} are not significant, and no additional vents are required.
- Dusts with a K_{St} value of 150 bar m s^{-1} are able to develop significant pressures, although the likelihood of explosion propagation through the elevator is low. Vents additional to those at the head and boot may be required on long elevators if the casing is comparatively weak.
- Dusts with K_{St} values above 150 bar m s^{-1} will propagate explosions, and vents additional to those in the head and boot are required on elevators taller than 6 m. The graph in Figure 13.4 should be used to estimate the reduced explosion pressure for a given K_{St} value and vent spacing. The strength of the elevator should then be designed appropriately.
- No data is available for dusts with K_{St} values greater than 210 bar m s^{-1}.

13.3.2 Recovery cyclones

Experiments under realistic operating conditions show that explosion pressures in vented cyclones can be very low[4]. The usual sizing method, however, should be used unless a sufficient case can be made for reducing the vent area.

The most favourable position for the vents is on the top surface of the cyclone body. Sometimes they can be positioned on top of the vortex tube but explosion pressures will, as a consequence, be higher and the vortex tube must be strong enough to withstand the explosion. Figure 13.5 demonstrates diagrammatically some possible venting arrangements.

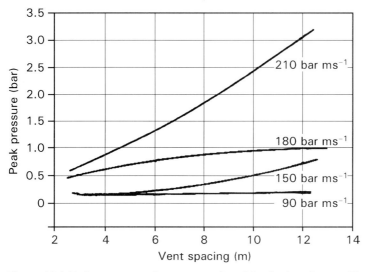

Figure 13.4 Peak pressure against vent spacing. 2-leg bucket elevator. Vent opening pressure 0.1 bar. Test results cover bucket spacing at 280 mm and 140 mm.

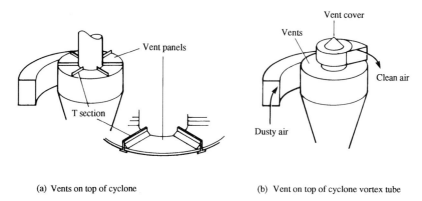

(a) Vents on top of cyclone   (b) Vent on top of cyclone vortex tube

Figure 13.5 Venting arrangements on a cyclone

13.3.3 Dust collector (filter/separator)

The usual sizing methods (see Chapter 7) will give a satisfactory value for the vent area. Venting should always be placed on the dirty side, as close to the likely ignition source as possible. Filter elements should not obstruct the vent area unless this obstruction has been taken into account in sizing the vent. If possible the flame should have an unobstructed passage to the vent opening.

225

When sizing vent openings in a filter the free volume of the enclosure should be used (that is, excluding bags), and not the total volume.

If the clean side volume is greater than half the dirty side volume it is prudent to provide the clean side with vents in case dust deposits have built up over time and are capable of being stirred up by an explosion. A typical filter is shown in Figure 13.6. Most filters can withstand an overpressure of 0.7 bar.

13.3.4 Spray dryers

The usual sizing methods (see Chapter 7) provide adequate vent area estimation when the L/D ratio of the dryer is less than 5. It has been argued that the usual sizing methods are conservative both because of the large volumes associated with this kind of plant and because the explosible dust cloud does not normally fill the vessel — it is generally considered to occupy the lower third of the volume.

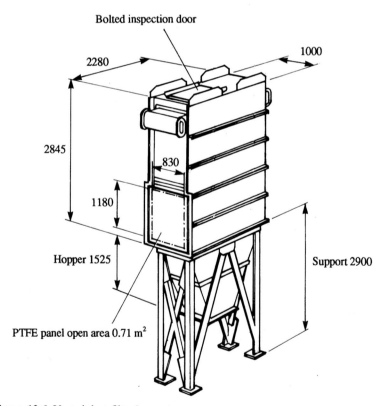

Figure 13.6 Vented dust filter/separator

However, this is not a sufficient reason for relaxing the venting requirements, because, in the event of an explosion, dust deposited on the walls of the dryer can be disturbed and so fuel the explosion. The total volume must be used in the vent sizing procedure, unless specialist advice indicates otherwise. An acceptable and detailed case must be made if a volume less than the total volume is used for the vent sizing method.

If hybrid mixtures of flammable gas and explosible dust are present in the dryer then the mixture needs to be tested according to the standard methods (see Chapter 2, Section 2.1 and Appendix 3). The construction of the dryer would need to be such that it can withstand a vented explosion of such a mixture. A basic design of a spray dryer is shown in Figure 13.7. The design strength of spray dryers is usually in the region of 0.2 bar, rarely rising above 0.4 bar.

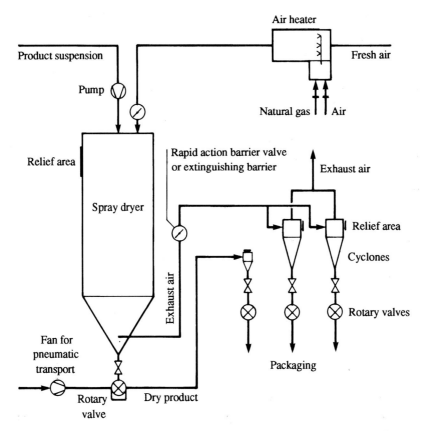

Figure 13.7 Basic design of spray dryer (Reproduced from Bartnecht, W., *Explosions: Course, prevention and protection* (Springer-Verlag) by permission of the author and publisher)

Venting of other types of dryer — pneumatic, rotary and band dryers — is discussed in an IChemE guide[1].

13.3.5 Grinders and mills

Venting is not usually applicable to grinders, which are generally built strong enough to withstand the explosion, but attached items of equipment such as collecting hoppers need venting. Because of the grinding tools, grinders have an enlarged inner surface area and the explosion pressure and rate of pressure rise are often reduced compared to what would be expected in an empty compact vessel. Air inlet and dust discharge openings may act as sufficient inherent venting for mills and grinders, but the attachment of ducts to the former will increase the explosion pressure and the danger of explosion propagation into other parts of the plant must not be overlooked. If venting of mills is possible it has been suggested that the usual sizing methods can be used[5]. It is recommended[6] that an installation such as the one in Figure 13.8 should be designed for at least 2–3 bar, with isolation techniques applied to the feed side and air exhaust.

13.3.6 Venting of storage bins

For storage bins vent areas should be sized according to the usual sizing methods (see Chapter 7), as in Figure 13.9, where a vent sized for $P_{stat} = 0.2$ bar, $P_{red} = 0.4$ bar and an St1 group dust has been fitted[7].

13.3.7 Venting of powder blenders

Where protection is necessary, vent areas should be calculated by means of the methods in Chapter 7. The blending motion must be stopped immediately once a vent is activated otherwise larger dust clouds may be generated.

Rotating blenders cannot be vented and alternative methods of protection are difficult to apply. Special care must be taken to exclude all ignition sources during operation and during loading.

13.3.8 Equipment that is difficult to vent

Some grinding, screening, classifying, packaging and blending equipment can be difficult to vent adequately. Such equipment should be located in an isolated cubicle, itself vented to a safe place (see Chapter 7, Section 7.3.2). Personnel should not be able to enter this cubicle while the equipment is operating.

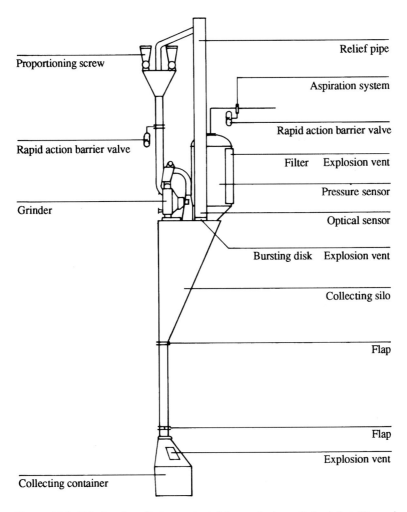

Proportioning screw

Rapid action barrier valve

Grinder

Collecting container

Relief pipe

Aspiration system

Rapid action barrier valve

Filter   Explosion vent

Pressure sensor

Optical sensor

Bursting disk   Explosion vent

Collecting silo

Flap

Flap

Explosion vent

Figure 13.8 Grinding installation protected by explosion relief venting (Reproduced from Bartnecht, W., *Explosions: Course, prevention, protection* (Springer-Verlag) by permission of the author and publisher)

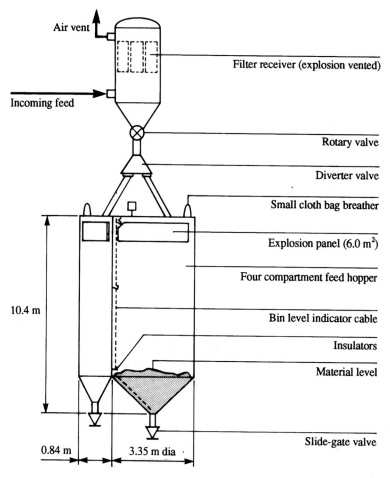

Air vent

Incoming feed

Filter receiver (explosion vented)

Rotary valve

Diverter valve

Small cloth bag breather

Explosion panel (6.0 m^2)

Four compartment feed hopper

10.4 m

Bin level indicator cable

Insulators

Material level

Slide-gate valve

0.84 m   3.35 m dia

Figure 13.9 Feed hopper system (Reproduced from 'Analysis of a Dust Deflagration', by Laurence G. Britton and David C. Kirby, *Plant/Operation Progress*, Volume 8, Number 3, pp. 177–180 (1989) by permission of the American Institute of Chemical Engineers AIChE)

References in Chapter 13

1. Abbott, J.A., 1990, *Prevention of Fires and Explosions in Dryers* (Institution of Chemical Engineers, Rugby, UK, ISBN 0 85295 257 0).
2. Maddison, N., 1991, Safety Consciousness in Drying Powders, *Processing*, June p. 15.
3. Holbrow, P., Lunn, G.A. and Tyldesley, A., 2001, Explosion Venting of Bucket Elevators, *Hazards XVI 'Analysing the past, planning the future'*, IChemE Symposium Series 147, Manchester, UK, p. 213.
4. Tonkin, P.S. and Berlemont, F.J., 1972, *Dust Explosions in a Large-Scale Cyclone Plant.* Fire Research Note 942, FRS, Building Research Establishment, Ltd.
5. Eckhoff, R.K., 1990, Sizing of Dust Explosion Vents in the Process Industries — Advances Made During the 1980s, *J. Loss Prevess Proc Ind.*, *3*, p. 268.
6. Schamlz, F., 1982, *Grinding and Mixing Plants, Spray Dryers*, Paper presented at The control and prevention of dust explosions, Basle, 16–17 November (IBC Technical Services Ltd.).
7. Britten, L.G. and Kirby, D.C., 1989, Analysis of a Dust Deflagration, *Plant/ Operations Progress*, *8* (3) p. 177.

Explosion propagation, protection of pipelines and isolation techniques

14

14.1 Introduction

The separate items of a dust-handling plant are usually connected together by, for example, ductwork, chutes, pipes and conveyors. An explosion, initiated in one plant item, e.g., a mill, can propagate along pipes and ducts etc. and start a subsequent explosion in other plant items, e.g., cyclones, dust collectors, receptacle hoppers and storage bins.

In the design of a dust-handling plant it is therefore important to take into account necessary measures to prevent:

- explosions, initiated in one plant item, propagating along ductwork to the other plant items;
- re-ignition after an explosion as a result of the introduction of fresh material or air;
- smouldering material and burning particles being transferred from one part of the plant into an explosible dust cloud in another part;
- the initiation of secondary explosions as a result of a vented explosion.

Various approaches and techniques that can be used to help achieve these objectives are discussed below. These are illustrative rather than comprehensive. It is important to recognise that their application and deployment in any given situation should rest on informed decisions based on a systematic hazard and risk assessment as required by the ATEX Directive[1].

14.2 Explosion propagation and protection of pipelines

Dust explosions can propagate through pipelines that link dust-handling plant. When the walls of a duct or pipeline confine a dust explosion, an explosion can attain high flame speeds and generate high pressures. The process of propagation and acceleration depends on a complex interaction between the combustion processes of the dust particles, heat transfer, fluid dynamic phenomena, such as dust dispersion, turbulence and pressure piling, and on the physical layout of the pipeline.

The confined combustion creates a gas flow in the pipeline into which the flame travels. Turbulence in the gas stream breaks up the flame front, increasing its area, accelerating the rate of combustion and leading to higher flow speeds and ever increasing turbulence. This positive feed back mechanism is a means by which the explosion can reach a very destructive potential. A simple relation between the speed of a propagating explosion and the pressure it generates can be derived by approximating the flame front as a piston that compresses a volume of unburned gas ahead of it.

The following equation defines this relationship:

$$(P_{expl} - P_0) = \rho_0 C_0 U_j$$

where P_{expl} is the explosion pressure, P_0 is the ambient pressure, ρ_0 the density of the unburned gas at ambient conditions, C_0 is the velocity of sound in the unburned gas and U_j is the flame speed. This relation is known as the acoustic approximation[2].

With simple mathematics, the acoustic approximation demonstrates some aspects of flame behaviour. For instance, the higher the flame speed, the higher the pressures developed. If U_j is slow relative to C_0, the compression of the unburned gas will move well ahead of the flame and can be vented through the open end of a pipeline. But as the difference between U_j and C_0 diminishes, the volume of compressed gas ahead of the flame also diminishes, and because of the increasing confinement of the combustion process higher explosion pressures are generated. When U_j equals and then exceeds C_0, the flame front overtakes the pressure front and a detonation is produced which travels at approaching the speed of sound in the burnt gas, $C_0 (T_b/T_u)^{1/2}$ where (T_b/T_u) is the ratio of the burnt and unburned gas temperatures. Pressures in excess of those produced in totally enclosed subsonic explosions can be developed in detonations because the confinement of the combustion process is so great. Detonations travel at supersonic speeds into the unburned gas. Detonation or detonation type phenomena have been shown to develop in dust-carrying pipelines[3]. Explosion pressure and flame speed measurements are shown in Figure 14.1.

Evidence from the literature on explosions in pipelines suggests that, in most circumstances, dust-carrying pipelines that are straight do not require explosion venting as an additional safety precaution, so long as adequate means are taken to protect attached vessels. In many test explosions, in circumstances where the primary explosion does not generate a high pressure — that is, in a well-vented

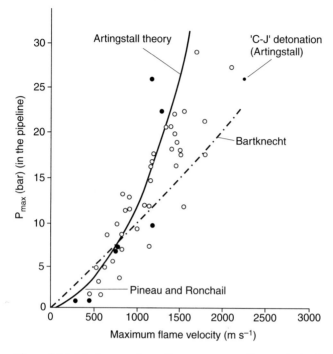

Figure 14.1 Maximum values of pressure versus flame velocity for 2 tests of two high volatile coals, size grade 250, compared with the findings of other investigators (Reproduced by permission of The Combustion Institute)

vessel, the highest pressures generated are measured in one or other of the linked vessels and not in the pipeline.

If there is time and opportunity for the explosion to become self-accelerating, however, and travel independently of the primary explosion, then very fast flames and very high pressures can be generated. Even in these circumstances, tests show that the pipeline does not rupture because the pressure peaks are of such short duration. Even when these fast flames enter the second vessel, the high pressures developed in the pipeline are not transmitted throughout the vessel volume. The pressures generated by the subsequent secondary explosion are much less than the peak pressures in the pipeline, and more on the level expected from vented deflagrations.

The best known guidance for estimating pressures in pipelines is given in NFPA68[4]. The guidance relevant to dust explosions is reproduced in Figures 14.2 and 14.3.

Figure 14.2 gives guidance for estimating the distance at which high pressures are generated by self-propagating flames in a straight pipeline open

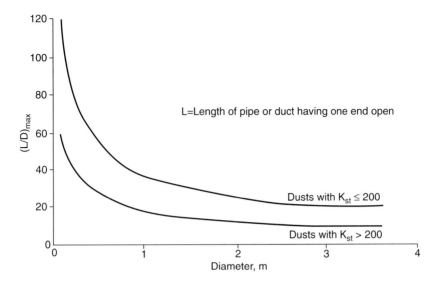

Figure 14.2 Distance along a straight pipe at which an over pressure of 10 bar will be developed in dust/air mixtures. The primary explosion should not exceed 0.5 bar overpressure. Based on guidance in NFPA 68

at one end. It gives reasonably accurate guidance for the distances required for the development of 10 bar explosion overpressure for conditions where the initiating event is not powerful, but neither is the pipe open at the ignition end. When the initiating event is powerful, high explosion pressures in a more or less contained primary vessel, for example, the guidance overestimates the pipe length. Generally, if the primary explosion generates a pressure greater than 0.5 bar, the guidance should not be used. The data generally support the guidance up to a pipe diameter of 0.6 m.

As pipes become very narrow it becomes increasingly difficult to sustain a propagating flame, and eventually impossible. This effect depends on the explosibility of the dust, the dust concentration and the conditions inside the pipe, including flow velocity and the strength of the initiating event. It is impossible to make any hard and fast rules, because the available data do not come from a wide set of consistent trials. However, when the pipe diameter is below 0.1 m, for St1 dusts and initiating events that do not generate high pressures, the probability of extensive flame propagation is low. If the initiating event does generate high pressure, from a contained explosion for instance, the flame can be forced through very narrow pipes for lengthy distances.

Figure 14.3 gives the NFPA68 guidance[4] on explosion pressures developed in a pipeline closed at one end. The guidance is presented in terms of the pipe

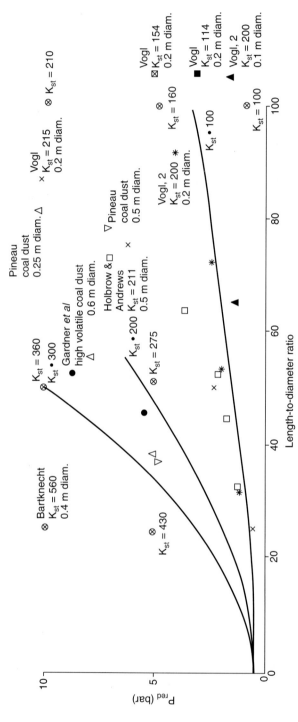

Figure 14.3 Maximum pressure during deflagrations of dust/air mixtures in a straight pipe closed at one end. The primary explosion should not exceed 0.5 bar overpressure. Based on guidance in NFPA 68

L/D ratio and the K_{St}-value of the dust, and is compared with data from several experimental studies[3,5-7].

The guidance underestimates the data, and predicts a shorter L/D to reach a given explosion pressure than tests show.

The data show some consistency between K_{St}-value and L/D ratio for pipe diameters of 0.2 m to 0.6 m. A reasonable conclusion is that the guidance in Figure 14.3 follows trends fairly well in this range of pipe diameters, although the predictions are conservative. However, in tests where a primary ignition takes place inside a contained enclosure, the guidance underestimates the pressures, because the initiating event is at a high pressure. The points from Gardner *et al.*[3] and Pineau[8] show this behaviour. Generally, the pressure generated in the initiating event should not exceed 0.5 bar if this guidance is to be used.

In practice, the strength of the pipeline should be such that it can withstand the explosion pressures likely to be encountered. If the explosion begins following an ignition in a well-vented enclosure the distance along the pipe, L, at which a specified overpressure will occur can be estimated from the equations:

$$L = D \times (324.8 \times (1 - \exp(-0.1072 \times P_{red}))) \qquad K_{St} \leq 100 \text{ bar m s}^{-1}$$
$$L = D \times (83.57 - 81.99 \times \exp(-0.1640 \times P_{red})) \qquad 100 < K_{St} \leq 200 \text{ bar m s}^{-1}$$
$$L = D \times (63.76 - 62.42 \times (\exp(-0.1484 \times P_{red}))) \quad 200 < K_{St} \leq 300 \text{ bar m s}^{-1}$$

where D is the pipe diameter, and D is from 0.2 to 0.6 m. These equations are derived from Figure 14.3. If the primary explosion is likely to exceed 0.5 bar overpressure, these equations should not be used.

In NFPA68[4] a constraint is given that the dust/air mixtures should flow at speeds no greater that 2 m s^{-1}. The experimental points, however, are from tests which have, in some cases, higher flow speeds, and these indicate that the NFPA68 guidance is of wider applicability than originally suggested. Experiments with flow velocities up to 40 m s^{-1} are included in Figure 14.3. Therefore the data covers the range of velocities used in typical pneumatic conveyance systems.

On the basis of this guidance, necessary protection for pipelines and interconnected plant can be chosen. The basis of safety will rest on a combination of the strength of the pipeline, isolation of the explosion effects and protection of the enclosures connected by the pipeline. Venting, suppression or containment can protect the enclosures and methods are available for predicting pressure effects in some vented (see Chapter 8) and enclosed (see Chapter 5) connected systems. The required strength of the pipeline depends on the pressures likely to be developed. If conditions are such that the explosion pressure will reach 10 bar, then an appropriate construction should be used, but there is no evidence that even the very high pressures measured by Vogl[5] and Gardner et al.[3] will rupture pipelines. These pressures are reached so abruptly and are of such a short duration at any given position that the pipeline does not respond to them. When the plant design is such that high pressures are not likely, a pipeline of lower strength construction can be used.

Isolation techniques, including cut-off valves, suppression barriers and diverters, can prevent the onset of high pressures and fast flame-speeds. In that case, apart perhaps for when diverters are used, straight pipelines of normal construction would be expected to contain an explosion without the need for additional precautions, such as venting.

If the pipeline contains bends and obstacles, then these exacerbate explosion propagation, and venting may be a desirable precaution. Guidance for the positioning of vents is available from NFPA68[4]. Vents should be placed close to obstacles such as elbows, tees, orifices, valves and anything which blocks more than 5% of the pipe cross-sectional area. Vents of area equal to that of the cross-section of the pipe should be placed at 3 and 6 diameters each side of the obstacles.

Positioning explosion isolation devices in pipelines requires information on the flame speeds, and explosion pressures that can be developed. Figures 14.2 and 14.3 allow an estimate of the distance at which given pressures are achieved; other information in the literature allows estimates of the distance a flame will travel in a given time.

From tests[9] in a pneumatic conveying system an empirical equation for calculating the flame propagation distance along pipes has been developed:

$$L = A \cdot \exp (B \cdot t) + C$$

where L is the flame propagation distance (m), t is the flame transit time (s), B is a coefficient (s^{-1}), and A and C are constants, with values:

$P_{red} \leq 0.2$ bar: $A = 8.5$, $C = -8.5$, $B = 0.0068$,
0.2 bar $< P_{red} \leq 1.0$ bar: $A = 8.5$, $C = -8.5$, $B = 0.0104$,
1.0 bar $< P_{red} \leq 2.0$ bar: $A = 8.5$, $C = -8.5$, $B = 0.0157$.

The equation has the following constraints:

1. $K_{St} \leq 200$ bar m s^{-1},
2. Pipe diameter ≥ 100 mm,
3. Conveying velocity ≤ 300 m s^{-1}
4. Volume of primary vessel > 9 m^3,
5. Pneumatic and mechanical dust feed.

Other empirical relationships[10] between propagation distance and time for several experimental configurations have been developed. These equations are:

$$L = (t - 0.017)/(10^{(0.555 - 0.375 * LOG \, (Pred))}) * 0.001,$$

for a standing $1 \, m^3$ primary vessel and a pipe diameter $\geq 0.1 \, m$ fitted at the vessel side.

$$L = t/(10^{(0.555 - 0.375 * LOG(Pred))}) * 0.001,$$

for a $0.5 \, m^3$ vessel or a reclining $1 \, m^3$ vessel and a pipe diameter $\geq 0.1 \, m$ fitted in the end wall.

$$L = t/(10^{(0.425 - 0.375 * LOG(Pred))}) * 0.001,$$

for a $4.25 \, m^3$ primary vessel and a pipe diameter $\geq 0.1 \, m$.

$$L = (t - 0.005)/(10^{(0.425 - 0.375 * LOG(Pred))}) * 0.001,$$

for a $4.25 \, m^3$ primary vessel and a pipe diameter $\geq 0.4 \, m$.

$$L = t/(10^{(0.765 - 0.375 * LOG(Pred))}) * 0.001,$$

for a $9.4 \, m^3$ primary vessel and a pipe diameter $\geq 0.1 \, m$.

The equations apply to dusts with K_{St} values $\leq 200 \, bar \, m \, s^{-1}$.

14.2.1 Protection against explosion propagation in pipelines

The following precautions can be considered:

- Ensure that in the design of the plant, taking into account the explosibility of the dust, the length and diameter of pipelines are chosen so that detonation cannot occur. The above relationships can aid the design process.
- Design the pipework and/or the whole plant to contain the maximum explosion pressure (see Chapter 5), and/or use explosion suppression (see Chapter 6), and/or vent appropriate plant items (see Chapter 7).
- Take preventive measures to limit the extent and the consequences of explosion propagation.

14.3 Prevention (or limitation) of explosion propagation (isolation techniques)

Techniques that commonly are applied include the following:

14.3.1 Explosion relief diverter

An explosion relief diverter (see Figure 14.4) can be fitted in the interconnecting pipeline. The diverter is not a true isolation device and it cannot be relied

239

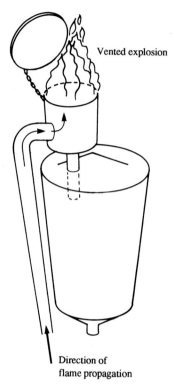

Figure 14.4 Explosion relief diverter

upon as a flame barrier[11]. However, its use means the explosion travelling along the connecting pipe is vented and the pressure released. A less violent explosion then travels forward, e.g., into a second vessel.

14.3.2 Rapid action valves

A variety of rapid action valves are available including flaps and slide valves (see Figure 14.5). Rapid action valves are most effective for pipeline diameters of 500 mm or less. The valve is usually installed 5–10 m along a duct or pipeline so that by the time the flame front reaches it, it is fully closed. A typical closing time for a rapid action valve is around 25 ms. The valve is usually activated by an appropriately sited explosion detector and operated pneumatically by compressed gas contained in a pressure vessel. Both pressure detectors (with threshold detection levels around 0.1 bar) and optical/radiation detectors are used. Because of the possibility of blinding an optical detector, pressure detectors are favoured in most dusty applications, but they may introduce a 'range of uncertainty' of operation, i.e., a weak explosion entering the duct may

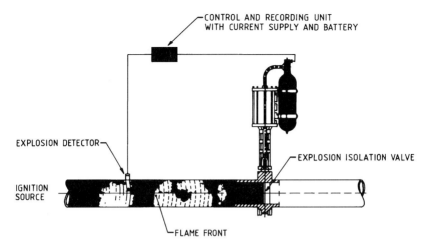

Figure 14.5 Rapid action valve (From Moore, P.E., Dust Explosion Suppression and Containment, IMechE Seminar on Prevention and Control of Dust Explosions. Northwich, Cheshire, 14 November, 1984)

not exceed the threshold pressure. For this reason, in some instances the use of both pressure and optical detection may be warranted.

14.3.3 Suppressant barriers

Instead of the physical barrier to explosion propagation provided by a rapid action valve, a barrier or plug of suppressant material (see Chapter 6 for a discussion of explosion suppression) can be injected into the duct or pipeline ahead of the flame front to provide effective explosion isolation (see Figure 14.6).

The explosion is detected using either a pressure detector installed on the upstream interconnected vessel, or a flame detector installed on the pipeline. The suppressant is deployed typically some 5–10 m along the duct to allow sufficient time for the suppressant to be deployed and build up an extinguishing concentration before the flame arrives at the barrier location. Barrier design demands that the barrier is positioned such that effectiveness is assured, and that a sustained discharge of suppressant achieves a sufficient extinguishing concentration across the whole pipeline diameter.

Since a suppressant barrier presents no obstruction, it is often the case that the pressure impulse from an explosion that is propagating down a pipeline can be contained to quite a low pressure with a suppressant barrier, and of course flame propagation is prevented. Suppressant barriers can be deployed in cluttered ducts — for example, in conveyor or elevator legs — to provide viable explosion protection.

241

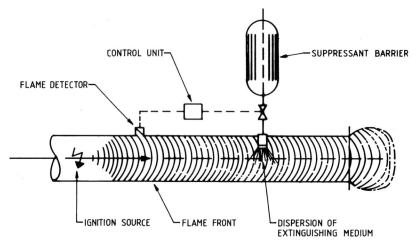

CONTROL UNIT

FLAME DETECTOR

SUPPRESSANT BARRIER

IGNITION SOURCE   FLAME FRONT   DISPERSION OF
EXTINGUISHING MEDIUM

Figure 14.6 Suppressant barrier (From Moore, P.E., Dust Explosion Suppression and Containment, IMechE Seminar on Prevention and Control of Dust Explosions. Northwich, Cheshire, 14 November, 1984)

It must be recognized that these active explosion isolation systems are dependent on the effective detection of the flame front. In the case of a timid explosion with negligible pressure effect, detection by explosion pressure alone is not likely to be effective. Some operators prefer to specify both pressure and flame detectors to maximize barrier efficiency.

Suppressant barriers often form an integral part of an explosion protection system in which the primary vessel is protected by explosion vents or explosion suppression. Detection of the explosion in the vessel also triggers the barrier to ensure that no flame propagates upstream or downstream from the explosion incident.

14.3.4 Material chokes

Judicious selection and design of conveying equipment can achieve a degree of isolation.

Screw conveyors[12] (see Figure 14.7) can provide 'a choke' of material to prevent the propagation of an explosion.

Rotary valves are widely used to control powder flow and if properly designed they also can prevent the propagation of a dust explosion. To achieve this they need to be robust enough to withstand the pressures involved, and the rotor needs to be designed to prevent passage of flame. The number of vanes, the thickness of and the clearance between vanes and the casing will all influence the effectiveness of a rotary valve as a flame trap. Rotary valves

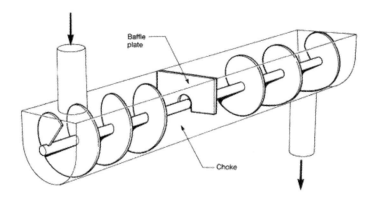

Figure 14.7 The use of a screw conveyor as a choke

should have all-metal veins if they are to act as explosion barriers. Rotary valves commonly are tested experimentally in Germany to check their performance, and, under the ATEX Directive, if, in future, claims are made by manufacturers about their application in explosion protection, testing may become mandatory. It should be noted that clearances in this type of valve tend to increase with wear, and if they are to remain effective as chokes over an extended period of time, the plant needs to be operated in a way that maintains a plug of material above the valve. Rotary valves can have a secondary explosion protection purpose. Following a dust explosion, burning powder will remain, and if this is conveyed on through a process, it may act as a source of ignition elsewhere. This can be prevented if rotary valves are linked to some form of explosion detector, such as a trip switch on a vent panel, and stop immediately in the event of an explosion.

If it is considered likely that it will not be possible to stop the choke device, i.e., rotary valve or conveyor, sufficiently quickly to prevent some burning material being swept through, then consideration needs to given to, for example, injecting an inerting concentration of suppressant locally in the plant, in order to prevent this occurring.

14.4 Prevention of re-ignition

In some plants it may not be possible to shut down immediately the supply of feed and air to a vessel in which an explosion has been detected. There is then a risk of re-ignition after the explosion has taken place leading to a second explosion. In this case it is often possible to render the feed inert by injecting suppressant material locally into the feed when an explosion is detected. The supply of fresh air into the process can be cut off, for example, by means of a rapid action valve.

14.5 Preventing the transfer of smouldering material and burning particles into an explosible dust cloud

Certain materials, for example, wood-chips, are prone to smouldering or burning due to the nature of their processing. The smouldering or burning material can then be carried to other parts of the process where an explosible dust cloud could be present, e.g., a silo (see Appendix 1 for an example of such an incident), by, for example, screw or belt conveyors, or a pneumatic transport system, all of which are commonly used. In processes where this is recognised as a problem it is good practice to install thermal or optical sensors to detect burning or smouldering material, and arrange for these to be interlocked to shut down the plant or activate a fixed fire extinguishing system installed in the plant. This usually takes the form of a water spray.

In instances where it is not considered possible to arrest the transfer of the burning particles quickly enough, then it might be appropriate to consider injecting an inerting concentration of a suppressant into the vessel into which the transport system discharges, where an explosible concentration of dust may exist.

References in Chapter 14

1. Council Directive of 23 March 1994 (ATEX-100A-Directive) on Equipment protective systems intended for use in potentially explosive atmospheres (94/9/EC), European Communities Council, *Official Journal of the European Communities*, 19 April 1994, 37 (L100).
2. Hertzberg, M. and Cashdollar, K.L. Introduction to dust explosions in *Industrial Dust Explosions*, K.L. Cashdollar and M. Hertzberg (Eds.), ASTM Special Technical Publication 958 (American Society of Testing and Materials).
3. Gardner, B.R., Winter, R.J. and Moore, M.J., 1986, *Explosion Development and Deflagration-to-Detonation Transition in Coal Dust/Air Suspensions*, 21st Symposium (International) on Combustion, The Combustion Institute p. 335.
4. NFPA, 1998, *Guide for Venting of Deflagrations*, (NFPA 68) (National Fire Protection Association, Quincy, USA).
5. Vogl, A., 1995, *The Course of Dust Explosions in Pipes of Pneumatic Systems*, Paper presented at the Symposium 'Esplosioni da polveri: valutazione, prevenzione e protezione', San Donato Milanese, 28th June 1995. La Ruiste dei Combustible, *49*, p. 381, (October).

6. Holbrow, P. and Andrews, S., 1997, *Protection of Dust Carrying Pipelines*, HSL Research Report, DE/97/05.

7. Bartknecht, W., 1981, *Explosions: Course, Prevention, Protection*, ISBN 0-387-10216-7 (Springer Verlag).

8. Pineau, J.P., 1984, *Dust explosions in vessels connected to ducts*, VDI — Berichte Nr. 494, p. 67.

9. Vogl, A., 1996, *Explosionsubertragung aus Behaltern in Rohrleitungen pneumatischer Anlagen*, VDI Berichte Nr. 1272, p. 215.

10. Roser, M., 1998, *Investigation of dust explosion phenomena in interconnected process vessels*, Ph.D. Thesis, Loughborough University.

11. Vogl, A., 1989, How effective are explosion relief stacks?, Paper presented at *Dust explosion protection*, Antwerp, 11–13 September (Europex International Symposium).

12. HSE, 1992, (HS(G)103) Safe handling of combustible dusts, HMSO.

Appendix 1
Incidents

Some illustrative examples of recent incidents are given below.

Although the technical causes for incidents and the protective measures needed are generally well understood, nonetheless incidents resulting in injury or serious damage continue to occur. One of the most common characteristics of incidents is the way a localized ignition spreads through a plant to multiply the effect of the initial fire or explosion, as the examples show.

Explosion in a grain storage facility

In August 1997, at Blaye in France, an explosion occurred in a grain storage facility, handling wheat, barley and maize. The facility comprised 44 vertical concrete silos, with a total storage volume of 47,000 m³. Two towers contained bucket elevators and dust collection equipment, while across the top in a concrete gallery were belt conveyors. No explosion relief was provided on the plant and internally the towers and gallery were open, thus allowing dust clouds and flame to spread. Ignition seems to have started in a fan forming part of the centralised dust collection system.

There was no warning of the explosion, and 11 people were killed when concrete debris rained down on the control room. Both towers, the gallery and 28 silos were completely wrecked. It is salutary to note that the whole grain handled might have been thought to be a low risk. The concentration of dust fine enough to explode lay in the range 0.02–0.16% for samples of the different products. The explosion properties likewise seemed modest. Samples tested passed a 500 micron sieve, they showed P_{max} values of just 6 bar, and K_{St} values in the range 60–70 bar ms^{-1}.

Explosion in a powdered silicon plant

An explosion ripped through a plant in the UK producing powdered silicon. The silicon lumps were ground in a ball mill, and pneumatically conveyed through a classifier to a cyclone and collection system. Explosion vents were provided on the cyclone and filter, but proved inadequate, at least partly because 5 mm steel plate had worn in places to paper thickness, thus weakening the overall mechanical integrity of the plant. Ignition started in the cyclone, which tore open, shearing 60 bolts on the top surface and 16 at a flange below. No means of isolating the various plant components was provided, so the explosion spread, wrecking also the fan casing, ducting, filter, rotary valves and dampers. The operator was blown off his feet and received burn injuries.

The ignition is believed to have been caused by electrostatic discharge from some unearthed part of the plant. The company clearly did not understand the hazards of the product they were processing.

Wood dust explosion in a furniture factory

An incident that could easily have been avoided involved a factory making flat pack furniture from chipboard. Board off-cuts were ground up in a simple mill, and the dust collected in a large filter. From there the dust was fed to a silo before being used as fuel for a boiler. An operator became aware of a burning smell, and with the foreman wandered round the plant looking for the source. They had just reached the filter, located in the yard just outside a main access route, when 22 explosion vent panels opened. Fortunately they were not seriously injured but the filter was badly damaged in the fire, which followed the explosion.

Investigation showed the fire had started in the mill. If the mill and fan had been turned off as soon as the fire was suspected, dust would have settled, and no explosion could have occurred.

Explosion in a coal grinding plant

A coal grinding plant associated with a cement works exploded because of poor operating procedures and inadequate understanding of the process. Lumps of coal were fed continuously through the mill and powder was collected in a cyclone. During mill operation warmed air, from an oil-fired heat exchanger, was passed through the mill to dry the powdered coal. Some of the air was recycled through the heat exchanger. Instrument problems led to a plant shut down for 12 minutes, and immediately on restart an explosion occurred. Appropriate vents relieved this, but the subsequent fire took an hour to extinguish.

It was shown later that powdered coal had been drawn into the recirculating air system, and some had deposited in the heat exchanger. The deposit was hot enough to allow burning to start, when the cooling effect of a continuous airflow was stopped. On restart it was evident that a burning deposit was drawn into the mill. The management had no idea what temperatures were reached in the air ducts, nor the minimum temperature that could start ignition of the coal. They had discontinued an earlier practice of adding powdered limestone to inert the system on starting up the mill.

Explosion in a plant making refined starch

Neither the provision of explosion vents nor a system for inerting the atmosphere in the plant proved adequate to prevent an explosion in a plant making refined starch. Powdered starch was blended and bleached in a vessel with mechanical systems of mixing and recirculating the product. Defects in the drive to the oscillating bars in the mixing vessel meant that friction could have caused ignition, but it could also have been caused by self heating when over-strength bleach was introduced.

The sample line measuring the oxygen content in the plant was blocked. The nitrogen generator was defective and could not deliver the designed volume of inert gas at the intended purity. The explosion vents were ducted to outside the building but the ducts were smaller than the vent panels, were partly obstructed with product, and no one knew how they had been designed. The explosion tore open the mixing vessel and a secondary explosion in the building removed many roof and wall panels.

Appendix 2
Legislation

Introduction

In the UK the Health and Safety at Work (HSW) Act[1] is the main legislative framework. The Act places general duties on each of the main parties to industrial activity — employers, self-employed, employees, manufacturers and designers, and owners of dangerous premises — to ensure the safety of those at work and people who may be affected by a work activity.

The old cornerstone, i.e., Section 31 of the Factories Act 1961, with its more prescriptive requirements relating to dust explosion prevention and protection, is being repealed. Inter alia, this has a specific prohibition on hot work of any kind, unless either all the explosible or flammable substances and any fumes evolving from them are first removed from the plant, or the atmosphere is inerted. A similar provision on hot work will be carried forward into new legislation. In any case, the general duties of the HSW Act would require it. Over the years many explosions have been caused by welding or other hot work on dust handling plant.

There is a key qualification for the duties in the HSW Act: that the end-result is to be achieved 'so far as is reasonably practicable'. The recognized interpretation of this qualification is that there must be a computation of risk and cost. So risk assessment and cost-benefit analysis come in on the ground floor. The risk to both employees and the public must be considered. This book illustrates most of the techniques that are used to ensure safety from the risk or consequences of a dust explosion. Whether a particular precaution is required in any particular circumstance depends on the legal test of what is reasonably practicable. Will the safety gains be proportionate to the costs involved?

The HSW Act should ensure that equipment at work is safe to use, but this requirement is extended by the Use of Work Equipment Regulations[2]. These require that where European harmonised safety requirements have been laid down new equipment supplied for use at work must comply fully with these requirements. These regulations will impact not only on manufacturers of

249

proprietary equipment but also on those who build equipment for their own use, and may not have evaluated fully the necessary safety features. Explosion vent panels or doors are a particular case, where most 'home-made' designs have never been properly tested, and they may well open too slowly, or require an excessive pressure to open at all.

The European Union is now the main engine for legislative change.

European influences

Single market legislation

Achieving the free movement of goods lies at the heart of achieving an open market for business in Europe. In order to fulfil this objective, the European Community Ministers agreed on a 'New Approach to Technical Harmonisation and Standards', to remove technical barriers to trade. This introduced 'New Approach' Directives (i.e., Community laws) that were to set out, inter alia, essential safety requirements, written in general terms. Goods that comply with these essential safety requirements (ESRs) can be freely traded in all community countries, and individual states cannot reject them on safety grounds. More than one Directive may apply to a single item of equipment. The CE mark is applied to the equipment to show it complies with relevant Directives; other standard markings give additional information. In the explosion protection field, to ensure high standards, some classes of equipment must be independently checked by appointed test houses, known as notified bodies.

Goods that do not comply with the essential safety requirements may not be sold in the Community. As the Directives themselves are written in general terms, for practical application they need to be amplified by the production of technical standards at various levels of detail. This work is ongoing in many fields. Once a standard is adopted as a harmonised European standard under a particular Directive or Directives, compliance with its details is sufficient to ensure that the equipment meets the ESRs of those Directives.

Directives relevant to explosion prevention and protection

There are two types of Directives. They relate respectively to those who supply equipment, and those who put it into use.

Supply

The Machinery Directive (89/392/EEC) demands (at Annex 1, Section 1.5.7) that machinery shall be so designed and constructed to prevent hazards due to fires and explosions[3] [Note: silos, hoppers and other equipment with no moving parts or external sources of power fall outside the scope].

The ATEX-100A-Directive (94/9/EC)[4] applies to those who make or sell equipment for use in potentially explosive atmospheres. Its requirements are more specific than the Machinery Directive. Equipment that meets the ESRs of ATEX will also meet Machinery Directive requirements in respect of fire and explosion hazards. The ATEX-100A-Directive applies to electrical and mechanical equipment and protective systems intended for use on the surface, and below ground. From 1 July 2003 (transitional arrangements apply until then) all equipment, protective systems, safety devices, etc. intended for use in potentially explosive atmospheres will have to comply with the Directive. In essence this means that:

• where possible the equipment should not form an explosive atmosphere;
• the equipment should be designed not to act as an ignition source;
• in the event of an explosion the equipment should be designed to limit the range of dangerous flames and pressures;
• in some cases the equipment will be subject to type-examination by a Notified Body;
• in many cases the equipment will be subject to conformity assessment procedures by a Notified Body;
• the equipment must carry a CE marking and other information (generally about intended use).

The ATEX-100A-Directive recognises three categories of equipment for use in most industries, and further categories for coal mines. Different safety requirements and conformity assessment procedures are given for the categories depending on the reliability of the protection needed. Mandatory third party certification applies to some types of equipment; this is a new requirement in the dust field. It also covers explosion protection equipment (protective systems), even though it may create no ignition hazard. Explosion vent panels, explosion suppression equipment, and explosion barrier systems will be within scope, and these will have, for the first time, to be third party certified.

Guidance on the Directive is available[5].

Many existing European electrical standards have been updated to adopt the ATEX terminology and requirements, but a large number of new standards are required for the non-electrical field, and for explosion protection systems.

Accordingly, the European standardisation body, CEN set up a new Technical Committee (TC305) to co-ordinate the development of standards in the field of explosion prevention and protection for mechanical equipment. A high level standard BS EN 1127-1: 1998 has been produced that describes the basic concepts and methodology of explosion prevention and protection in support of both the Machinery and ATEX Directives. TC305 has five working groups: WG 1 — Test methods for determining the flammability, ignitability and explosibility characteristics of substances; WG 2 — Equipment for use in potentially explosive atmospheres; WG 3 — Devices and systems for explosion prevention and protection; WG 4 — Terminology and methodology; WG 5 — Mining. TC 305 is currently developing a whole raft of concept standards that set out the various ways in which mechanical equipment can be prevented from causing an ignition risk. The first of these, the basic requirements has been issued as EN 13463 part 1. More detailed machinery standards are also under development for suppression equipment, explosion vent panels and explosion isolation devices, powder conveying machinery, wood waste collection plants and other equipment.

Use

In order to promote harmonised minimum standards of health and safety for workers across the community, European Directives set out a basic framework, extended by a series of more specific legislation. In the field of fire and explosion hazards two Directives are particularly relevant. The Chemical Agents Directive (98/24/EC)[6] and the ATEX 137 user Directive (1999/92/EC)[7]. Both address fire and explosion hazards, and they will be implemented in the UK as a single set of regulations[8], coming fully into force by June 2003. They require an assessment of the risks arising from the use of dangerous substances, including explosible dusts, and recognise a hierarchy of precautions: preventing the formation of hazardous quantities or concentrations of flammable materials; avoiding ignition sources that could give rise to fires and explosions; and mitigating the consequences of any fire or explosion that may arise. These basic principles are not new, but there are some requirements in the dust-handling field that are new.

As part of the risk assessment that will be required wherever explosible dusts are handled, a hazardous area classification exercise should be carried out. This should then be used as the basis for selecting equipment. It does not imply that all old equipment, built before the ESRs of the ATEX Directive were written, has to be replaced, instead the safety of individual items needs to be considered and justified.

Other requirements include written instructions for work in hazardous areas, where the risk assessment identifies that they are necessary, and warning signs to indicate the extent of hazardous areas, again tempered by the phrase 'where necessary'.

References in Appendix 2

1. Health and Safety at Work etc. Act, 1974, c37.
2. Provision and Use of Work Equipment Regulations 1998, SI 1998/2306, amended by SI 1999/860 and 1999/2001.
3. Supply of Machinery (Safety) Regulations 1992, SI 1992/3073.
4. Council Directive of 23 March 1994 (ATEX-100A-Directive) on Equipment protective systems intended for use in potentially explosive atmospheres (94/9/EC), European Communities Council, *Official Journal of the European Communities*, 19 April 1994, 37 (L100)(implemented in the UK as the Equipment and Protective Systems for use in Potentially Explosive Atmospheres Regulations 1996).
5. ATEX guidelines (First Edition), Guidelines on the application of European Parliament and Council Directive 94/9/EC of 23 March 1994 on the approximation of the laws of the Member States concerning equipment and protective systems intended for use in potentially explosive atmospheres. European Commission, May 2001, Office for Official Publications of the European Communities, L-2985, Luxembourg. The ATEX guide and other related information can be found on
http://europa.eu.int/comm/enterprise/atex/index.
6. Council Directive 98/24/EC on 'The Protection of the Health and Safety of Workers from the Risks Related to Chemical Agents at Work' (14th Individual Directive within the meaning of Article 16(1) of Directive 89/391/EEC).
7. Council Directive 1999/92/EC on 'Minimum Requirements for Improving the Health and Safety Protection of Workers Potentially at Risk from Explosive Atmospheres' (15th Individual Directive within the meaning of Article 16(1) of Directive 89/391/EEC).
8. Dangerous Substances and Explosive Atmospheres Regulations, 2002.

Appendix 3
Descriptions of explosibility apparatus

1. Vertical tube apparatus

This is the standard explosibility test currently accepted by the UK's Health and Safety Executive for the initial classification of dusts as Group A or Group B (see Chapter 2, Section 2.1.1).

The vertical tube apparatus[1] is shown in Figure A3.1. The usual ignition source is an electric spark produced by a high voltage transformer having a 10 kV, 0.024 amp output, and bridging a 0.5 cm gap between electrodes. Some dusts do not ignite readily by electric spark and an alternative ignition source is a heated wire coil made from 20 SWG Kanthal 'A' wire and consisting of about eight turns with an external diameter of 1 cm. The coil is heated to approximately 1000°C by a transformer having an output of 10 volts and 20 amps.

The dust is dispersed vertically from the dispersion cup around the mushroom-shaped deflector by either an instantaneous or continuous blast of air. If flame propagation is observed in the tube the dust is designated Group A. If flame propagation is not observed then the amount of dust and the method of dispersion is varied. If flame propagation is still not observed further drying and sieving of the sample takes place. The dried and sieved fractions are tested individually so that a Group B classification is based on exhaustive testing.

It is general practice for further testing to be done in the Godbert–Greenwald furnace apparatus if a dust with a Group B classification is to be used at a temperature above 110°C (see Chapter 2, Section 2.1.2).

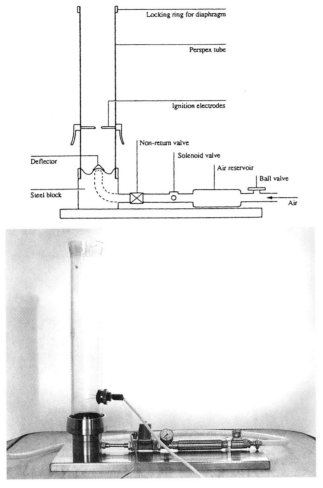

Figure A3.1 Vertical tube apparatus, coil ignition. (Reproduced by permission of FRS, Building Research Establishment Ltd. Crown Copyright)

2. Godbert–Greenwald furnace apparatus

The Godbert–Greenwald[1] furnace is shown in Figure A3.2. It comprises a 21.6 cm long, 3.6 cm id vitreosil tube wound with 20 SWG Kanthal 'A' wire which gives an even temperature distribution along the length of the tube. The tube is mounted vertically in a 20 SWG stainless steel, 15 cm diameter cylinder, and furnace temperatures up to 1000°C can be obtained. Explosibility testing is done at 800°C.

A small amount of the Group B dust, typically 0.2 g, is placed in the dust holder. The dust is dispersed into the furnace tube by an air blast. The criterion

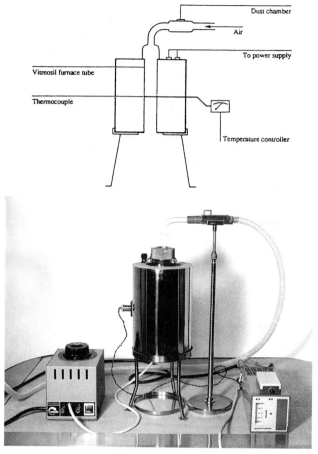

Figure A3.2 Godbert–Greenwald furnace. (Reproduced by permission of FRS, Building Research Establishment Ltd.)

for ignition is that flames are observed at the bottom of the tube. If no flame propagation occurs the dust is thoroughly tested by varying the dust amount and the dispersion conditions. If flame propagation occurs during the sequence of tests, the dust is re-classified as Group A; if no flame is observed the dust remains with a Group B classification.

Dusts that remain classified as Group B may require further testing for explosibility (see Chapter 2, Section 2.1.3) in the 1 m^3 vessel or the 20 litre sphere (see below) to take into account, for example, more energetic ignition sources, or higher pressures, or other process conditions. The explosibility is judged on the basis of the pressure rise.

The Godbert–Greenwald furnace, or the BAM furnace (see below), is used also for measuring the minimum ignition temperature (MIT) of a dust cloud (see Chapter 2, Section 2.3.3).

3. BAM furnace apparatus

The BAM furnace[2] is a horizontal, tube-like furnace (length 170 mm) with a hot impact plate approximately in the middle (see Figure A3.3). The dust is blown against the plate with a blast air produced by squeezing the rubber bulb. The temperature of the furnace is increased in increments until an ignition occurs. The ignition temperature is taken as the temperature of the impact plate, the hottest part of the furnace during the test.

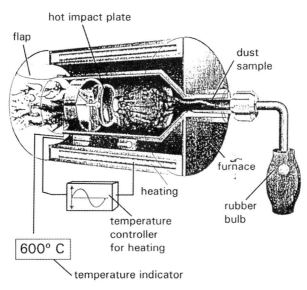

Figure A3.3 BAM furnace. (Test apparatus for determining the minimum ignition temperature of dust clouds)

4. 1 m³ Test apparatus*

Classifying a dust as Group A gives only a qualitative assessment of the risk. A quantitative assessment requires further testing to measure the maximum

---

*CEN Technical Committee 305 is preparing a new standard method for the determination of P_{max} and $(dP/dt)_{max}$. This will recommend use of the 1 m³ apparatus as the standard apparatus, but will also allow the use of alternatives such as the 20 litre sphere if conformity can be demonstrated.

explosion pressure, P_{max}, and the maximum rate of pressure rise, $(dP/dt)_{max}$ (see Chapter 2, Section 2.2). These characteristics are measured in either the $1\,m^3$ test apparatus or the 20 litre sphere apparatus (see below).

The $1\,m^3$ vessel[3] is recognized as an accepted international standard test apparatus and is shown in Figure A3.4. The explosion vessel is pressure-resistant and has a length approximately equal to its diameter. The dust is introduced into a 5.4 litre dust container external to the main vessel but connected to it through a fast-acting valve. The dust is held under an air pressure of 20 bar and is dispersed into the $1\,m^3$ vessel through a semi-annular, perforated half-ring with 13 holes each of 6 mm diameter. This procedure is often called the VDI method of dust injection. After an ignition delay, t_d, of 0.6 s, the dust cloud is ignited by an ignition source positioned at the centre of the vessel. The ignition source comprises two pyrotechnical igniters, and has a total energy of 10 kJ.

The development of the explosion pressure with time is monitored, and the peak values of maximum explosion pressure and maximum rate of pressure rise obtained after testing over a wide range of dust concentrations are recorded. If, at large dust concentrations a 5.4 litre dust container proves too small to contain the dust, a 10 litre container can be used. However, the value of t_d must be changed to 0.9 s so that results when using the 10 litre container are comparable to those with a 5.4 litre container.

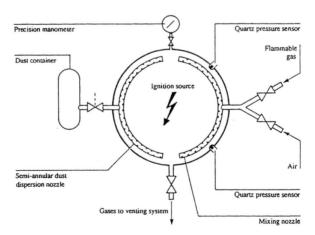

Figure A3.4 Test apparatus $(V = 1m^3)$ for the determination of explosion data of combustible dusts (schematic) (Reproduced from Bartnecht, W., 1989, *Explosions: Course, prevention, protection* (Springer-Verlag) by permission of the author and publisher.)

5. 20 Litre sphere apparatus*

The 20 litre sphere[4] is a smaller version of the 1 m^3 test vessel described above, and is shown in Figure A3.5. Prior to testing the dust is confined, under an air pressure of 20 bar, in a 600 ml dust container external to the 20 litre sphere. The dust is injected into the sphere through a fast acting valve and dispersed by a

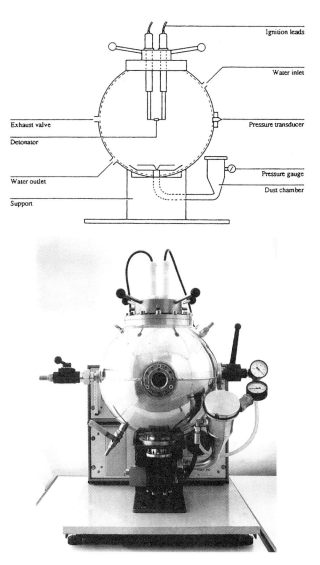

Figure A3.5 Modified 20 litre spherical explosion apparatus. (Reproduced by permission of FRS, Building Research Establishment Ltd. Crown Copyright.)

deflector plate near to the point of injection. The ignition delay, t_d, is 0.06 s (60 ms). Before a test the 20 litre sphere is evacuated to a pressure of 0.4 bar absolute. When the dust is injected the pressure rises to 1 bar absolute and the explosion is thus ignited at normal atmospheric pressure. The ignition source comprises pyrotechnical igniters with a total energy of 10 kJ positioned at the vessel centre. The peak values of maximum explosion pressure and maximum rate of pressure rise are obtained after testing over a range of dust concentrations.

The 20 litre spherical tester is recommended as a standard explosibility test in many countries including the USA and the UK.

References in Appendix 3

1. Field, P., 1982, *Dust Explosions* (Volume 4 of *Handbook of Powder Technology*), ISBN 0167 3785 (Elsevier).
2. International Safety Security Association, 1997, *Determination of the Combustion and Explosion Characteristics of Dusts* (ISSA Prevention Series No. 2018 (E), Mannheim, ISBN 92-843-1092; ISSN 1015-8022)
3. Bartknecht, W., 1981, *Explosions: Course, Prevention, Protection*, ISBN 0 387 10216 7 (Springer-Verlag).
4. Bartknecht, W., 1989, *Explosions: Course, Prevention, Protection*, ISBN 0 387 50100 2 (Springer-Verlag).

Appendix 4
Dust fires

The hazard

Wherever dusts are handled, layers or deeper deposits may form. Fires may start in a layer or deposit, most commonly caused by hot surfaces or spontaneous heating. With most dusts, such a fire will develop slowly, in marked contrast to a dust explosion, and the immediate danger may be small. However, if the dust is disturbed into a cloud, or transported on to another part of a plant where a cloud exists, an explosion may then follow.

Fires are particularly likely where material is held for a longer period than normal at an elevated temperature. This may be the result of an unplanned shut down, poor flow through the system, so that some product stays too long in the same place, or failure of a cooling system to operate as intended.

Precautions

Whatever the cause, plans and equipment should be in place to:

- detect fires at an early stage;
- avoid the build up of heat within a large pile if spontaneous heating is possible;
- plan ways in which a smouldering fire may be extinguished.

This usually involves the application of a cooling medium, an inerting medium, or where it can be done safely, emptying the product from the plant. It is particularly important to avoid generating dust clouds during an emptying process. If inerting is adopted, it may take days or even weeks for a large mass to cool down sufficiently to avoid all risk of re-ignition when air is admitted.

Detection of fires

Fires in large-scale dust handling plants are difficult to detect. There may well be no flames, and smoke detectors are not usually reliable in dusty atmospheres. The most common techniques for identifying fires or conditions leading to the onset of fire are spark detectors, temperature monitors, and continuous monitors for combustion products such as carbon monoxide. Spark detectors can only be used where the product is moving, e.g., in some type of conveying system. Temperature sensors can easily miss localised hot spots, and are often too slow to react to be useful. Sensitive gas detectors are most useful where there is a controlled flow of air through the system.

To detect localised heating in a silo, for example, an array of thermocouples may be used, but there may be large temperature gradients within a heap that has low thermal conductivity, and early detection cannot be assured. Sometimes visual inspection of product coming through a process can give an indication of overheating, if for instance darkened particles are found.

It may be possible to detect low levels of gaseous combustion products, if the system is reasonably closed. Carbon monoxide sensors have been used successfully for a range of dusts, but other gases may be evolved from particular products, e.g., acrolein is evolved from decomposing milk powder and this has been used as the basis of fire detection systems.

Precautions to avoid build up of heat

With products prone to self-heating, some precautions to avoid build up of heat are recommended. In particular the temperature of fresh product added into a storage silo or bin may need to be strictly controlled. Storage vessels should be emptied completely periodically, to avoid dead spots where there is no turnover of product. Some products may simply be recirculated through a conveying system and back to store as a way of dissipating heat. In other cases long temperature probes may be inserted into a stockpile as a way of identifying any temperature rise inside the pile.

Extinguishing a fire

If a fire does start, the speed at which it grows may well be determined by the availability of air, as much as the properties of the dust. There are usually three options to extinguish a deep-seated fire in a silo or similar container. These are to add water, fill the container with inert gas, or to try and remove the product from the container. All have potential problems.

Adding water to some metals may cause a fire to flare up, while adding water to burning coal can cause carbon monoxide to be formed if the temperature is high enough. If a hatch is opened to allow water to be sprayed in, the inflow of air may also cause a smouldering fire to burst suddenly into flames, endangering those by the hatch. Powerful jets of water have been known to raise a dust cloud from a heap, and initiate a dust explosion. Some products swell and become sticky when wet, e.g., sewage sludge, and subsequently are very difficult to empty from a container once wetted. If a silo is completely filled with water, the additional weight may exceed the design strength and cause the structure to collapse. If despite these risks, water is the preferred way of tackling a fire inside equipment, it is preferable to provide some way in which it may be sprayed in from a fixed system through spray heads provided for the purpose, which can be easily coupled up to water supply when needed.

Inert gases such as carbon dioxide or nitrogen may be fed into a closed vessel, but they provide little cooling effect, and it is difficult to displace all the air within a heap of dust. They can be an effective way of extinguishing fires, but in a large vessel, very large volumes of gas may be needed, and it may well take days or even weeks to finally extinguish all traces of a smouldering fire. More than one injection point is recommended on a large container.

In some cases the best approach is to remove as much product as possible from a storage container, if this can be done without raising a dust cloud. Water sprays can be applied to material as it is transferred into smaller open containers. If bridging or rat holing within the silo is possible however, the sudden collapse of the pile may create the conditions for a dust explosion. The flow properties of the dust must be taken into consideration.

Appendix 5
K_{St} – Nomographs

The K_{St} Nomograph Method

The information required for the K_{St} nomograph method is:

- The reduced explosion pressure (bar a);
- The volume of the dust-handling plant (m^2);
- The explosibility characteristic – the K_{St} value of the dust as measured in a standard test ($bar\,m\,s^{-1}$);
- The static opening pressure of the vent cover, P_{stat} (bar a). It is assumed that the vent has low inertia with an area density less than $10\,kg\,m^{-2}$. No provision is made for vent covers of high inertia.

These nomographs are applicable in the following conditions:

- Vent bursting pressures, P_{stat}, greater than 1.1 bar a;
- Reduced explosion pressures, P_{red}, greater than 1.2 bar a;
- K_{St} values greater than 10 $bar\,m\,s^{-1}$ and less than 600 $bar\,m\,s^{-1}$;
- Values of P_{max} less than 11 bar a for St 1 and St 2 dusts ($K_{St} \leq 300\,bar\,m\,s^{-1}$) and P_{max} values less than 13 bar a for St 3 dusts ($300 < K_{St} \leq 600\,bar\,m\,s^{-1}$);
- Vessel volumes less than $1000\,m^3$;
- Length to diameter ratio of the vessel less than $5:1$;
- No vent ducts are fitted to the vent.

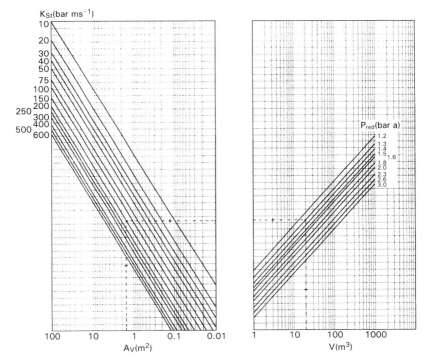

Figure A5.1 K_{St} Nomograph: $P_{stat} = 1.1$ bar a.

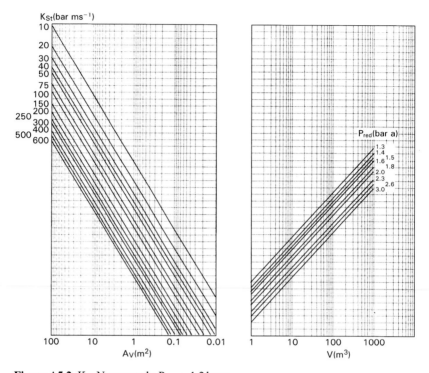

Figure A5.2 K_{St} Nomograph: $P_{stat} = 1.2$ bar a.

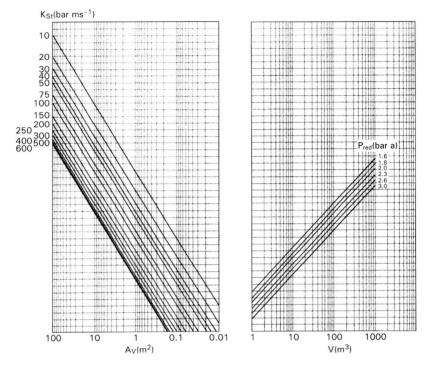

K$_{St}$(bar ms^{-1})

A$_V$(m^2)

P$_{red}$(bar a)

V(m^3)

Figure A5.3 K$_{St}$ Nomograph: P$_{stat}$ = 1.5 bar a.

267

Appendix 6
Estimates for reduced explosions

A) Estimates of reduced explosion pressures for straight vent ducts

Note: All pressures are given in bar a.

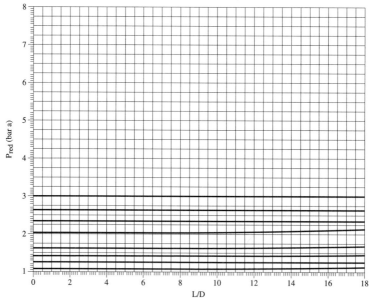

Figure A6.1. $K_{St} = 10$ and $20\,bar\,m\,s^{-1}$, $P_{stat} = 1.1\,bar\,a.$
Duct configuration: straight.

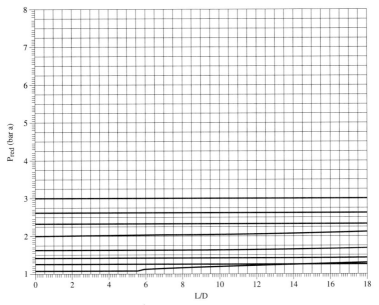

Figure A6.2. $K_{St} = 30 \, \text{bar m s}^{-1}$, $P_{stat} = 1.1 \, \text{bar a}$.
Duct configuration: straight.

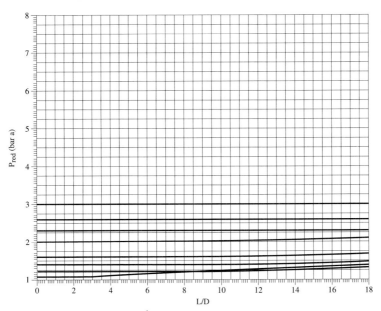

Figure A6.3. $K_{St} = 40 \, \text{bar m s}^{-1}$, $P_{stat} = 1.1 \, \text{bar a}$.
Duct configuration: straight.

269

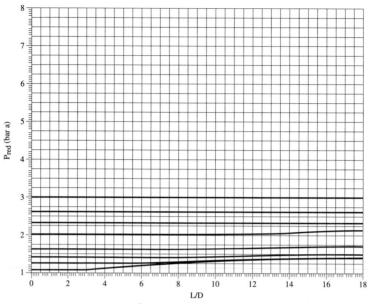

Figure A6.4. $K_{St} = 50\,\mathrm{bar\,m\,s^{-1}}$, $P_{stat} = 1.1\,\mathrm{bar\,a}$.
Duct configuration: straight.

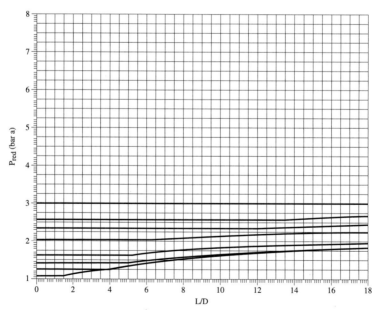

Figure A6.5. $K_{St} = 75\,\mathrm{bar\,m\,s^{-1}}$, $P_{stat} = 1.1\,\mathrm{bar\,a}$.
Duct configuration: straight.

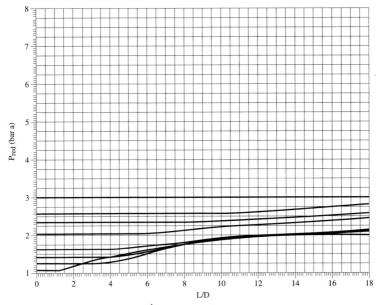

Figure A6.6. $K_{St} = 100\,\mathrm{bar\,m\,s^{-1}}$, $P_{stat} = 1.1\,\mathrm{bar\,a}$.
Duct configuration: straight.

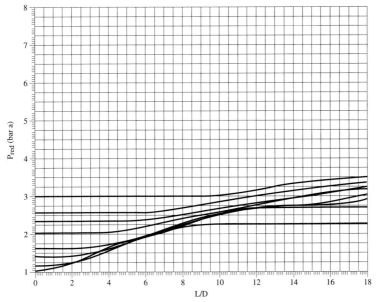

Figure A6.7. $K_{St} = 150\,\mathrm{bar\,m\,s^{-1}}$, $P_{stat} = 1.1\,\mathrm{bar\,a}$.
Duct configuration: straight.

271

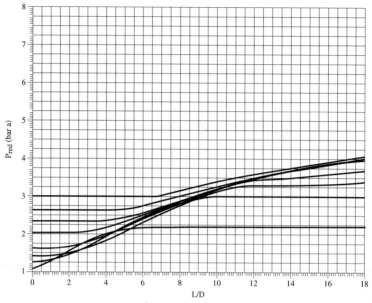

Figure A6.8. $K_{St} = 200\, \mathrm{bar\, m\, s}^{-1}$, $P_{stat} = 1.1\, \mathrm{bar\, a}$.
Duct configuration: straight.

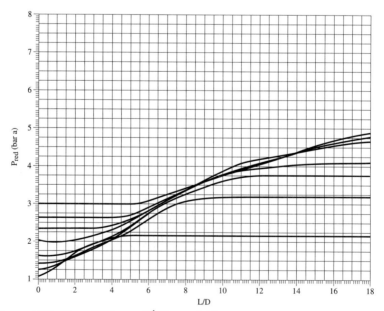

Figure A6.9. $K_{St} = 250\, \mathrm{bar\, m\, s}^{-1}$, $P_{stat} = 1.1\, \mathrm{bar\, a}$.
Duct configuration: straight.

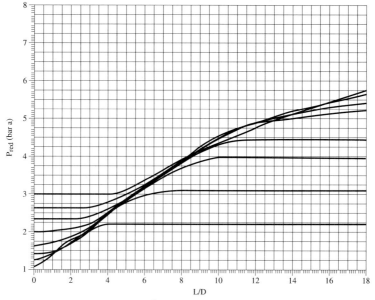

Figure A6.10. $K_{St} = 300\,\mathrm{bar\,m\,s^{-1}}$, $P_{stat} = 1.1\,\mathrm{bar\,a}$.
Duct configuration: straight.

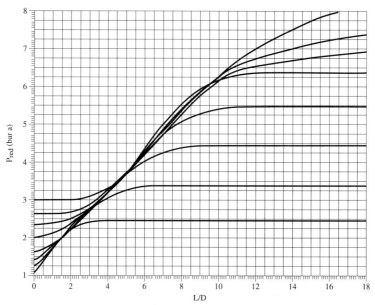

Figure A6.11. $K_{St} = 400\,\mathrm{bar\,m\,s^{-1}}$, $P_{stat} = 1.1\,\mathrm{bar\,a}$.
Duct configuration: straight.

273

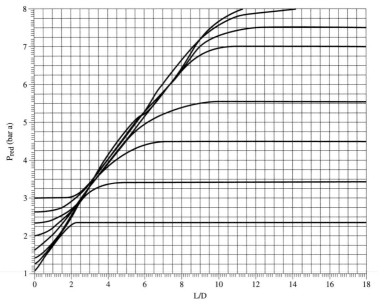

Figure A6.12. $K_{St} = 500 \, \text{bar} \, \text{m} \, \text{s}^{-1}$, $P_{stat} = 1.1 \, \text{bar} \, \text{a}$.
Duct configuration: straight.

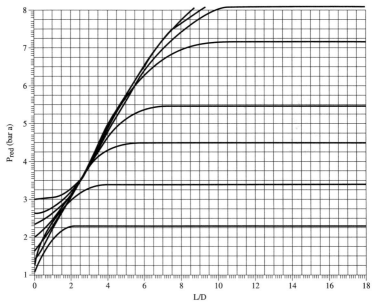

Figure A6.13. $K_{St} = 600 \, \text{bar} \, \text{m} \, \text{s}^{-1}$, $P_{stat} = 1.1 \, \text{bar} \, \text{a}$.
Duct configuration: straight.

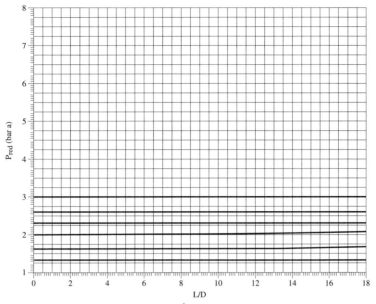

Figure A6.14. $K_{St} = 10$ and $20\,bar\,m\,s^{-1}$, $P_{stat} = 1.2\,bar\,a$.
Duct configuration: straight.

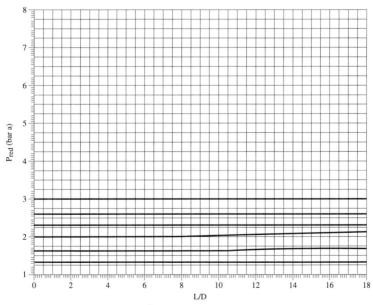

Figure A6.15. $K_{St} = 30\,bar\,m\,s^{-1}$, $P_{stat} = 1.2\,bar\,a$.
Duct configuration: straight.

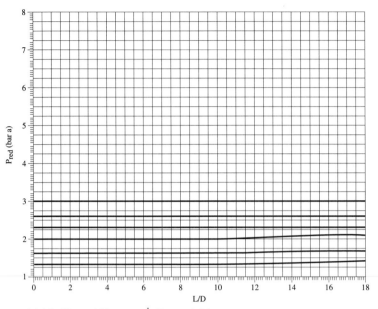

Figure A6.16. $K_{St} = 40 \, \text{bar} \, \text{m} \, \text{s}^{-1}$, $P_{stat} = 1.2 \, \text{bar} \, \text{a}$.
Duct configuration: straight.

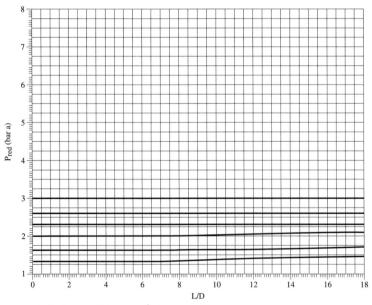

Figure A6.17. $K_{St} = 50 \, \text{bar} \, \text{m} \, \text{s}^{-1}$, $P_{stat} = 1.2 \, \text{bar} \, \text{a}$.
Duct configuration: straight.

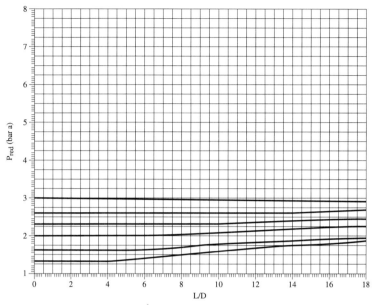

Figure A6.18. $K_{St} = 75\,\text{bar}\,\text{m}\,\text{s}^{-1}$, $P_{stat} = 1.2\,\text{bar}\,\text{a}$.
Duct configuration: straight.

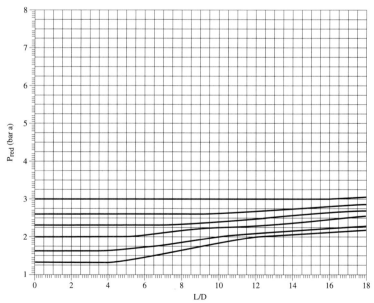

Figure A6.19. $K_{St} = 100\,\text{bar}\,\text{m}\,\text{s}^{-1}$, $P_{stat} = 1.2\,\text{bar}\,\text{a}$.
Duct configuration: straight.

277

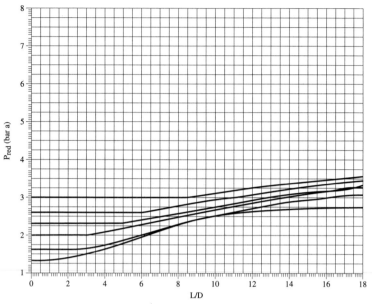

Figure A6.20. $K_{St} = 150\,\mathrm{bar\,m\,s^{-1}}$, $P_{stat} = 1.2\,\mathrm{bar\,a}$.
Duct configuration: straight.

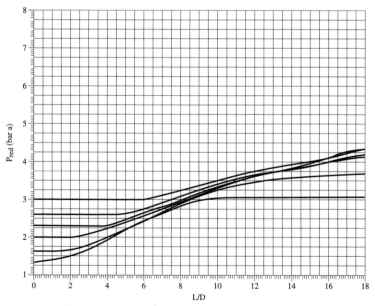

Figure A6.21. $K_{St} = 200\,\mathrm{bar\,m\,s^{-1}}$, $P_{stat} = 1.2\,\mathrm{bar\,a}$.
Duct configuration: straight.

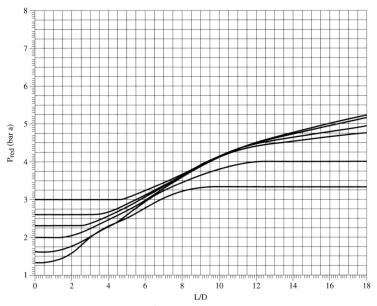

Figure A6.22. $K_{St} = 250\,\mathrm{bar\,m\,s^{-1}}$, $P_{stat} = 1.2\,\mathrm{bar\,a}$.
Duct configuration: straight.

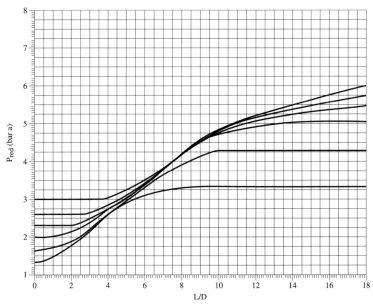

Figure A6.23. $K_{St} = 300\,\mathrm{bar\,m\,s^{-1}}$, $P_{stat} = 1.2\,\mathrm{bar\,a}$.
Duct configuration: straight.

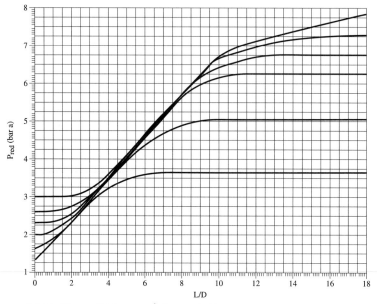

Figure A6.24. $K_{St} = 400 \, \text{bar m s}^{-1}$, $P_{stat} = 1.2 \, \text{bar a}$.
Duct configuration: straight.

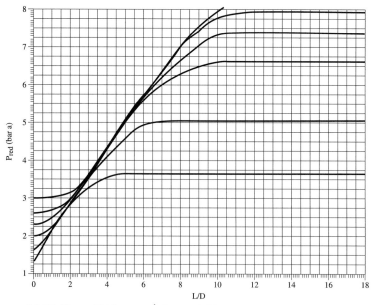

Figure A6.25. $K_{St} = 500 \, \text{bar m s}^{-1}$, $P_{stat} = 1.2 \, \text{bar a}$.
Duct configuration: straight.

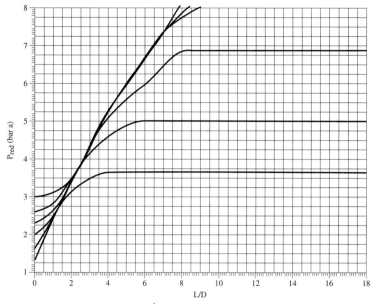

Figure A6.26. $K_{St} = 600\,\text{bar m s}^{-1}$, $P_{stat} = 1.2\,\text{bar a}$.
Duct configuration: straight.

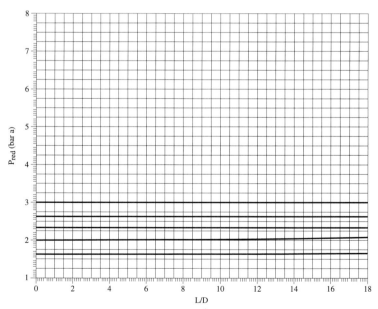

Figure A6.27. $K_{St} = 10$, 20 and $30\,\text{bar m s}^{-1}$, $P_{stat} = 1.5\,\text{bar a}$.
Duct configuration: straight.

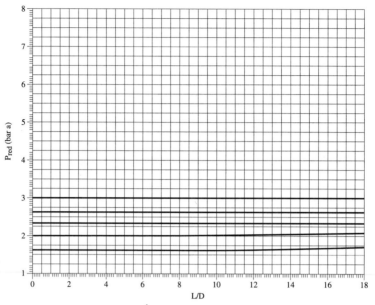

Figure A6.28. $K_{St} = 40 \, \text{bar} \, \text{m} \, \text{s}^{-1}$, $P_{stat} = 1.5 \, \text{bar} \, \text{a}$.
Duct configuration: straight.

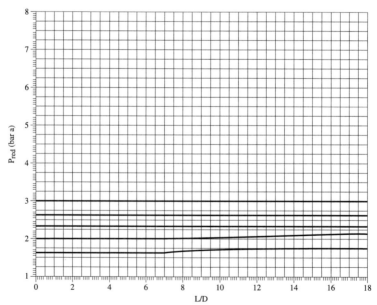

Figure A6.29. $K_{St} = 50 \, \text{bar} \, \text{m} \, \text{s}^{-1}$, $P_{stat} = 1.5 \, \text{bar} \, \text{a}$.
Duct configuration: straight.

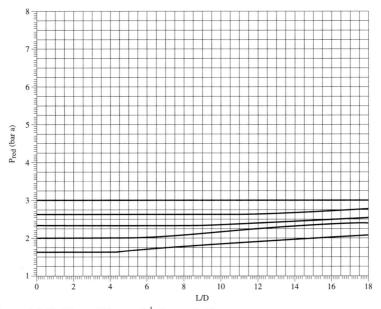

Figure A6.30. $K_{St} = 75\,\mathrm{bar\,m\,s^{-1}}$, $P_{stat} = 1.5\,\mathrm{bar\,a}$.
Duct configuration: straight.

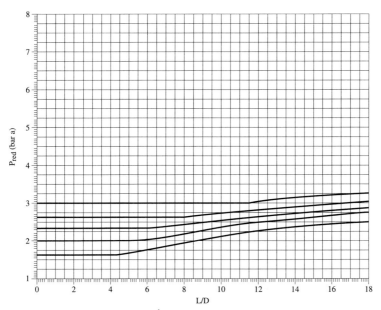

Figure A6.31. $K_{St} = 100\,\mathrm{bar\,m\,s^{-1}}$, $P_{stat} = 1.5\,\mathrm{bar\,a}$.
Duct configuration: straight.

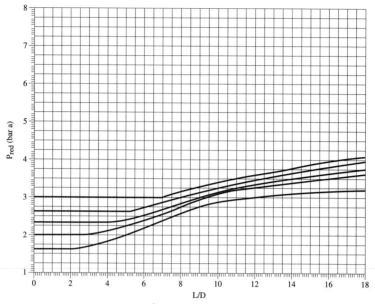

Figure A6.32. $K_{St} = 150\,\text{bar}\,\text{m}\,\text{s}^{-1}$, $P_{stat} = 1.5\,\text{bar}\,\text{a}$.
Duct configuration: straight.

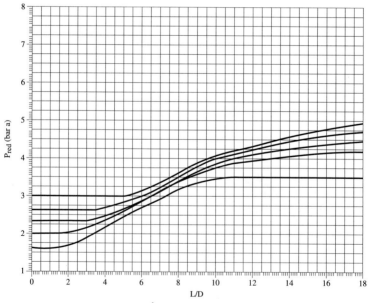

Figure A6.33. $K_{St} = 200\,\text{bar}\,\text{m}\,\text{s}^{-1}$, $P_{stat} = 1.5\,\text{bar}\,\text{a}$.
Duct configuration: straight.

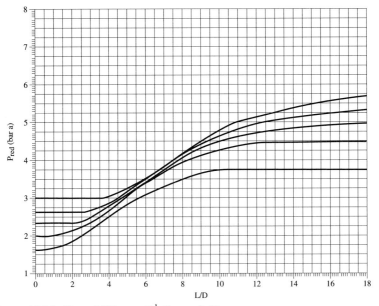

Figure A6.34. $K_{St} = 250\,\mathrm{bar\,m\,s}^{-1}$, $P_{stat} = 1.5\,\mathrm{bar\,a}$.
Duct configuration: straight.

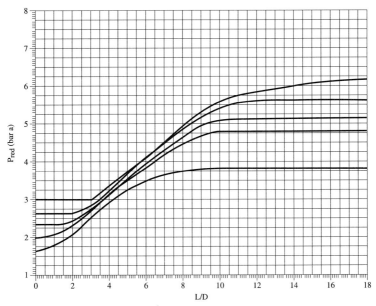

Figure A6.35. $K_{St} = 300\,\mathrm{bar\,m\,s}^{-1}$, $P_{stat} = 1.5\,\mathrm{bar\,a}$.
Duct configuration: straight.

285

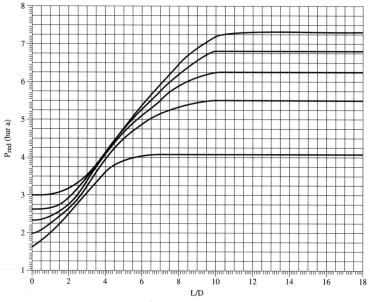

Figure A6.36. $K_{St} = 400 \, \text{bar m s}^{-1}$, $P_{stat} = 1.5 \, \text{bar a}$.
Duct configuration: straight.

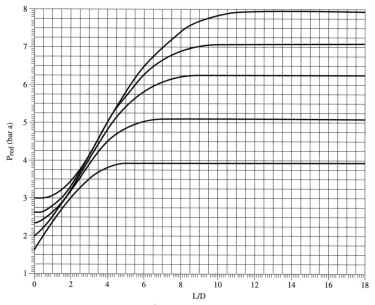

Figure A6.37. $K_{St} = 500 \, \text{bar m s}^{-1}$, $P_{stat} = 1.5 \, \text{bar a}$.
Duct configuration: straight.

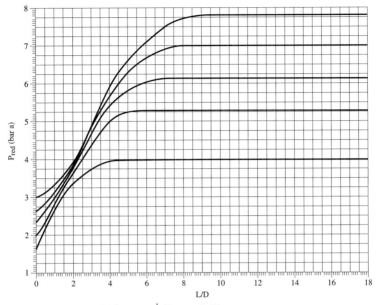

Figure A6.38. $K_{St} = 600 \, \text{bar m s}^{-1}$, $P_{stat} = 1.5 \, \text{bar a}$.
Duct configuration: straight.

287

B) Estimates of reduced explosion pressures for vent ducts with a single sharp 45° bend

Note: All pressures are given in bar a.

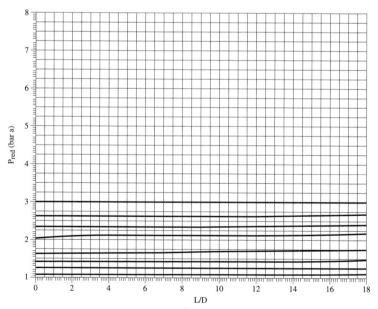

Figure A6.39. $K_{St} = 10$ and $20\,\mathrm{bar\,m\,s^{-1}}$, $P_{stat} = 1.1\,\mathrm{bar\,a}$.
Duct configuration: single sharp 45° bend.

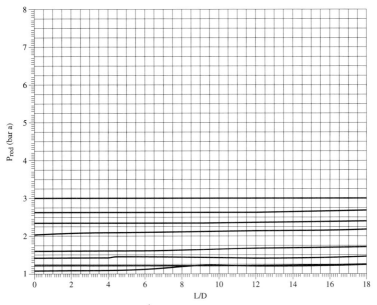

Figure A6.40. $K_{St} = 30\,\mathrm{bar\,m\,s^{-1}}$, $P_{stat} = 1.1\,\mathrm{bar\,a}$.
Duct configuration: single sharp $45°$ bend.

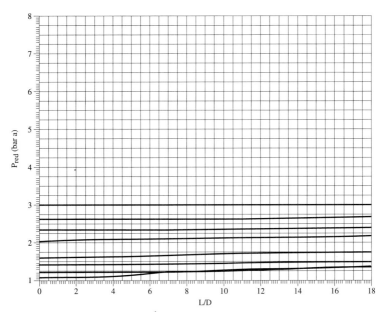

Figure A6.41. $K_{St} = 40\,\mathrm{bar\,m\,s^{-1}}$, $P_{stat} = 1.1\,\mathrm{bar\,a}$.
Duct configuration: single sharp $45°$ bend.

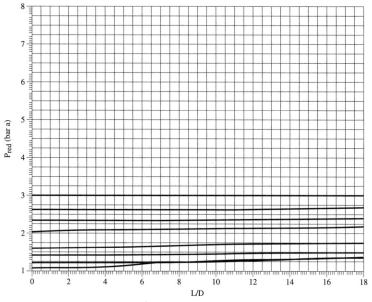

Figure A6.42. $K_{St} = 50\,\mathrm{bar\,m\,s}^{-1}$, $P_{stat} = 1.1\,\mathrm{bar\,a}$.
Duct configuration: single sharp 45° bend.

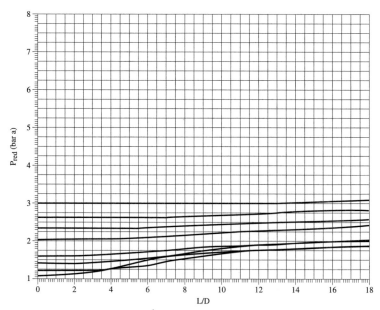

Figure A6.43. $K_{St} = 75\,\mathrm{bar\,m\,s}^{-1}$, $P_{stat} = 1.1\,\mathrm{bar\,a}$.
Duct configuration: single sharp 45° bend.

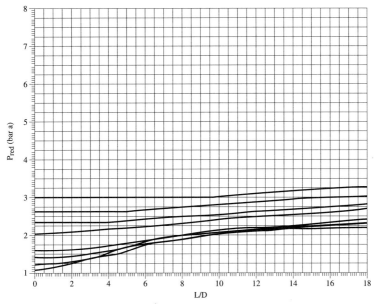

Figure A6.44. $K_{St} = 100\,bar\,m\,s^{-1}$, $P_{stat} = 1.1\,bar\,a$.
Duct configuration: single sharp 45° bend.

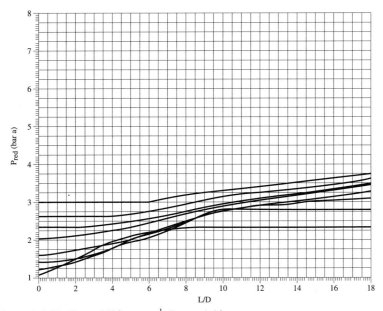

Figure A6.45. $K_{St} = 150\,bar\,m\,s^{-1}$, $P_{stat} = 1.1\,bar\,a$.
Duct configuration: single sharp 45° bend.

291

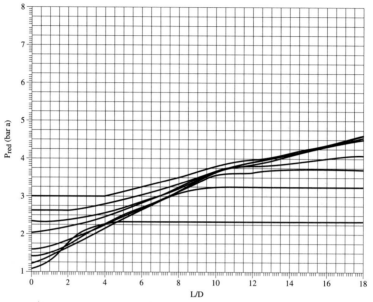

Figure A6.46. $K_{St} = 200\,\mathrm{bar\,m\,s^{-1}}$, $P_{stat} = 1.1\,\mathrm{bar\,a}$.
Duct configuration: single sharp 45° bend.

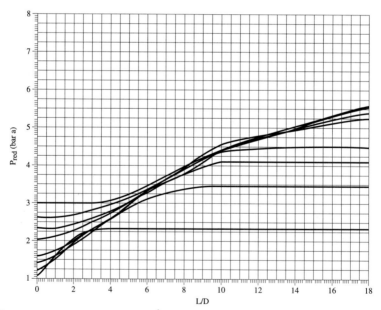

Figure A6.47. $K_{St} = 250\,\mathrm{bar\,m\,s^{-1}}$, $P_{stat} = 1.1\,\mathrm{bar\,a}$.
Duct configuration: single sharp 45° bend.

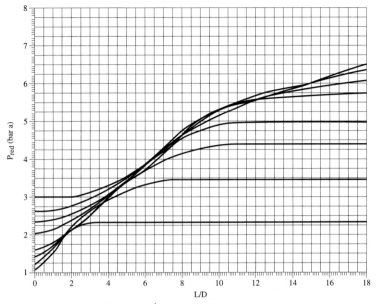

Figure A6.48. $K_{St} = 300 \, \text{bar} \, \text{m} \, \text{s}^{-1}$, $P_{stat} = 1.1 \, \text{bar a}$.
Duct configuration: single sharp 45° bend.

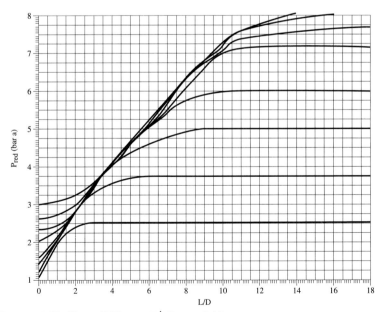

Figure A6.49. $K_{St} = 400 \, \text{bar} \, \text{m} \, \text{s}^{-1}$, $P_{stat} = 1.1 \, \text{bar a}$.
Duct configuration: single sharp 45° bend.

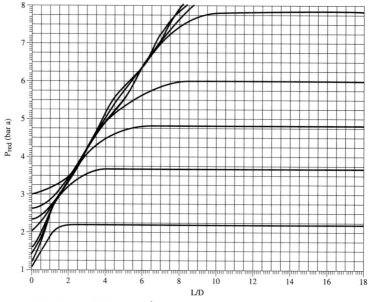

Figure A6.50. $K_{St} = 500\,\text{bar}\,\text{m}\,\text{s}^{-1}$, $P_{stat} = 1.1\,\text{bar}\,\text{a}$.
Duct configuration: single sharp 45° bend.

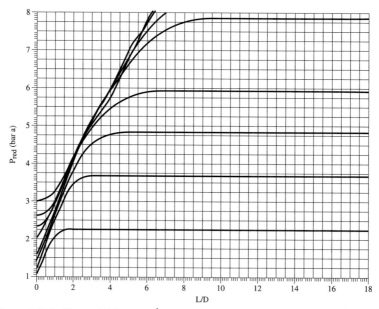

Figure A6.51. $K_{St} = 600\,\text{bar}\,\text{m}\,\text{s}^{-1}$, $P_{stat} = 1.1\,\text{bar}\,\text{a}$.
Duct configuration: single sharp 45° bend.

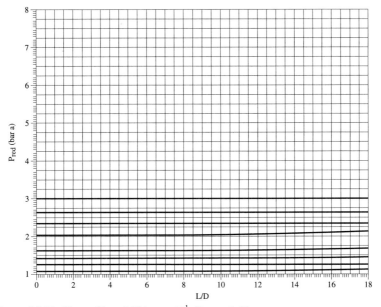

Figure A6.52. $K_{St} = 10$ and $20\,\mathrm{bar\,m\,s^{-1}}$, $P_{stat} = 1.2\,\mathrm{bar\,a}$.
Duct configuration: single sharp $45°$ bend.

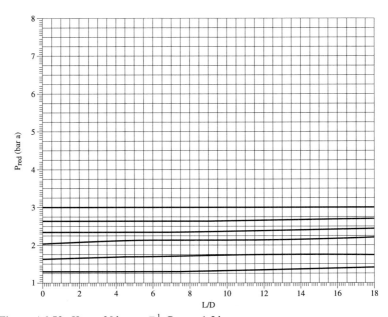

Figure A6.53. $K_{St} = 30\,\mathrm{bar\,m\,s^{-1}}$, $P_{stat} = 1.2\,\mathrm{bar\,a}$.
Duct configuration: single sharp $45°$ bend.

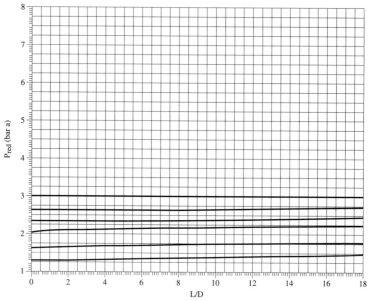

Figure A6.54. $K_{St} = 40\,\mathrm{bar\,m\,s}^{-1}$, $P_{stat} = 1.2\,\mathrm{bar\,a}$.
Duct configuration: single sharp 45° bend.

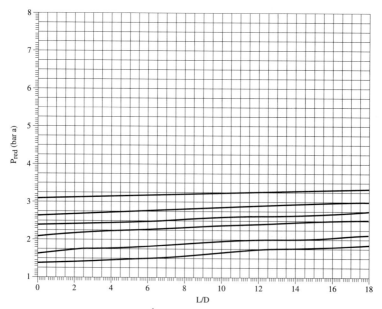

Figure A6.55. $K_{St} = 50\,\mathrm{bar\,m\,s}^{-1}$, $P_{stat} = 1.2\,\mathrm{bar\,a}$.
Duct configuration: single sharp 45° bend.

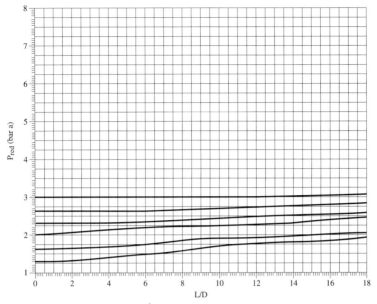

Figure A6.56. $K_{St} = 75\,\mathrm{bar\,m\,s^{-1}}$, $P_{stat} = 1.2\,\mathrm{bar\,a}$.
Duct configuration: single sharp 45° bend.

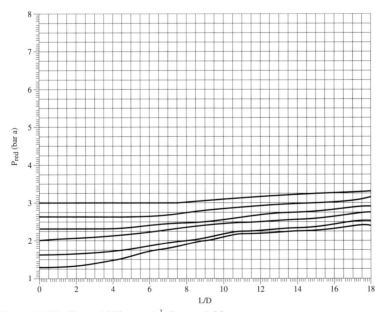

Figure A6.57. $K_{St} = 100\,\mathrm{bar\,m\,s^{-1}}$, $P_{stat} = 1.2\,\mathrm{bar\,a}$.
Duct configuration: single sharp 45° bend.

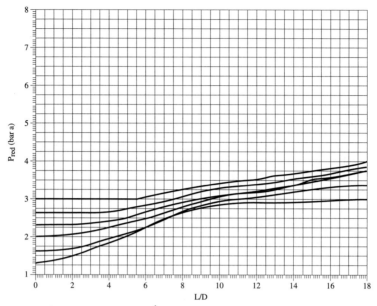

Figure A6.58. $K_{St} = 150\,\mathrm{bar\,m\,s^{-1}}$, $P_{stat} = 1.2\,\mathrm{bar\,a}$.
Duct configuration: single sharp 45° bend.

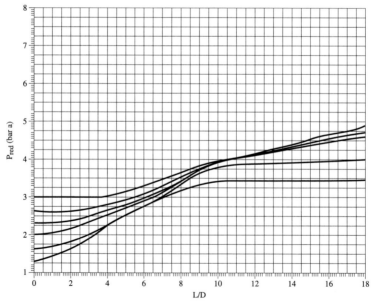

Figure A6.59. $K_{St} = 200\,\mathrm{bar\,m\,s^{-1}}$, $P_{stat} = 1.2\,\mathrm{bar\,a}$.
Duct configuration: single sharp 45° bend.

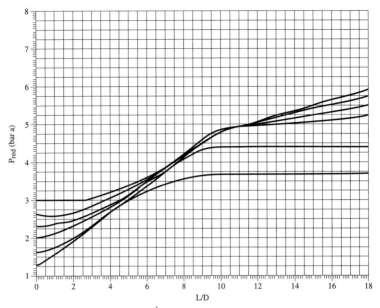

Figure A6.60. $K_{St} = 250\,\text{bar}\,\text{m}\,\text{s}^{-1}$, $P_{stat} = 1.2\,\text{bar a}$.
Duct configuration: single sharp 45° bend.

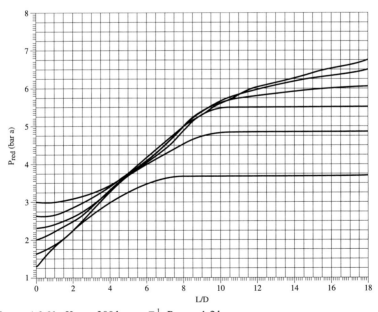

Figure A6.61. $K_{St} = 300\,\text{bar}\,\text{m}\,\text{s}^{-1}$, $P_{stat} = 1.2\,\text{bar a}$.
Duct configuration: single sharp 45° bend.

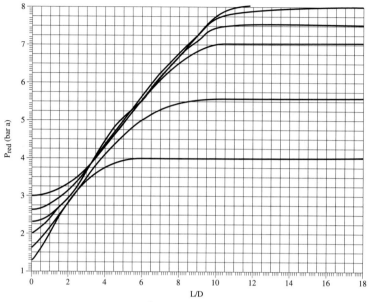

Figure A6.62. $K_{St} = 400\,\mathrm{bar\,m\,s^{-1}}$, $P_{stat} = 1.2\,\mathrm{bar\,a}$.
Duct configuration: single sharp 45° bend.

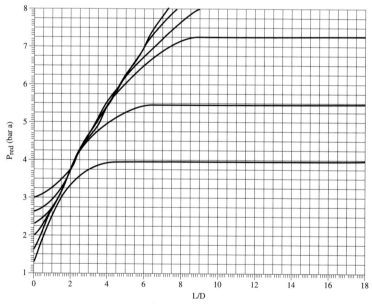

Figure A6.63. $K_{St} = 500\,\mathrm{bar\,m\,s^{-1}}$, $P_{stat} = 1.2\,\mathrm{bar\,a}$.
Duct configuration: single sharp 45° bend.

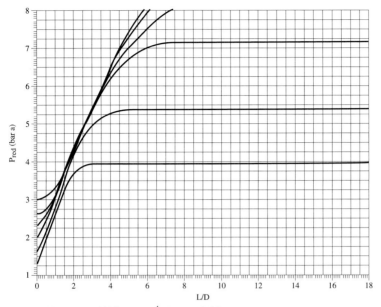

Figure A6.64. $K_{St} = 600\,\mathrm{bar\,m\,s^{-1}}$, $P_{stat} = 1.2\,\mathrm{bar\,a}$.
Duct configuration: single sharp $45°$ bend.

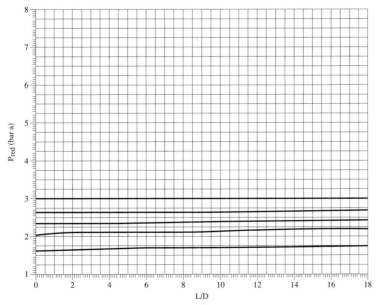

Figure A6.65. $K_{St} = 10$, 20 and $30\,\mathrm{bar\,m\,s^{-1}}$, $P_{stat} = 1.5\,\mathrm{bar\,a}$.
Duct configuration: single sharp $45°$ bend.

301

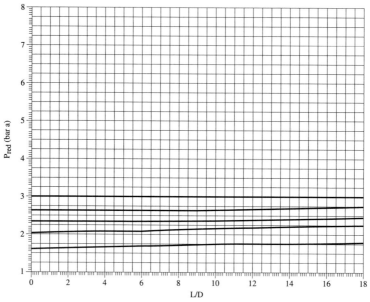

Figure A6.66. $K_{St} = 40\,\text{bar m s}^{-1}$, $P_{stat} = 1.5\,\text{bar a}$.
Duct configuration: single sharp 45° bend.

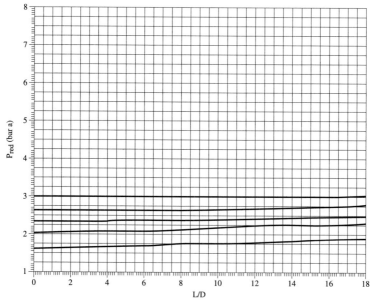

Figure A6.67. $K_{St} = 50\,\text{bar m s}^{-1}$, $P_{stat} = 1.5\,\text{bar a}$.
Duct configuration: single sharp 45° bend.

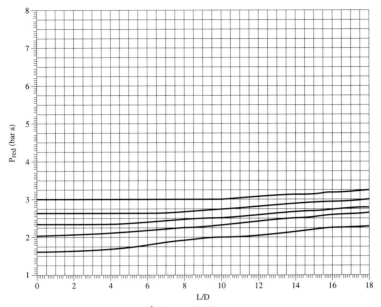

Figure A6.68. $K_{St} = 75 \, \mathrm{bar\,m\,s^{-1}}$, $P_{stat} = 1.5 \, \mathrm{bar\,a}$.
Duct configuration: single sharp 45° bend.

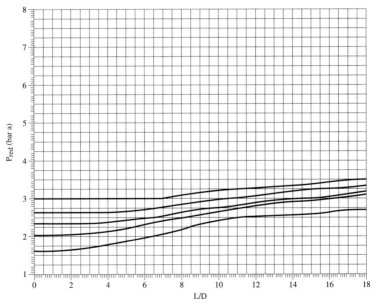

Figure A6.69. $K_{St} = 100 \, \mathrm{bar\,m\,s^{-1}}$, $P_{stat} = 1.5 \, \mathrm{bar\,a}$.
Duct configuration: single sharp 45° bend.

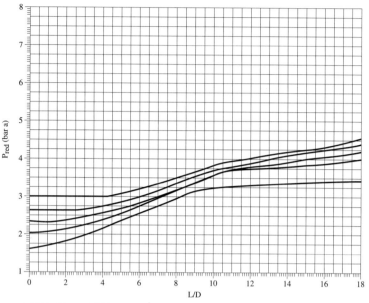

Figure A6.70. $K_{St} = 150\,\mathrm{bar\,m\,s^{-1}}$, $P_{stat} = 1.5\,\mathrm{bar\,a}$.
Duct configuration: single sharp 45° bend.

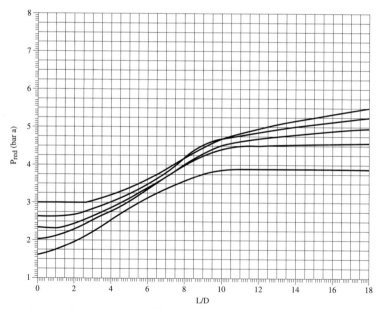

Figure A6.71. $K_{St} = 200\,\mathrm{bar\,m\,s^{-1}}$, $P_{stat} = 1.5\,\mathrm{bar\,a}$.
Duct configuration: single sharp 45° bend.

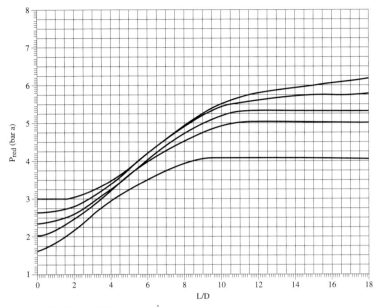

Figure A6.72. $K_{St} = 250\,\text{bar m s}^{-1}$, $P_{stat} = 1.5\,\text{bar a}$.
Duct configuration: single sharp 45° bend.

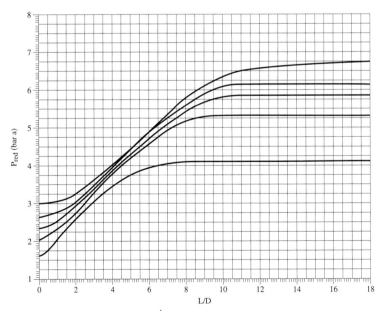

Figure A6.73. $K_{St} = 300\,\text{bar m s}^{-1}$, $P_{stat} = 1.5\,\text{bar a}$.
Duct configuration: single sharp 45° bend.

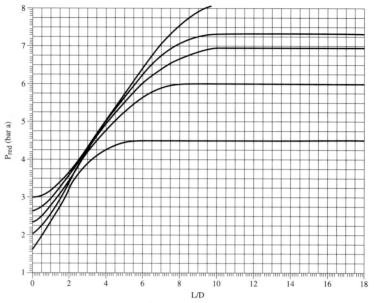

Figure A6.74. $K_{St} = 400 \, \text{bar m s}^{-1}$, $P_{stat} = 1.5 \, \text{bar a}$.
Duct configuration: single sharp 45° bend.

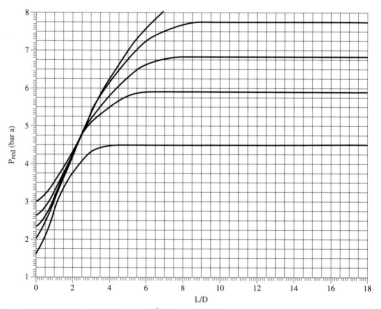

Figure A6.75. $K_{St} = 500 \, \text{bar m s}^{-1}$, $P_{stat} = 1.5 \, \text{bar a}$.
Duct configuration: single sharp 45° bend.

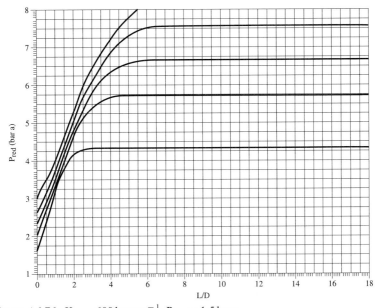

Figure A6.76. $K_{St} = 600\,\mathrm{bar\,m\,s^{-1}}$, $P_{stat} = 1.5\,\mathrm{bar\,a}$.
Duct configuration: single sharp $45°$ bend.

C) Estimates of reduced explosion pressures for vent ducts with a single sharp 90° bend

Note: All pressures are given in bar a.

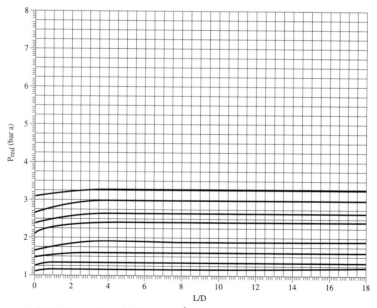

Figure A6.77. $K_{St} = 10$ and $20 \, \text{bar m s}^{-1}$, $P_{stat} = 1.1 \, \text{bar a}$.
Duct configuration: single sharp 90° bend.

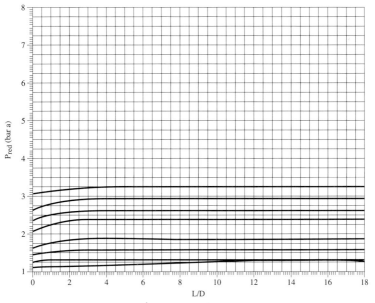

Figure A6.78. $K_{St} = 30\,\mathrm{bar\,m\,s^{-1}}$, $P_{stat} = 1.1\,\mathrm{bar\,a}$.
Duct configuration: single sharp 90° bend.

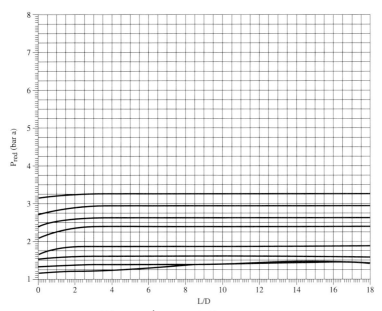

Figure A6.79. $K_{St} = 40\,\mathrm{bar\,m\,s^{-1}}$, $P_{stat} = 1.1\,\mathrm{bar\,a}$.
Duct configuration: single sharp 90° bend.

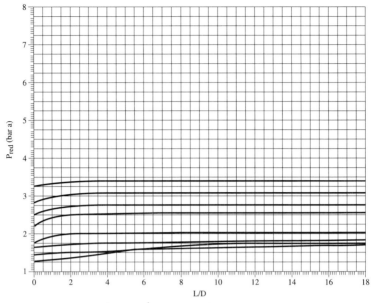

Figure A6.80. $K_{St} = 50\,\text{bar}\,\text{m}\,\text{s}^{-1}$, $P_{stat} = 1.1\,\text{bar}\,\text{a}$.
Duct configuration: single sharp 90° bend.

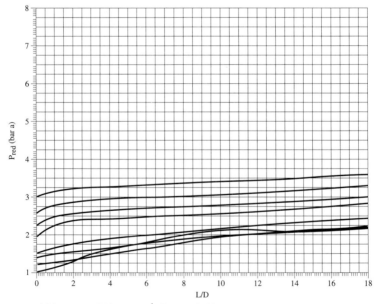

Figure A6.81. $K_{St} = 75\,\text{bar}\,\text{m}\,\text{s}^{-1}$, $P_{stat} = 1.1\,\text{bar}\,\text{a}$.
Duct configuration: single sharp 90° bend.

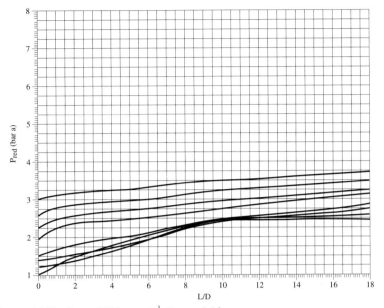

Figure A6.82. $K_{St} = 100\,\mathrm{bar\,m\,s^{-1}}$, $P_{stat} = 1.1\,\mathrm{bar\,a}$.
Duct configuration: single sharp 90° bend.

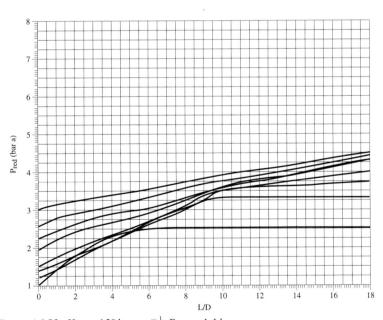

Figure A6.83. $K_{St} = 150\,\mathrm{bar\,m\,s^{-1}}$, $P_{stat} = 1.1\,\mathrm{bar\,a}$.
Duct configuration: single sharp 90° bend.

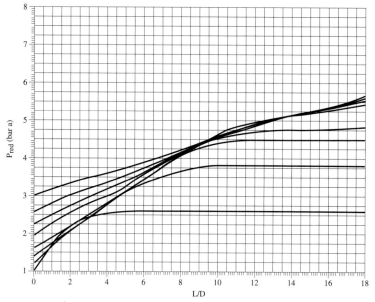

Figure A6.84. $K_{St} = 200 \, \text{bar m s}^{-1}$, $P_{stat} = 1.1 \, \text{bar a}$.
Duct configuration: single sharp 90° bend.

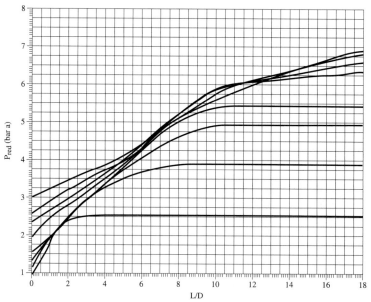

Figure A6.85. $K_{St} = 250 \, \text{bar m s}^{-1}$, $P_{stat} = 1.1 \, \text{bar a}$.
Duct configuration: single sharp 90° bend.

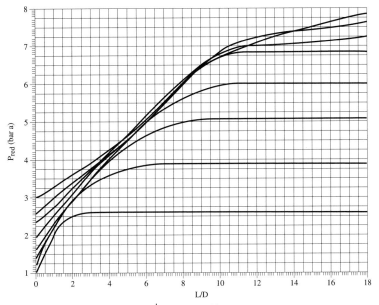

Figure A6.86. $K_{St} = 300 \, \text{bar m s}^{-1}$, $P_{stat} = 1.1 \, \text{bar a}$.
Duct configuration: single sharp 90° bend.

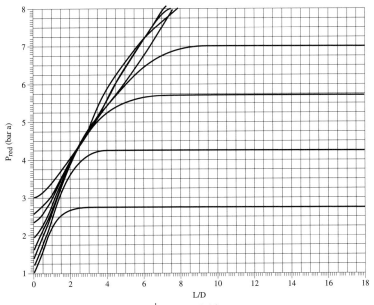

Figure A6.87. $K_{St} = 400 \, \text{bar m s}^{-1}$, $P_{stat} = 1.1 \, \text{bar a}$.
Duct configuration: single sharp 90° bend.

313

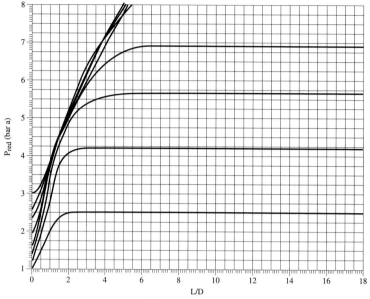

Figure A6.88. $K_{St} = 500 \, \text{bar m s}^{-1}$, $P_{stat} = 1.1 \, \text{bar a}$.
Duct configuration: single sharp 90° bend.

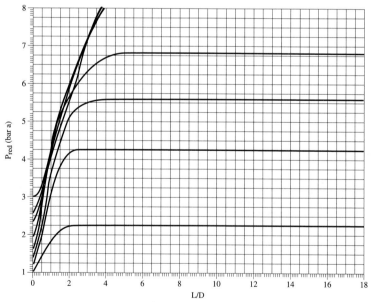

Figure A6.89. $K_{St} = 600 \, \text{bar m s}^{-1}$, $P_{stat} = 1.1 \, \text{bar a}$.
Duct configuration: single sharp 90° bend.

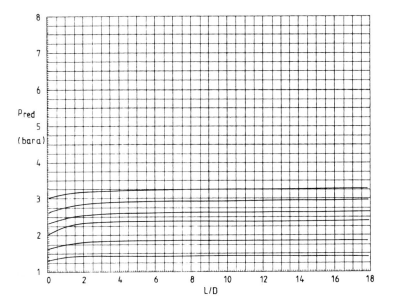

Figure A6.90. $K_{St} = 10$ and $20\,\mathrm{bar\,m\,s^{-1}}$, $P_{stat} = 1.2\,\mathrm{bar\,a}$.
Duct configuration: single sharp $90°$ bend.

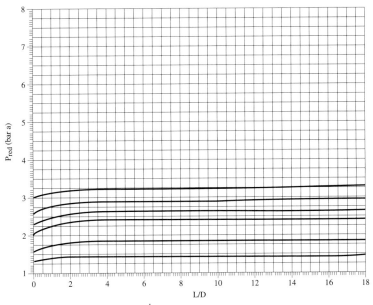

Figure A6.91. $K_{St} = 30\,\mathrm{bar\,m\,s^{-1}}$, $P_{stat} = 1.2\,\mathrm{bar\,a}$.
Duct configuration: single sharp $90°$ bend.

315

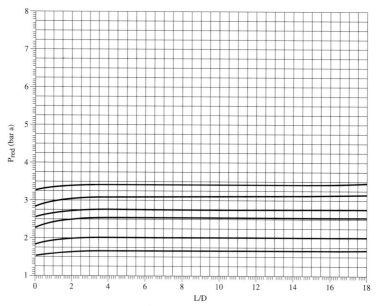

Figure A6.92. $K_{St} = 40\,\mathrm{bar\,m\,s^{-1}}$, $P_{stat} = 1.2\,\mathrm{bar\,a}$.
Duct configuration: single sharp 90° bend.

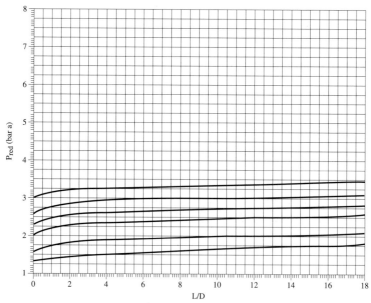

Figure A6.93. $K_{St} = 50\,\mathrm{bar\,m\,s^{-1}}$, $P_{stat} = 1.2\,\mathrm{bar\,a}$.
Duct configuration: single sharp 90° bend.

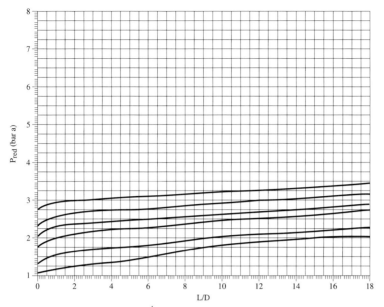

Figure A6.94. $K_{St} = 75\,\text{bar m s}^{-1}$, $P_{stat} = 1.2\,\text{bar a}$.
Duct configuration: single sharp 90° bend.

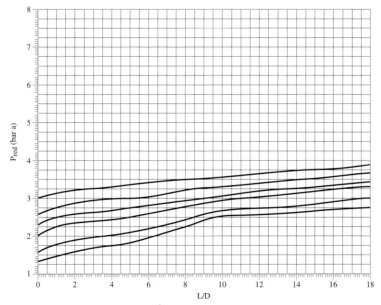

Figure A6.95. $K_{St} = 100\,\text{bar m s}^{-1}$, $P_{stat} = 1.2\,\text{bar a}$.
Duct configuration: single sharp 90° bend.

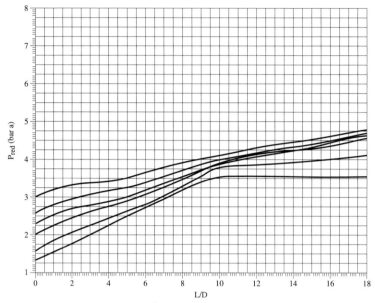

Figure A6.96. $K_{St} = 150\,\mathrm{bar\,m\,s}^{-1}$, $P_{stat} = 1.2\,\mathrm{bar\,a}$.
Duct configuration: single sharp 90° bend.

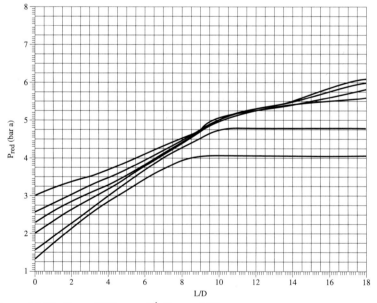

Figure A6.97. $K_{St} = 200\,\mathrm{bar\,m\,s}^{-1}$, $P_{stat} = 1.2\,\mathrm{bar\,a}$.
Duct configuration: single sharp 90° bend.

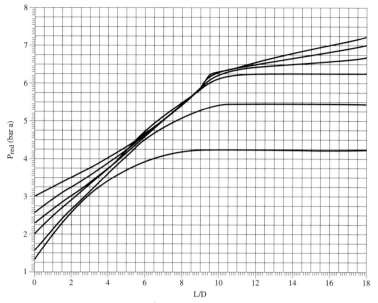

Figure A6.98. $K_{St} = 250 \, \text{bar m s}^{-1}$, $P_{stat} = 1.2 \, \text{bar a}$.
Duct configuration: single sharp 90° bend.

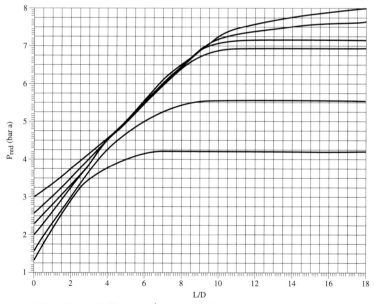

Figure A6.99. $K_{St} = 300 \, \text{bar m s}^{-1}$, $P_{stat} = 1.2 \, \text{bar a}$.
Duct configuration: single sharp 90° bend.

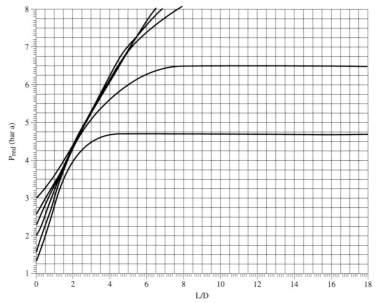

Figure A6.100. $K_{St} = 400\,\mathrm{bar\,m\,s^{-1}}$, $P_{stat} = 1.2\,\mathrm{bar\,a}$.
Duct configuration: single sharp 90° bend.

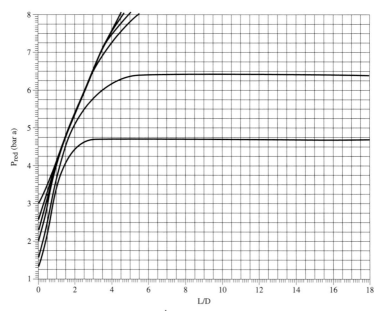

Figure A6.101. $K_{St} = 500\,\mathrm{bar\,m\,s^{-1}}$, $P_{stat} = 1.2\,\mathrm{bar\,a}$.
Duct configuration: single sharp 90° bend.

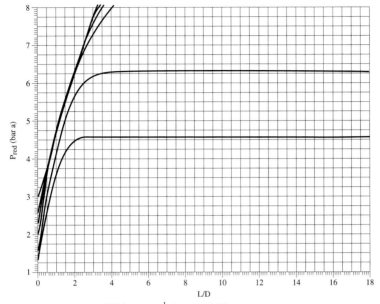

Figure A6.102. $K_{St} = 600 \, \text{bar m s}^{-1}$, $P_{stat} = 1.2 \, \text{bar a}$.
Duct configuration: single sharp 90° bend.

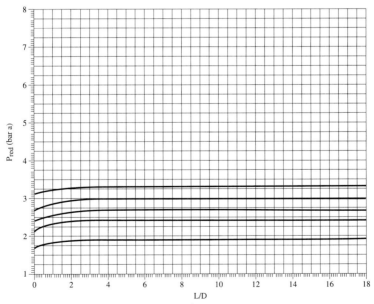

Figure A6.103. $K_{St} = 10$ and $20 \, \text{bar m s}^{-1}$, $P_{stat} = 1.5 \, \text{bar a}$.
Duct configuration: single sharp 90° bend.

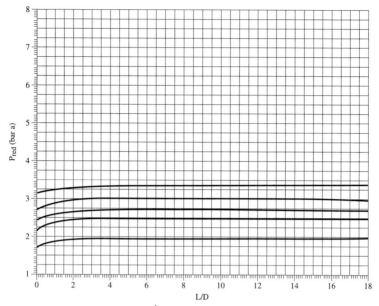

Figure A6.104. $K_{St} = 30 \, \text{bar m s}^{-1}$, $P_{stat} = 1.5 \, \text{bar a}$.
Duct configuration: single sharp 90° bend.

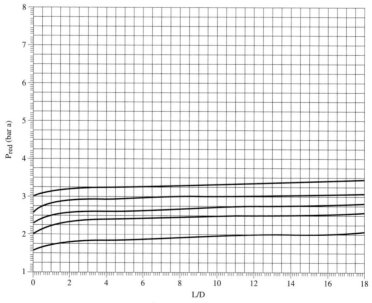

Figure A6.105. $K_{St} = 40 \, \text{bar m s}^{-1}$, $P_{stat} = 1.5 \, \text{bar a}$.
Duct configuration: single sharp 90° bend.

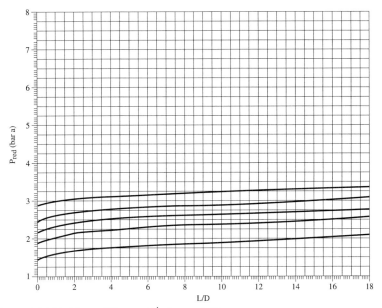

Figure A6.106. $K_{St} = 50\,\mathrm{bar\,m\,s}^{-1}$, $P_{stat} = 1.5\,\mathrm{bar\,a}$.
Duct configuration: single sharp 90° bend.

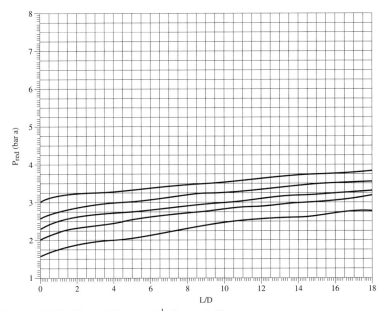

Figure A6.107. $K_{St} = 75\,\mathrm{bar\,m\,s}^{-1}$, $P_{stat} = 1.5\,\mathrm{bar\,a}$.
Duct configuration: single sharp 90° bend.

323

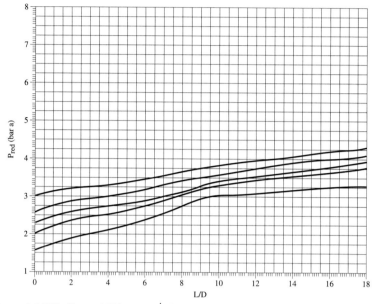

Figure A6.108. $K_{St} = 100\,\text{bar m s}^{-1}$, $P_{stat} = 1.5\,\text{bar a}$.
Duct configuration: single sharp 90° bend.

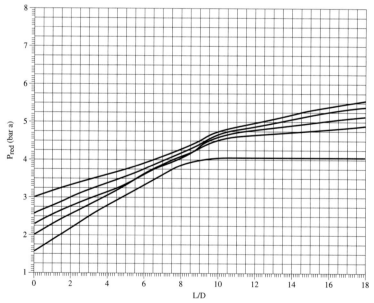

Figure A6.109. $K_{St} = 150\,\text{bar m s}^{-1}$, $P_{stat} = 1.5\,\text{bar a}$.
Duct configuration: single sharp 90° bend.

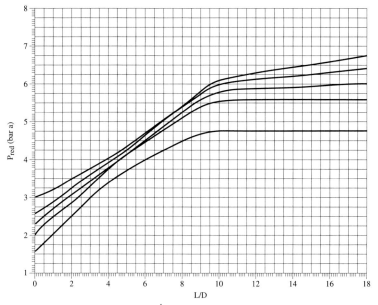

Figure A6.110. $K_{St} = 200\,\text{bar}\,\text{m}\,\text{s}^{-1}$, $P_{stat} = 1.5\,\text{bar}\,\text{a}$.
Duct configuration: single sharp 90° bend.

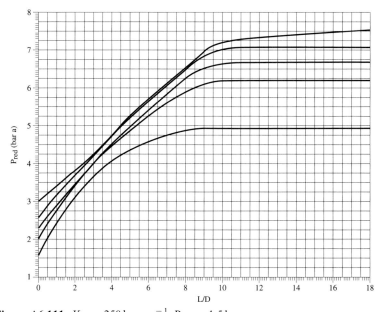

Figure A6.111. $K_{St} = 250\,\text{bar}\,\text{m}\,\text{s}^{-1}$, $P_{stat} = 1.5\,\text{bar}\,\text{a}$.
Duct configuration: single sharp 90° bend.

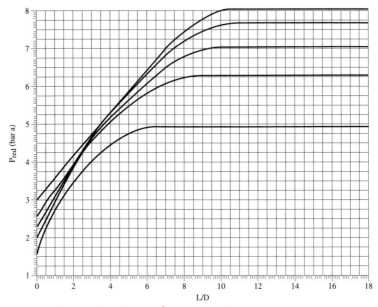

Figure A6.112. $K_{St} = 300 \, \text{bar m s}^{-1}$, $P_{stat} = 1.5 \, \text{bar a}$.
Duct configuration: single sharp 90° bend.

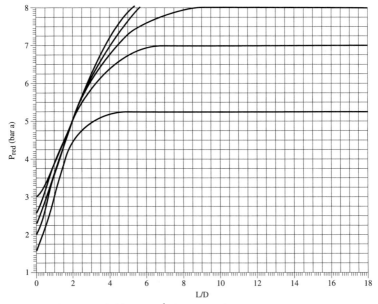

Figure A6.113. $K_{St} = 400 \, \text{bar m s}^{-1}$, $P_{stat} = 1.5 \, \text{bar a}$.
Duct configuration: single sharp 90° bend.

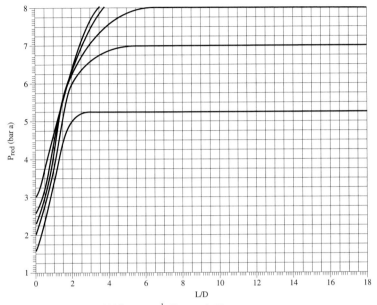

Figure A6.114. $K_{St} = 500\,\text{bar}\,\text{m}\,\text{s}^{-1}$, $P_{stat} = 1.5\,\text{bar}\,\text{a}$.
Duct configuration: single sharp 90° bend.

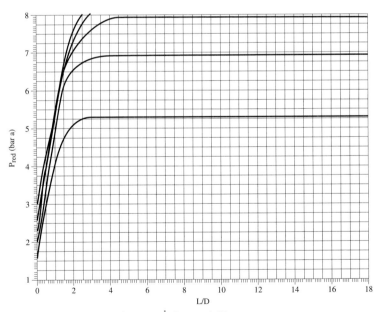

Figure A6.115. $K_{St} = 600\,\text{bar}\,\text{m}\,\text{s}^{-1}$, $P_{stat} = 1.5\,\text{bar}\,\text{a}$.
Duct configuration: single sharp 90° bend.

327

D) Estimates of the reduced explosion pressures for St 3 metal ducts

Note: All pressures are given in bar a.

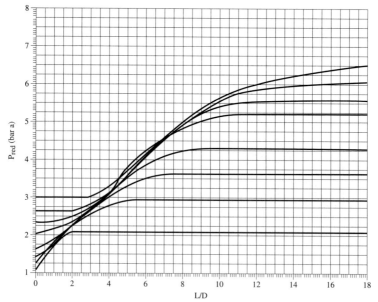

Figure A6.116. $K_{St} = 400 \, \text{bar m s}^{-1}$, $P_{stat} = 1.1 \, \text{bar a}$.
Duct configuration: straight.

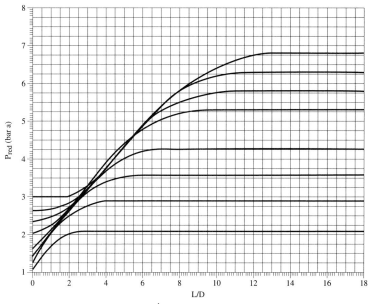

Figure A6.117. $K_{St} = 500\,\text{bar}\,\text{m}\,\text{s}^{-1}$, $P_{stat} = 1.1\,\text{bar}\,\text{a}$.
Duct configuration: straight.

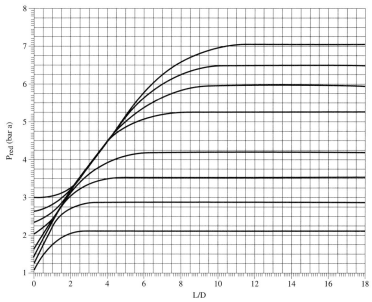

Figure A6.118. $K_{St} = 600\,\text{bar}\,\text{m}\,\text{s}^{-1}$, $P_{stat} = 1.1\,\text{bar}\,\text{a}$.
Duct configuration: straight.

329

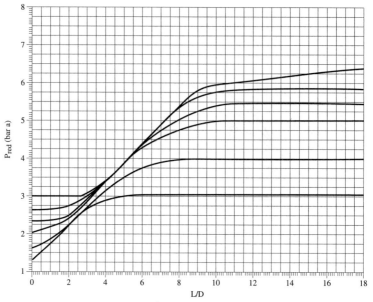

Figure A6.119. $K_{St} = 400 \, \text{bar m s}^{-1}$, $P_{stat} = 1.2 \, \text{bar a}$.
Duct configuration: straight.

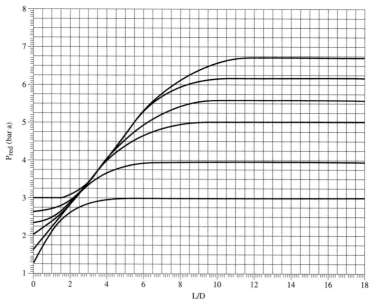

Figure A6.120. $K_{St} = 500 \, \text{bar m s}^{-1}$, $P_{stat} = 1.2 \, \text{bar a}$.
Duct configuration: straight.

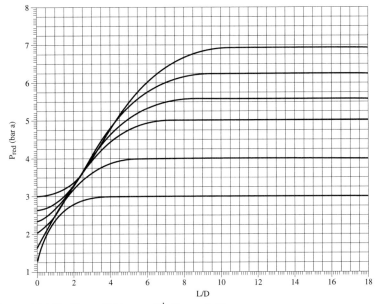

Figure A6.121. $K_{St} = 600\,\text{bar m s}^{-1}$, $P_{stat} = 1.2\,\text{bar a}$.
Duct configuration: straight.

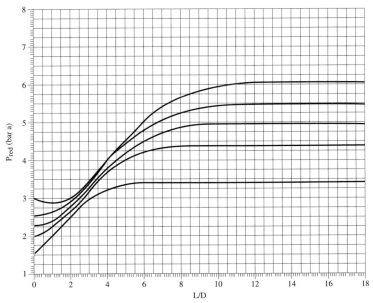

Figure A6.122. $K_{St} = 400\,\text{bar m s}^{-1}$, $P_{stat} = 1.5\,\text{bar a}$.
Duct configuration: straight.

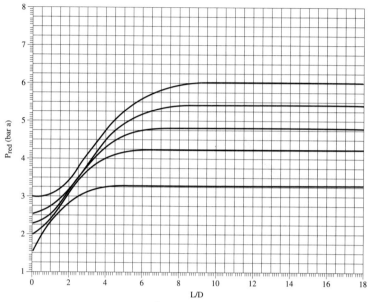

Figure A6.123. $K_{St} = 500\,\text{bar}\,\text{m}\,\text{s}^{-1}$, $P_{stat} = 1.5\,\text{bar}\,\text{a}$.
Duct configuration: straight.

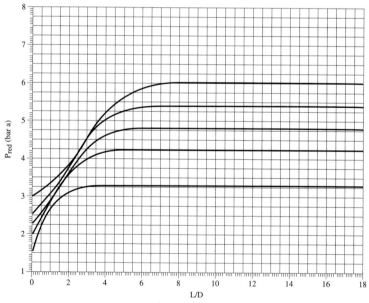

Figure A6.124. $K_{St} = 600\,\text{bar}\,\text{m}\,\text{s}^{-1}$, $P_{stat} = 1.5\,\text{bar}\,\text{a}$.
Duct configuration: straight.

332

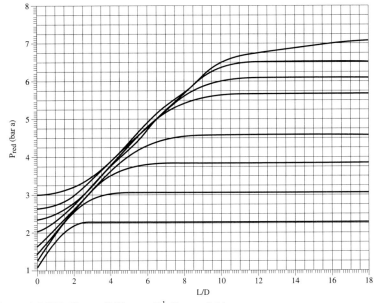

Figure A6.125. $K_{St} = 400 \, \text{bar m s}^{-1}$, $P_{stat} = 1.1 \, \text{bar a}$.
Duct configuration: single sharp $45°$ bend.

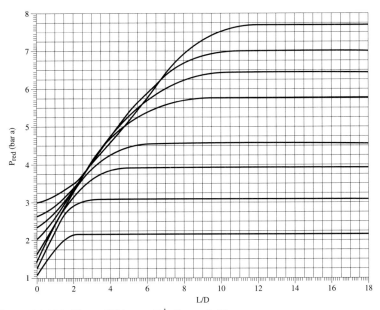

Figure A6.126. $K_{St} = 500 \, \text{bar m s}^{-1}$, $P_{stat} = 1.1 \, \text{bar a}$.
Duct configuration: single sharp $45°$ bend.

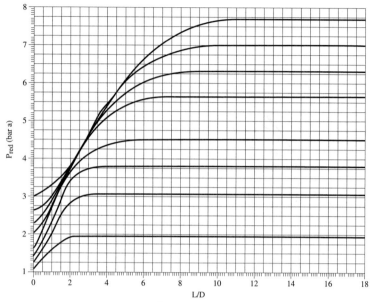

Figure A6.127. $K_{St} = 600 \, \text{bar} \, \text{m} \, \text{s}^{-1}$, $P_{stat} = 1.1 \, \text{bar} \, \text{a}$.
Duct configuration: single sharp 45° bend.

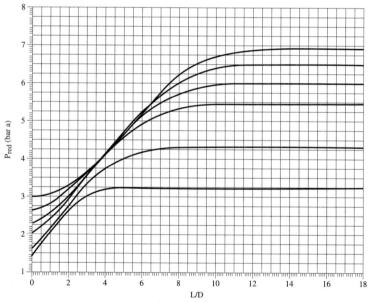

Figure A6.128. $K_{St} = 400 \, \text{bar} \, \text{m} \, \text{s}^{-1}$, $P_{stat} = 1.2 \, \text{bar} \, \text{a}$.
Duct configuration: single sharp 45° bend.

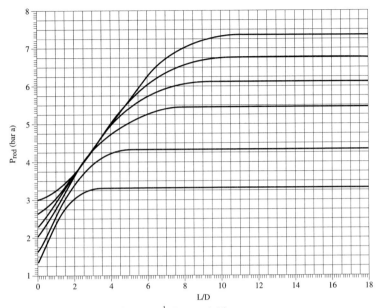

Figure A6.129. $K_{St} = 500 \, \text{bar m s}^{-1}$, $P_{stat} = 1.2 \, \text{bar a}$.
Duct configuration: single sharp $45°$ bend.

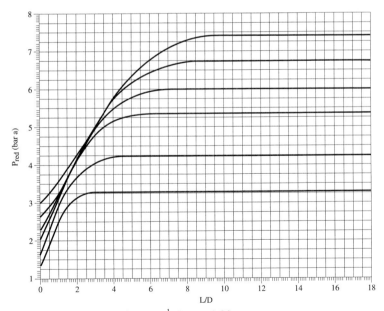

Figure A6.130. $K_{St} = 600 \, \text{bar m s}^{-1}$, $P_{stat} = 1.2 \, \text{bar a}$.
Duct configuration: single sharp $45°$ bend.

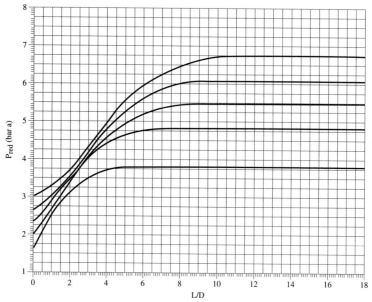

Figure A6.131. $K_{St} = 400\,\mathrm{bar\,m\,s^{-1}}$, $P_{stat} = 1.5\,\mathrm{bar\,a}$.
Duct configuration: single sharp 45° bend.

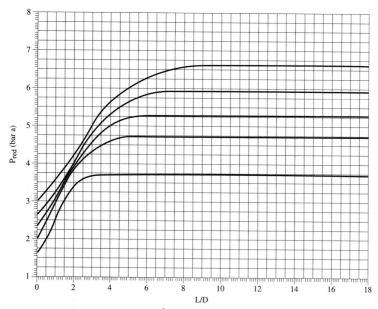

Figure A6.132. $K_{St} = 500\,\mathrm{bar\,m\,s^{-1}}$, $P_{stat} = 1.5\,\mathrm{bar\,a}$.
Duct configuration: single sharp 45° bend.

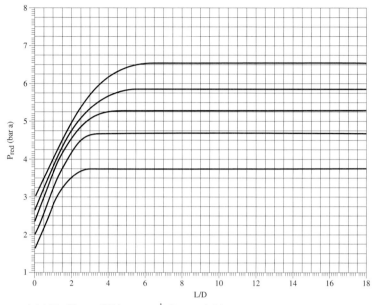

Figure A6.133. $K_{St} = 600\,\text{bar}\,\text{m}\,\text{s}^{-1}$, $P_{stat} = 1.5\,\text{bar}\,\text{a}$.
Duct configuration: single sharp 45° bend.

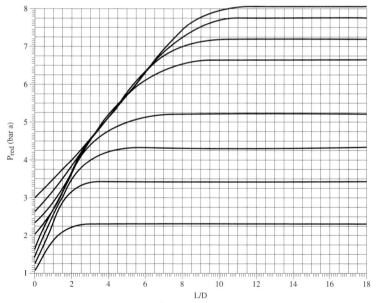

Figure A6.134. $K_{St} = 400\,\text{bar}\,\text{m}\,\text{s}^{-1}$, $P_{stat} = 1.1\,\text{bar}\,\text{a}$.
Duct configuration: single sharp 90° bend.

337

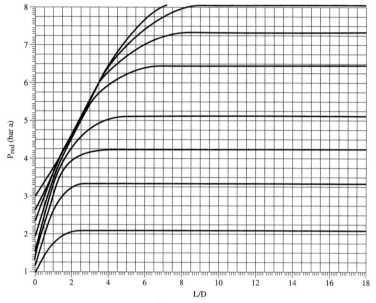

Figure A6.135. $K_{St} = 500 \, bar \, m \, s^{-1}$, $P_{stat} = 1.1 \, bar \, a$.
Duct configuration: single sharp 90° bend.

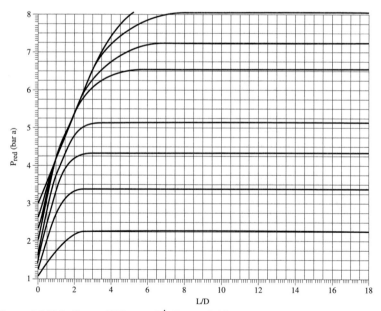

Figure A6.136. $K_{St} = 600 \, bar \, m \, s^{-1}$, $P_{stat} = 1.1 \, bar \, a$.
Duct configuration: single sharp 90° bend.

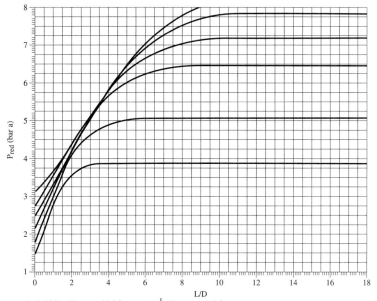

Figure A6.137. $K_{St} = 400\,\text{bar}\,\text{m}\,\text{s}^{-1}$, $P_{stat} = 1.2\,\text{bar}\,\text{a}$.
Duct configuration: single sharp 90° bend.

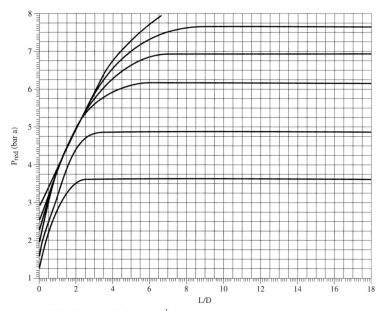

Figure A6.138. $K_{St} = 500\,\text{bar}\,\text{m}\,\text{s}^{-1}$, $P_{stat} = 1.2\,\text{bar}\,\text{a}$.
Duct configuration: single sharp 90° bend.

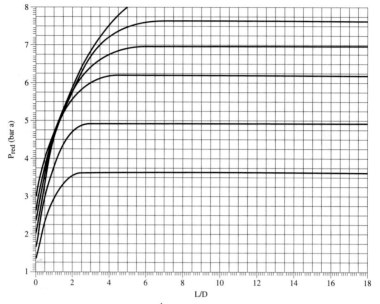

Figure A6.139. $K_{St} = 600 \, \text{bar m s}^{-1}$, $P_{stat} = 1.2 \, \text{bar a}$.
Duct configuration: single sharp 90° bend.

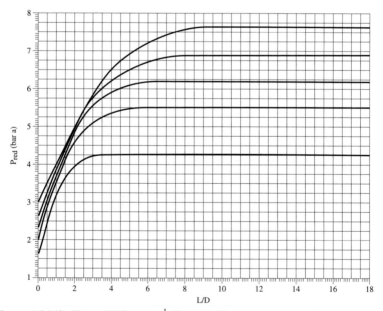

Figure A6.140. $K_{St} = 400 \, \text{bar m s}^{-1}$, $P_{stat} = 1.5 \, \text{bar a}$.
Duct configuration: single sharp 90° bend.

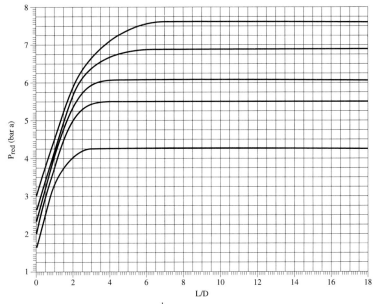

Figure A6.141. $K_{St} = 500 \, \text{bar m s}^{-1}$, $P_{stat} = 1.5 \, \text{bar a}$.
Duct configuration: single sharp 90° bend.

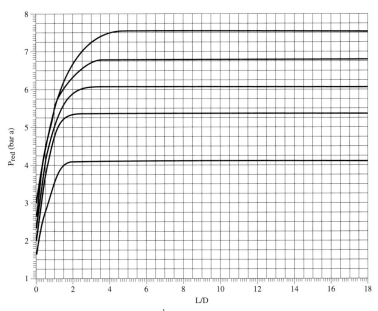

Figure A6.142. $K_{St} = 600 \, \text{bar m s}^{-1}$, $P_{stat} = 1.5 \, \text{bar a}$.
Duct configuration: single sharp 90° bend.

Glossary*

ATEX-100A Directive (94/9/EC):
Equipment and protective systems intended for use in potentially explosive atmospheres.

ATEX comes from the French 'ATmosphere EXplosif'.

See also Appendix 2.

ATEX 137A Directive (1999/92/EC):
'On minimum requirements for improving the health and safety protection of workers potentially at risk from explosive atmospheres'.

This Directive and the Chemical Agents Directive (see below) both address fire and explosion hazards, and they will be implemented in the UK as a single set of regulations, coming fully into force by June 2003. They require an assessment of the risks arising from the use of dangerous substances, including explosible dusts, and recognise a hierarchy of precautions: preventing the formation of hazardous quantities or concentrations of flammable materials; avoiding ignition sources that could give rise to fires and explosions; and mitigating the consequences of any fire or explosion that may arise. These basic principles are not new, but there are some requirements in the dust-handling field that are new.

See also Appendix 2.

CEN
European Committee for Standardisation.

CENELEC (CLC)
European Committee for Electrotechnical Standardisation.

---

* With acknowledgement to BSI for permission to reproduce in this glossary definitions from BS EN 1127–1: 1998, *Explosive atmospheres — Explosion prevention and protection, Part 1: Basic concepts and methodology.*

CEN TC 305

CEN Technical Committee 305: '*Potentially explosive atmospheres: explosion prevention and protection*'.

Scope: To develop standards where necessary in the fields of:

- Test methods for determining the flammability characteristics (ignition, propagation, explosion effects, etc.) of substances;
- Equipment and protective systems for use in potentially explosive atmospheres;
- Equipment and systems for explosion prevention and protection.

BSI has a 'shadow' committee:

BSI Technical Committee FSH/23: '*Fire and explosion prevention and protection in plant and machinery*'.

Terms of reference:

- To prepare standards relating to fire and explosion prevention and protection in plant and machinery.
- To steer UK participation in CEN/TC 305 and to provide recommendations in an advisory capacity for UK participation in other international organisations concerned with fire and explosion in plant and machinery.

Chemical Agents Directive (98/24/EC):

'On the protection of the health and safety of workers from the risks related to chemical agents at work'.

This Directive and the ATEX 137A Directive (q.v.) will be implemented in the UK as a single set of regulations, coming fully into force by June 2003.

Cube-root (or cubic) law

See K_{St} value.

Deflagration

Explosion propagating at subsonic velocity.
[ISO 8421-1, 1987-03-01, 1.11]

Detonation

Explosion propagating at supersonic velocity and characterised by a shock wave.
[ISO 8421-1, 1987-03-01, 1.12]

Equipment

'Equipment' means machines, apparatus, fixed or mobile devices, control components and instrumentation thereof and detection and prevention systems which, separately or jointly, are intended for the generation, transfer, storage, measurement, control and conversion of energy for the processing of material, and which are capable of causing an explosion through their own potential sources of ignition.
[ATEX-100A Directive 94/9/EC, Chapter I, Article 1]

Explosibility

The ability of a dust to take part in a cloud explosion when dispersed in air at a suitable concentration and in the presence of an effective ignition source. It denotes both a qualitative assessment of this ability — either explosible or non-explosible; and a quantitative measure of the likely explosion violence — usually the rate of pressure rise in an enclosed explosion. Standard tests are described in Chapter 2, and Appendix 3.

Explosible dust cloud

A cloud of explosible dust in air producing a potentially explosive atmosphere.

Explosion

Abrupt oxidation or decomposition reaction producing an increase in temperature, pressure, or in both simultaneously.
[ISO 8421-1, 1987-03-01, 1.13]

Explosion limits

The limits, i.e., the LEL and UEL, q.v., of the explosion range. See Chapter 1, Section 1.1, and Chapter 2, Section 2.3.1.

Explosion range

Range of the concentration of a flammable substance in air within which an explosion can occur.

Explosion-resistant

Property of vessels and equipment designed to be either explosion-pressure-resistant or explosion-pressure-shock-resistant.

Explosion-pressure-resistant

Property of vessels and equipment designed to withstand the expected explosion pressure without becoming permanently deformed. See Chapter 5, Section 5.1.

Explosion-pressure-shock-resistant

Property of vessels and equipment designed to withstand the expected explosion pressure without rupturing, but allowing permanent deformation. See Chapter 5, Section 5.1

Explosive atmosphere

Mixture with air, under atmospheric conditions, of flammable substances in the form of gases, vapours, mists or dusts, in which, after ignition has occurred, combustion spreads to the entire unburned mixture.
(See also Directive 94/9/EC, Chapter I, Article 1.)

Flammable substance

Substance in the form of gas, vapour, liquid, solid, or mixtures of these, able to undergo an exothermic reaction with air when ignited.

Hazardous explosive atmosphere

Explosive atmosphere which, if it explodes, causes damage.

Hybrid mixture

Mixture of flammable substances with air in different physical states. An example of a hybrid mixture is the mixture of methane, coal dust and air.

K_{St} value

A dust-specific measure of the explosibility, in units of bar m s^{-1}, and calculated using the equation:

$$K_{St} = (dP/dt)_{max} V^{1/3}$$

where V is the vessel volume. The equation is the so-called 'cubic' or 'cube-root' law. The K_{st} value is considered to be volume independent. The measurement is described in Chapter 2, Section 2.2, and Appendix 3.

Inerting

Addition of inert substances to prevent explosive atmospheres. See Chapter 4.

Intended use

The use of equipment, protective systems and devices in accordance with the equipment group and category as specified in the ATEX-100A Directive 94/9/EC, Annex I, and taking into account all the information supplied by the manufacturer which is required for the safe functioning of equipment, protective systems and devices.
(See also Directive 94/9/EEC, Chapter I, Article 1.)

Limiting oxygen concentration (LOC)
Maximum oxygen concentration in a mixture of a flammable substance and air and an inert gas, in which an explosion will not occur, determined under specified test conditions. See Chapter 4, Section 4.3.

Lower explosion limit (LEL)
The lower limit of the explosion range. See Chapter 1, Section 1.1.

Machinery
An assembly of linked parts or components, at least one of which moves, with the appropriate actuators, control and power circuits, etc. joined together for a specific application, in particular for the processing, treatment, moving or packaging of a material (material is equivalent to substance or product).

The term 'machinery' also covers an assembly of machines which, in order to achieve the same end, are arranged and controlled so that they function as an integral whole.

[Machinery Directive 89/392/EEC, Article 1.2]

See also Appendix 2.

Maximum explosion pressure (P_{max})
Maximum pressure occurring in a closed vessel during the explosion of an explosible dust atmosphere determined under specific test conditions. Standard tests are described in Chapter 2, Sections 2.1 and 2.2.

Maximum rate of explosion pressure rise ((dp/dt)$_{max}$)
Maximum value of the pressure rise per unit time during explosions of all explosive atmospheres in the explosion range of a combustible substance in a closed vessel under specified test conditions. Standard tests are described in Chapter 2, Sections 2.1 and 2.2, and Appendix 3.

Minimum ignition energy (MIE)
Lowest electrical energy stored in a capacitor that upon discharge is sufficient to effect ignition of the most ignitable atmosphere under specified test conditions. See Chapter 2, Section 2.3.2, and Appendix 3.

Minimum ignition temperature (MIT) of a dust cloud
The lowest temperature of a hot surface on which the most ignitable mixture of the dust with air is ignited under specified test conditions. See Chapter 2, Section 2.3.3.

Minimum ignition temperature (MIT) of a dust layer

The lowest temperature of a hot surface at which ignition occurs in a dust layer under specified test conditions. See Chapter 2, Section 2.4.3.

Nomograph

A chart, or diagram, of scaled lines or curves used to help in calculations, comprising three scales in which a line joining values on two determines a third.

Potentially explosive atmosphere

An atmosphere which could become explosive due to local and operational conditions.
[ATEX-100A Directive 94/9/EC, Chapter I, Article 1].

Protective system

'Protective system' means design units that are intended to halt incipient explosions immediately and/or to limit the effective range of explosion flames and explosion pressures. Protective systems may be integrated into equipment or separately placed on the market for use as autonomous systems.
[ATEX-100A Directive 94/9/EC, Chapter I, Article 1]

Reduced explosion pressure, P_{red}

Pressure generated by an explosion of an explosive atmosphere in a vessel, which is protected by either explosion relief or explosion suppression. See Chapter 6, Section 6.1 and Chapter 7, Section 7.1.

(Spontaneous heating) Self-ignition (of dust in bulk)

Ignition of dusts caused by the rate of heat generation from oxidation and/or exothermic decomposition reactions of the dust being greater than the rate of heat loss to the surroundings. See Chapter 3, Section 3.2.3.

St groups

A grouping of explosible dusts according to the St value. See Chapter 2, Section 2.2.

Upper explosion limit (UEL)

The upper limit of the explosion range. See Chapter 1, Section 1.1.

Vent cover bursting pressure, P_{stat}

The pressure at which the explosion relief vent closure bursts under static conditions. See Chapter 7, Section 7.1 and Chapter 11, Section 11.3.

Index